Davey

Westwood

THE LAST MIGRATION

VINCENT CRONIN

The Last
Migration

RUPERT HART-DAVIS
& THE BOOK SOCIETY
1957

This edition issued on first publication by The Book
Society Ltd in association with Rupert Hart-Davis Ltd
April 1957

PRINTED IN GREAT BRITAIN
BY WESTERN PRINTING SERVICES LTD BRISTOL

FOR
CHANTAL

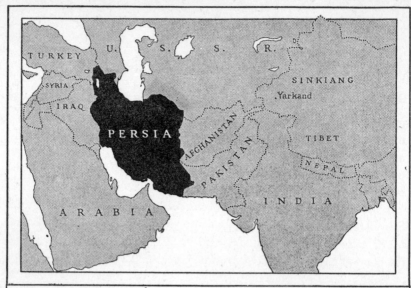

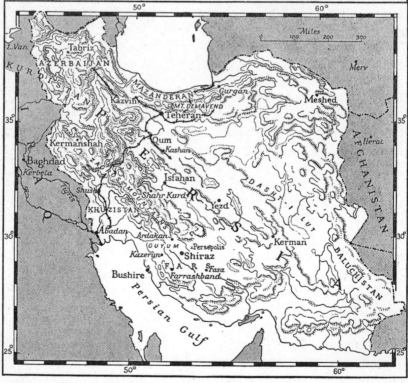

PROLOGUE

"A FRUITFULL countrey, inhabited with pasturing people, which dwell in the Summer season upon mountaines, and in Winter they remoove into the valleyes without resorting to townes or any other habitation: and when they remoove, they doe journey in carravans or troops of people and cattell, carrying all their wives, children and baggage upon bullocks."

This sentence, from Hakluyt's *Principal Voyages*, was written by the Elizabethan merchant, sea-captain and traveller, Anthony Jenkinson. Much of his life Jenkinson spent trying to reach Cathay. He watched the entry of Sulaiman the Magnificent into Aleppo, he had the honour of being robbed by the King of Bokhara, he set up the red cross of St. George on the Caspian Sea, he passed through the maelstrom and, reaching Moscow in a sledge, dined by candlelight with Ivan the Terrible. But he never succeeded in entering Cathay, never met the Emperor of China. Disturbances at Tashkent and Kashgar closed the caravan trails through Central Asia, while the sea route led only to carefully guarded coastal enclaves.

Jenkinson had to be content with a visit to Persia, where from the Great Sophy, Tahmasp, he sought letters of safe-conduct and privileges for English merchants. Later a useful trade was opened whereby England exchanged tin, scarlet cloth and copper for raw silk, spices and yew. The raw silk has doubtless long ago been ripped by moths, the yew bow-staves broken or burned, and of that visit Jenkinson's own account—the first by an Englishman—remains the still unspoiled fruit. In it occurs the passage about "pasturing people", the first Persians Jenkinson saw in their own country.

The lines caught my attention and, having finished Jenkinson's narrative, I turned back to reread them. Stranger than language and spelling, rhythm and grammar was the scene itself, this meeting at the end of the known world between the widest travelled Englishman of his day and a people for whom travel was not the exception but the rule. Even the adventurous Jenkinson finally settled to a squire's life in

7

Northamptonshire, but these Persians, I imagined, if they were true nomads, would have continued their journey without ever arriving— nomads, by definition, being men who must continually move in order to pasture the beasts on which they depend for food.

Jenkinson makes it clear that only some Persians led this special life. According to Herodotus, the first European historian to describe Persia, the land of the Great King contained many tribes, of which four were wandering herdsmen. That was in the fifth century before Christ. Long before Jenkinson's visit in 1562 the pasturing people had been travelling: were they travelling still? Modern authorities on Persia provided the answer. No less than a quarter of an estimated population of twenty millions were nomad or semi-nomad. Their way of life, far from being a transitional stage between food-collecting and agriculture, had probably existed as long as man himself, being partly conditioned by climate and, in most parts of Persia except the north-west, by soil too poor for crops. Whereas the habits of other nomad peoples—Bedouin of Arabia, indigo-veiled Tuareg of the Sahara, pygmies of East Africa— could be known vicariously through many excellent descriptions, of the Persian nomads I found it difficult to form a clear picture. As far as I could discover, few travellers had lived among them and fewer still had left accounts more detailed than Jenkinson's. Yet the Elizabethan's words continued to ring in my ears, tantalizing, a siren song. I wanted to know more about these "pasturing people". The only way was to go and see for myself.

First, I learned something of their origin. These nomads with their seasonal migrations were themselves the product of much more extensive migrations by whole peoples, sometimes along the whole length of Asia. Tradition held that the earliest known inhabitants of Persia, who shared an Aryan language with the eventual conquerors of Europe, came from an earthly paradise called Aryanem-Vaejo: perhaps southwestern Siberia. When the Spirit of Evil made this land ice-bound, they moved south to Bokhara and Merv. Locusts drove them from Bokhara, and hostile tribes forced them to Balkh. Thence one group migrated to India, another, less numerous, to Persia. Here the smaller group was joined by new peoples from Southern Russia, from the steppes on the north of Khorasan and from Bactria, over the Hindu Kush. Like their electrum ornaments, which are all they have left behind, these first Persians were an alloy. And for some four thousand years they were

8

regularly increased and made yet more diverse by such migratory movements as the Seljuq and Mongol invasions.

Today far the purest of these different strata which compose Persia are the immigrants who have remained nomadic. The nature of the land, mountainous, desert, difficult of communication, has preserved their identity. They remain largely independent, but pay taxes and furnish soldiers in time of war. Their leaders are petty kings, and one of the Shah's titles is King of Kings. In the past if a Shah proved himself worthless, a powerful tribe might depose him, as the Bakhtiari did in 1909. Equally, if he made too exacting demands, a Shah might fear for his Peacock Throne. But such assertions of power by chieftains have been rare. The tribes have generally led peaceable lives, though in times of danger their virility has often saved the day for Persia.

I learned to distinguish five main nomadic areas. To the north-west in Kurdistan lived Kurmanju-speaking Kurds; in Azerbaijan (which because of the Russian border was closed to travellers) a scattering of Turkomans; in the south-east Baluchi, their long black hair worn in curls and moistened with rancid butter; in Khuzistan Persian tribes such as Lurs and Bakhtiari to the north; Arab tribes in the Western lowlands; and, in the province of Fars, many tribes of diverse origin.

Fars, formerly Parsa and the basis of the name Persia, is the country's heart-land; from Fars had sprung the Achaemenian founders of the Persian Empire; in Shiraz, its capital, were born and buried the poets Saadi and Hafiz, whom Persians honour among their greatest men. Most important, the province lies far from disputed frontiers where travel might be restricted. I decided, therefore, to make the object of my Persian journey one of the nomad peoples of Fars.

Further inquiries revealed that some of the leaders of a people whom I shall call the Falqani were believed to speak French, the second language of educated Persians. This weighed heavily with me, for what Persian I should have time to learn would doubtless prove inadequate in a country notorious for its dialects. A close friend of one of these leaders happened to be studying medicine in England and supplied me with a letter of introduction to a young man, son of a chieftain, named Rohim Falqani. He also told me that the Falqani made a long spring journey from the plains into the Zagros mountains. This sounded well worth sharing, and I timed my journey to arrive in early spring.

To avoid Turkey and her allies, Jenkinson had sailed on the *Swallow*

9

from Gravesend to a port near Archangel, crossed Russia and entered Persia through Astrakhan. To avoid Russia and her allies, the modern traveller by land must make his way through the waterlogged plains of Thrace and cross Turkey, either directly by Lake Van or southwards through the Cilician Gates; thence to Aleppo, Damascus, across the Syrian desert to Baghdad, and finally up into the high Persian plateau. Following the second route, I crossed the frontier on March the twenty-first, Nowruz—the Persian New Year's Day, and three nights later arrived in Teheran. Here I learned that to travel anywhere outside the capital I must obtain a pass. Not even Persians could travel without one of these red cards, signed by the Army and the Police. But during the New Year holiday offices and ministries were shut. I should have to wait a week.

During my stay I learned something of the recent history of the Falqani, under Reza, father of the present Shah. A former Cossack army officer, Reza had seized the throne in 1925. Having strengthened and enlarged the Army and established a secret police, he assumed dictatorial powers in order to pursue a policy of autocratic nationalism. He confiscated land at will until most of the province of Mazanderan had become his personal property. In the name of the New Persia he unveiled the women and openly persecuted the mullahs—teachers of sacred law and religious leaders—because their creed was not indigenous. He also ordered the language to be purified to exclude words of Arabic origin: an impossible task eventually abandoned.

The continued presence of nomad tribes Reza Shah considered a blot on his progressive country. Conservative by tradition, they opposed many of the usurper's innovations. They refused, for instance, to wear the compulsory new dress for men: Western-style suits with peaked caps; and the new gendarmerie found it difficult to enforce this rule on a sturdy people forever on the move in mountainous country. Seeing in the tribes a challenge to his policy and a potential threat to his throne, Reza Shah decided to settle the most powerful among them as the surest means of crushing their proud spirit and ending their backward ways. The task was entrusted to the Army and carried out in haste. No suitable agricultural land existed, water was lacking, implements were not provided, the climate in the plains proved fatally severe. Weakened by this strange sedentary life, many of the tribespeople fell ill and died.

Among the first settled were the Falqani. Some leaders were killed, others deposed and kept under open arrest in Teheran. The Falqani remained settled for about ten years until 1941, when the Allied powers invaded Persia and forced Reza Shah, who had German sympathies and was by then suffering from acute megalomania (bordering, some believe, on insanity), to abdicate. He was exiled to South Africa where, in 1944, he died. On his abdication the tribes, weaker in numbers and in wealth, again resumed their nomad life.

So much I learned, not without difficulty, for Teheranis seemed reluctant to speak of the tribes. My new acquaintances tried to discourage me from visiting the Falqani. One said the tribes were dying out, that I could see costumes, tools, art much more easily in the tribal museum built by Reza Shah. Another said that during their spring migration they were constantly on the move, wrapped in a cloud of dust: it would be difficult for them to entertain, or even receive, a stranger. Yet another hinted that after the recent anti-British demonstrations under Mosadegh it would be wiser not to venture far from the capital. A fourth claimed that a more accurate picture of Persia could be obtained from visiting the new waterworks in Teheran or one of the modern sugar factories.

But I applied for my pass and after spending many hours on three consecutive days in various government departments I was handed a red card bearing my photograph. The names of the places I could visit were written on it in ink: Isfahan, Shiraz and several villages north and east of Shiraz which I had been told were of particular interest. But to my surprise the pass made no mention of Farrashband, the small town south of Shiraz which served as a centre of Falqani winter quarters. Yet I expressly remembered including Farrashband on my application form. When I raised the matter, the authorities apologized for what, they said, must have been a clerical error. No, there was nothing to prevent my going to Farrashband—provided I obtained a new pass. More photographs would be required; the next day was Friday, a holiday. Say in a week's time the pass should be ready. I had already lost almost a fortnight; with the lengthening days the Falqani would be preparing to leave their winter quarters. If I delayed longer, I might miss my chance of sharing their long journey north. And, remembering what my friends had said, I wondered whether I should be more successful with a second pass than with my first. I decided to waive these formalities and go directly to Shiraz. I would communicate with Rohim if he was there, otherwise make my own way further south.

A two-day drive through salt desert, then across pink sandstone uplands and finally beside sweeping scrub-covered foothills of the Zagros range, brought me to Shiraz, a town of a hundred thousand inhabitants lying in a valley surrounded by brown hills. Here the Falqani chiefs owned a house called Garden of the Pines. The morning after my arrival I called there, and having stated my purpose was welcomed by an agent of the family. He explained that Rohim was with his people, probably in or near Farrashband. Only Rohim's wife, with her infant son, was living at Garden of the Pines and she, according to Persian etiquette, could not receive a stranger.

That afternoon I drove out of Shiraz by the southern gate. A mile from the town I was halted at a check-point heavily guarded by troops. Where did I want to go? To Farrashband? No one, said the sergeant in charge, could travel there without a pass. He looked at the card I had been given in Teheran, verified the photograph, slowly spelled out the place-names, then shook his head. I must turn back.

Again I called on Rohim's agent. "Apply to military headquarters for a new pass," he suggested. "There is a Zoroastrian fire temple at Farrashband. Explain that you want to look at that. Say nothing about your intended visit to Rohim."

Were such tactics really necessary, I asked? The agent said Yes, and gave me further complicated instructions. When I inquired the reason for this secrecy, he told me that Rohim would explain.

At first the Major to whom I applied declined to issue the pass. All such applications, he said, must be approved by Teheran. Finally I persuaded him to telegraph to his superiors. A week later orders arrived that my pass should be granted.

After four hours' drive across mountains I arrived at a large village in the plains. Date palms—giant green fans—shaded brown mud huts and an open bazaar, but did not stir the heavy, fly-laden air. Like Shiraz, Farrashband swarmed with troops. I was stopped at a check-point, from where four soldiers were ordered to escort me to the nearby Zoroastrian fire temple. Under a hot sun we climbed to the summit of a hill crowned by a dingy rubble of square-hewn stones. These I praised, tapped, sketched. Fortunately none of the soldiers was an expert in the finer points of Zoroastrian fire temples, and my evident ignorance passed unnoticed. An hour later we returned to Farrashband, where my escort drifted away. Rohim's agent had told me to lodge with a cobbler called Hussein, who would choose an opportune moment to lead me to the Falqani house. I found Hussein, a timid, rather gloomy little man, and spent the late afternoon with him, drinking tea. Several times he said, as though reassuring himself rather than me, that Rohim was very powerful—one of the most powerful men in all Persia—and that once I saw him all my difficulties would end.

As soon as darkness fell he led me through a maze of winding alleys. At the gate of a large garden leading to the Falqani house we were challenged by two armed sentries. We argued with them but they would not let us pass. Finally I asked to be taken to the commanding officer, a Colonel Sirdar. I showed my red card and told him that my passport bore the words "without let or hindrance". Surely I was entitled to see whomsoever I pleased in Farrashband. No, said the Colonel. My pass entitled me only to visit the fire temple, and he pointed out that this was indeed written on the card. Since I had now seen the ruin, I must return as soon as possible to Shiraz.

Next morning I pressed my case and Colonel Sirdar reluctantly agreed to telegraph to Shiraz asking whether I might visit the Falqani house. Three hours later a reply was received confirming the Colonel's decision.

During the drive back to Shiraz, I reflected on recent events. Was I deliberately being prevented from seeing the Falqani, and if so why? Even in Teheran, I recalled, I had been urged to change my plans. Four different reasons had been given me there, and I now inclined to doubt them all. I believed the real reason remained hidden.

Rohim's agent railed against the authorities and offered his sympathy. Times were difficult, he said. But at a precise explanation it was not for him, a mere servant, to guess. I must ask Rohim. I then persuaded him to try to deliver my letter of introduction, and a second letter which I now wrote asking Rohim, if possible, to meet me in Shiraz where, after a short visit to other villages of Fars province listed in my original pass, I said I should be returning in a week's time.

I spent the interval visiting places on the Falqani migration route, including a key village called Guyum, and the southern slopes of the Zagros. I also saw and came to know tribespeople of the Arabic-speaking Khamseh, eastern neighbours of the Falqani. Their way of life, like that of all the nomads of Fars, conformed to Jenkinson's description except in one detail. As beasts of burden they used horses, mules and sometimes camels, not bullocks, which were confined to the tropical, almost jungle Caspian coast Jenkinson had visited. That itself was an exception to the general lie of the Persian land: dry and producing scant vegetation. The Khamseh proved even more interesting than I had expected, but my curiosity was not satisfied. I told myself that I had come to Persia expressly to see the Falqani and unless I saw them I would count my journey a failure.

I returned to Shiraz. My letters had been delivered, but Rohim had not arrived and was not expected. I waited, at first patiently like a Persian, then with sinking hope, for I could not afford to stay indefinitely. Finally I decided to return to Teheran in the hope of obtaining at least an explanation. I set my date of departure.

Two afternoons before that date I received a message telling me to come to Garden of the Pines. The agent received me and said that Rohim had just arrived. He was in the house changing his clothes. If I would wait in the garden he would join me.

The valley was guarded by a circle of brown hills, and the garden by a high earthen wall. Within, avenues of cypresses alternating with pines protected a square pool of water surrounded by roses. Two sheep browsed on an expanse of unkempt grass; the fountain was silted and from the rose bushes, unpruned that spring, dangled a disarray of small blooms, scarlet, pink, yellow. I sat on an iron-framed wooden bench overlooking the water, watching goldfish glide through the clouded pool, appearing for a moment only to disappear. Behind stood the large house, a window or door slamming repeatedly in the breeze, no human sound coming from the balconies and high rooms. On each of my visits the pool, wall and hills had seemed outposts of a closed reservation, which now at last I believed I should enter.

In a few minutes there walked towards me a man of about twenty-eight, tall, narrow-hipped, broad-shouldered, swelling out the jacket of his Western-style black suit. His face was unusual for a Persian: oval, with high cheek bones and strongly slanting eyes, the expression rather grim, softened only at the corners of the mouth by a half-smile of greeting.

"I am Rohim Falqani," he said in French. "I am so sorry to keep you waiting." After an exchange of politenesses he sat down and continued. "I apologize for—all this trouble. You are my guest, and so far I have been able to show poor hospitality. If there is anything I can do for you, you have only to ask."

I thanked him, and we spoke for a few minutes about our mutual friend in London.

Then Rohim said, half-inquiring: "In your letter you talked of seeing how we Falqani live?"

"More than that. I should like to accompany you into the Zagros."

His face hardened, but he said nothing. Then I spoke of the difficulty in delivering my letter of introduction.

"My agent told me," he said. He rose and paced beside the pool. "Some people in Teheran would prefer that we had not met. And they certainly do not want you to see the tribe."

"Why?" I asked.

"A short question," he frowned, "but the answer would be rather long."

"However long, I should like to hear it."

He seemed to weigh the request. From a faded rose he drew a handful of limp petals and, preoccupied, scattered them in the pool. After a moment he turned. "We have a saying—Let the guest command his host." He made an effort to smile. "Very well, I shall obey."

Again he sat down beside me on the iron bench. He apologized that his English was halting, and continued to speak in French.

"It began last spring, this time a year ago, when the storks—the pilgrim storks—were flying back from the warmer country round Mecca."

He spoke in a deep, matter-of-fact voice, and seemed to scorn colourful phrases. Instead, he had a curious way of delineating things in his story—a fort, a melon, a greyhound—with a quick, exact gesture of his hands. What most struck me in his manner was that even at moments when his emotions were clearly very much involved, his face remained impassive.

He talked until dusk, then broke off without having finished. He invited me to enter the house, and in the gypsum-covered central room, lined with alcoves, a dinner of pilav, bread and melon jam was served. After dinner Rohim showed me photographs of some of the people about whom he had spoken and certain relevant objects: a silver cup, a clay bowl painted with green leaves and purple flowers, a tiny

15

jewelled copy of the Koran. Then he continued talking far into the night. Not until a quarter past three did he finish. For a few minutes we sat silent, while the kerosene lamps flared. I was astonished by what he had told me. Nothing I had read in the newspapers or heard from acquaintances had prepared me for such a revelation, and in spite of myself I exclaimed:

"Can all this be true?"

Rohim looked hurt. "Do you doubt my word?"

I tried to cover my impoliteness. "The unusual always shocks. Instinctively one doubts."

"Unusual, perhaps, to a European. Here such happenings are all too common."

I recalled my own impressions since arriving: of ruse and secrecy; personal, as opposed to institutional, power; and, underlying the appearance of order, a general lawlessness, whereby the improbable seemed continually to be happening. These, combined with Rohim's sincere, straightforward manner, inclined me to believe his account. With warmth I thanked him for taking me into his confidence. We spoke awhile on general subjects; then, as it was so late, Rohim invited me to spend the night at Garden of the Pines. I accepted. But his narrative was not conducive to sleep. I lay awake till dawn, visualizing some of his words, puzzling over others.

Next morning Rohim asked me how I should like to spend the day.

"You harbour an ungrateful guest," I replied. "What you told me last night has only made me wish to learn more. Could I possibly meet some of the people you spoke about—your family and friends?"

The request evidently surprised him, but he said he thought it could be arranged.

"Also, last night you said you were omitting certain incidents. Others you passed over quickly. I should like to fill in those gaps and details."

"Why are you so interested?" he asked.

I told Rohim that I thought the events of more than local importance and that, with his consent, I should like to make them known outside Persia.

"I have no objection," Rohim said. "On the contrary, you have come very far. It would be a pity to return without the whole truth. But to obtain it will take a long time. Have you the patience to wait?"

Since I could not travel south of Shiraz, Rohim invited me to stay at

Garden of the Pines while he arranged for friends, members of his family and tribespeople to come and talk with me. When he saw that I was in earnest, Rohim more and more favoured my plan. He took great pains to clarify puzzling points and to explain political and religious issues. It amused him to watch my methods, especially my search for written evidence.

"Here we have no facts in your sense," he said. "And so Persia has no true written history. One or two men, in their lifetime, glimpse the truth and show it in action. But usually what they did and stood for is soon forgotten."

So I started out on the previous spring's migration, and lived through the events of that whole year. The tribesmen I met gave their version of the events Rohim had described. Being illiterate, they had excellent memories. They answered my questions readily and tended to repeat actual dialogue. More important still, the Falqani, servants and chieftains alike, led a communal life, open to the sky and to their fellow-men. This unity bred communication. And when a man's thoughts did remain unspoken, his friends knew how to divine them from gesture and expression. Nothing, not even motives and doubts, was hidden from them. And, at Rohim's request, they spoke their minds freely to me.

Having learned all I could at Garden of the Pines, I returned to Teheran. There I met others whose names had recurred in Shiraz. I checked my information and collected more concerning events relevant to the Falqani which had occurred in Teheran. The pattern changed. Epic began to run a three-legged race with the ludicrous. Again instinctively I doubted; again I had recourse to the touchstone of my own experience. Often in Teheran I had felt myself taking part, against an oriental setting, in one of the more extravagant scenes from a Gilbert and Sullivan operetta. Charming manners masked intrigue, which was carried on with sublime indifference to even the most obvious facts. Since this was precisely the feature of events relating to the Falqani, and the events were well authenticated, I could not withhold belief.

By the time I left Persia, having travelled widely in Falqani country, spoken to and questioned many of the protagonists, I had pieced together the previous year's history of the tribe and their leader.

The outcome, satisfying in one respect, proved paradoxical and very disconcerting in another. The more I learned, the more clearly I saw the difficulty of revealing events exactly as they had happened. Nowhere is fact so esteemed as in the West; nowhere (unless it concern the irrelevancies of a dead past) is its disclosure so hedged with taboos. Sensibilities and reputations, both personal and national; ties of friendship; the obligations of a guest: to sacrifice these even on so high an altar would clearly have been improper.

Persians distinguish between *afsaneh*, which means story, *tarikh*, meaning history; and *dastan*, lying somewhere between these two: the form in which imagination casts near-factual history—almost myth, but without the English word's implication of falsity. Much of the Persian past is preserved as *dastan*: even a historical figure like Bahram Gur is remembered precisely under those aspects which, though absent from surviving coins and inscriptions, are typical of his character and reign: as hunter of the wild ass, as the ruler who introduced into Persia Indian musicians and dancers to gladden his people.

Many of the incidents recounted of Bahram Gur and against his enemies did not happen exactly as they are told, but they are not thereby considered false—at least in Persia, for they are held to embody particular situations more effectively than those which did happen, just as of two ballets set to a single piece of music, one by the composer, the other by a choreographer, that of the choreographer may more faithfully express the music.

A form which Persians apply for choice to their own past seemed to me not inappropriate to a book about Persians of the present day. I have adopted it, and recast the information obtained from Rohim and his tribesmen, much as the deeds of Bahram Gur have been recast by Persians themselves. The result follows: a single year from Falqani annals.

CHAPTER ONE

DARKNESS covered this part of the earth. Hidden light gradually turned the black sky to grey, revealing the outlines of a valley, flat and still. Empty, too, it seemed, until the growing glimmer picked out a white horse, bridled and saddled. From the darkness a man emerged, mounted heavily, as though not yet fully awake, and rode slowly towards the palest part of the sky. Reaching the first ridge on the valley's edge, he looked towards the rising sun.

Its light showed a fine-boned face on which the flesh lay firm, with long, slightly curved nose; thick black hair above a high straight brow, and animated dark eyes, rather narrow and long, as though made to scan wide horizons. He sat high and erect on his horse, his long fingers light along the reins, gazing steadfastly at the sun. Muscles, firm and prominent as those in his horse's flank, swelled a tight tunic. After a few moments, as though having caught the sun's fire, he turned quickly and trotted down the ridge. The valley before him was being created by the sun: fawn earth, with the weft of grass almost worn threadbare; corralled herds of brown, grey and black beasts; last of all, black dwellings, perhaps a thousand uncompromising oblong shapes like the pattern on an old earthenware jar: pools of stillness, patches of night. The horseman rode back into the valley, still motionless, as though the settlement had survived its population: graves waiting for the last trumpet to sound. He pressed his thighs against the horse's flanks and cantered to a tent on the southernmost side of the encampment. At his approach there came out a figure dressed, like the rider, in a tunic with divided sleeves and divided skirt, bound by a large blue silk cummerbund, with a close-fitting brown felt hat tilted back at an angle, brimless, but having long flaps turned vertically upwards. On his feet gleamed white, hand-made cord shoes. He carried a long, straight, horn-shaped musical instrument.

"Is it time, Ghazan Khan?"

"Time and more than time."

His voice, neither deep nor shrill, had an edge to it, a voice for cutting through difficulties. The man with the wooden horn at once ran up to a continuation of the same commanding ridge, from which outcropped a platform of stone. Here he stood regaining his breath, while the Khan followed slowly, then raised the surnay to his lips.

Ghazan knew the notes so well that when they sounded they seemed an echo of his own unspoken wishes. The artless skirling music called and incited. The still valley like a sounding-box rang a welcome to the dawn. Again and again a short rising phrase was repeated, as the sun rose free of the mountain peaks, and under the twin impulses of light and music the camp stirred. Now from one tent, now from another, figures stumbled sleepily. Smoke of fires began to rise straight in the chill dawn; food was prepared and hurriedly eaten. The trumpeter lowered his surnay and returned to his tent, while the stirring below in the plain grew till no part was untouched. Then, far to the north, Ghazan saw the first black square dwelling collapse, followed by another close by. The neat straight lines billowed and fell, the goatskin felt was stamped flat, rolled and stowed among the other baggage now being prepared. As far as the eye could see, tents were being folded up, until, an hour after the surnay call, every one of the thousand black pools had evaporated under the new sun.

Ghazan rode back and entered the encampment—fragments spread-eagled as though by earthquake. Disorder everywhere: clothes, bedding, animals, humans intermingled like folded rocks. It seemed they would never form up. All that the black tents had hidden was being corded on passive kneeling camels and on donkeys held by children: kettles, wooden and copper cooking-pots, sacks of grain and rice, dried meat and curds, looms, drums and surnays, clucking hens and roosters in pouches slung across donkeys, as well as the living-quarters themselves: cushions, rugs, tent-poles, the black goatskin tent, guy-ropes and stakes fashioned of bone, even the wattled rushes which divided the erect tent. All these were packed to the sound of barking dogs, bleating sheep and goats, neighing horses; the bray of mules, the occasional deep roar of a camel.

As one family loaded the last of their possessions, a boy would find a water-pipe, a roll of cotton or a jar containing ferment overlooked in the scurry. Amid shouts and laughter bales had to be uncorded, still further filled, then with imprecise, excited fingers tied once more on to the pack-animals. Meanwhile the herdsmen were uniting their flocks in large groups, chasing strays, shouting to dogs, throwing stones to disperse or close up ranks, driving forward others with sticks, while some helped their women and infants on to the back of camel or horse.

Gradually the solution cohered: some fifty groups of a hundred or so were composed, each with its flocks on either side of the main body of riders, which formed the coloured centre of a brown and black design. Ghazan rode to the head of the column, where he was joined by forty horsemen armed with rifles, a few rounds of ammunition in their leather jerkins, and by two attendants, the Khan's personal possessions in leather panniers slung across their horses. Ghazan set his white horse to a walk, heading north, while first the head of the column, then gradually all the remaining groups with their flocks, moved forward, raising a trail of dust.

There was no path. Ghazan led the tribe directly up into the sandstone hills, moving from side to side when the slope was steep. From the highest point of the pass he looked back on the cold side of the year. The plain bore no mark of recent habitation. Even the wattle corrals had been carried away. Only piles of stones, heaped in blunt low walls to break the wind from each tent's sleeping family, marked human progress, but these were timeless signs that might have been left generations ago. Otherwise the plain stretched brown and bare.

Yes, it was time they started. Once more he was leading his people away from the sun's heat. Today was the dawn not of one day only but of the whole year. All winter they had been well in their low-lying quarters, a mere two thousand feet above the level of the Gulf, but now spring swung Persia towards a vertical sun, lowland grass was drying up, and no streams ran there to renew the green. Soon the plains would become a sun-baked brick floor, the brackish wells dark with malarial insects. The life given in winter would be snatched back in summer. It would be death to remain.

For thirteen of his thirty years Ghazan had led the annual spring ascent. Each year determined a new orbit, though always within certain wide but unvarying limits, for each spring distributed according to a different pattern the rain and life-giving grass. Grass—thick, succulent, soft with juice, high as a horse's girth—this he hoped to find in a few days; at present the scattered, almost colourless blades hardly broke through the stony desert, but so long as it gave life to the life-giving flocks, they must follow its devious carpet.

On either side rose undulating hills, bare of ...
the main body of riders, the women and childr...
on the backs of pack-animals, kept to the easi...
men drove the black goats and grey sheep, h...
from their buttocks, along the high slopes.
task of assuring some eight miles of progre...
deviating flocks might cover twice that dista...
herds sufficient grazing for their long day's ...
Ghazan had foreseen from the light rainfall, ...
usual, and the herds lagged. He thought of ve...
a parallel pass, then remembered that on his las...
had shown signs of failing. At a pinch the h...
without drinking, the donkeys five days, the ...
every second night the two hundred thousan...
him must drink their fill, to be able to ...
with their milk. So they could not wande...
streams until the Shiraz road was crossed.
mountains, they could travel almost at will a...
sides, a diversion would take time. Once the...
unprotected, Ghazan would allow no delays...

By mid-morning they had penetrated deep ...
with thorny jujubes and oaks, stunted and g...
soil. They had met no living creature but occasi...
buff partridge, a thousand or more strong, ...
eaters; they had seen no habitation or sign of ...
had traversed that morning belonged to Gha...
villages—that the tribe would cross in the nex...
ancestral heritage, a trust from God for his pe...
every part of this minor world: his brain was a ...
each range, each fold in the ground, each ur...
He could mark from one year to the next ...
flattened this hilltop, the drought which had pa...
desert, slight rifts in a terrain which man alter...
varying climate. He had long since surveyed it...
with a loving eye, until now he knew the fee...
slope.

He called no halt that day. When the su...
herdsmen trooped to their pack-animals. The ...

22

CHAPTER ONE

DARKNESS covered this part of the earth. Hidden light gradually turned the black sky to grey, revealing the outlines of a valley, flat and still. Empty, too, it seemed, until the growing glimmer picked out a white horse, bridled and saddled. From the darkness a man emerged, mounted heavily, as though not yet fully awake, and rode slowly towards the palest part of the sky. Reaching the first ridge on the valley's edge, he looked towards the rising sun.

Its light showed a fine-boned face on which the flesh lay firm, with long, slightly curved nose; thick black hair above a high straight brow, and animated dark eyes, rather narrow and long, as though made to scan wide horizons. He sat high and erect on his horse, his long fingers light along the reins, gazing steadfastly at the sun. Muscles, firm and prominent as those in his horse's flank, swelled a tight tunic. After a few moments, as though having caught the sun's fire, he turned quickly and trotted down the ridge. The valley before him was being created by the sun: fawn earth, with the weft of grass almost worn threadbare; corralled herds of brown, grey and black beasts; last of all, black dwellings, perhaps a thousand uncompromising oblong shapes like the pattern on an old earthenware jar: pools of stillness, patches of night. The horseman rode back into the valley, still motionless, as though the settlement had survived its population: graves waiting for the last trumpet to sound. He pressed his thighs against the horse's flanks and cantered to a tent on the southernmost side of the encampment. At his approach there came out a figure dressed, like the rider, in a tunic with divided sleeves and divided skirt, bound by a large blue silk cummerbund, with a close-fitting brown felt hat tilted back at an angle, brimless, but having long flaps turned vertically upwards. On his feet gleamed white, hand-made cord shoes. He carried a long, straight, horn-shaped musical instrument.

"Is it time, Ghazan Khan?"

"Time and more than time."

His voice, neither deep nor shrill, had an edge to it, a voice for cutting through difficulties. The man with the wooden horn at once ran up to a continuation of the same commanding ridge, from which outcropped a platform of stone. Here he stood regaining his breath, while the Khan followed slowly, then raised the surnay to his lips.

Ghazan knew the notes so well that when they sounded they seemed an echo of his own unspoken wishes. The artless skirling music called and incited. The still valley like a sounding-box rang a welcome to the dawn. Again and again a short rising phrase was repeated, as the sun rose free of the mountain peaks, and under the twin impulses of light and music the camp stirred. Now from one tent, now from another, figures stumbled sleepily. Smoke of fires began to rise straight in the chill dawn; food was prepared and hurriedly eaten. The trumpeter lowered his surnay and returned to his tent, while the stirring below in the plain grew till no part was untouched. Then, far to the north, Ghazan saw the first black square dwelling collapse, followed by another close by. The neat straight lines billowed and fell, the goatskin felt was stamped flat, rolled and stowed among the other baggage now being prepared. As far as the eye could see, tents were being folded up, until, an hour after the surnay call, every one of the thousand black pools had evaporated under the new sun.

Ghazan rode back and entered the encampment—fragments spread-eagled as though by earthquake. Disorder everywhere: clothes, bedding, animals, humans intermingled like folded rocks. It seemed they would never form up. All that the black tents had hidden was being corded on passive kneeling camels and on donkeys held by children: kettles, wooden and copper cooking-pots, sacks of grain and rice, dried meat and curds, looms, drums and surnays, clucking hens and roosters in pouches slung across donkeys, as well as the living-quarters themselves: cushions, rugs, tent-poles, the black goatskin tent, guy-ropes and stakes fashioned of bone, even the wattled rushes which divided the erect tent. All these were packed to the sound of barking dogs, bleating sheep and goats, neighing horses; the bray of mules, the occasional deep roar of a camel.

As one family loaded the last of their possessions, a boy would find a water-pipe, a roll of cotton or a jar containing ferment overlooked in the scurry. Amid shouts and laughter bales had to be uncorded, still further filled, then with imprecise, excited fingers tied once more on to the pack-animals. Meanwhile the herdsmen were uniting their flocks

20

in large groups, chasing strays, shouting to dogs, throwing stones to disperse or close up ranks, driving forward others with sticks, while some helped their women and infants on to the back of camel or horse.

Gradually the solution cohered: some fifty groups of a hundred or so were composed, each with its flocks on either side of the main body of riders, which formed the coloured centre of a brown and black design. Ghazan rode to the head of the column, where he was joined by forty horsemen armed with rifles, a few rounds of ammunition in their leather jerkins, and by two attendants, the Khan's personal possessions in leather panniers slung across their horses. Ghazan set his white horse to a walk, heading north, while first the head of the column, then gradually all the remaining groups with their flocks, moved forward, raising a trail of dust.

There was no path. Ghazan led the tribe directly up into the sandstone hills, moving from side to side when the slope was steep. From the highest point of the pass he looked back on the cold side of the year. The plain bore no mark of recent habitation. Even the wattle corrals had been carried away. Only piles of stones, heaped in blunt low walls to break the wind from each tent's sleeping family, marked human progress, but these were timeless signs that might have been left generations ago. Otherwise the plain stretched brown and bare.

Yes, it was time they started. Once more he was leading his people away from the sun's heat. Today was the dawn not of one day only but of the whole year. All winter they had been well in their low-lying quarters, a mere two thousand feet above the level of the Gulf, but now spring swung Persia towards a vertical sun, lowland grass was drying up, and no streams ran there to renew the green. Soon the plains would become a sun-baked brick floor, the brackish wells dark with malarial insects. The life given in winter would be snatched back in summer. It would be death to remain.

For thirteen of his thirty years Ghazan had led the annual spring ascent. Each year determined a new orbit, though always within certain wide but unvarying limits, for each spring distributed according to a different pattern the rain and life-giving grass. Grass—thick, succulent, soft with juice, high as a horse's girth—this he hoped to find in a few days; at present the scattered, almost colourless blades hardly broke through the stony desert, but so long as it gave life to the life-giving flocks, they must follow its devious carpet.

On either side rose undulating hills, bare of tree and bush, and while the main body of riders, the women and children and city of tents borne on the backs of pack-animals, kept to the easier line of the pass, herdsmen drove the black goats and grey sheep, heavy rolls of fat hanging from their buttocks, along the high slopes. To Ghazan fell the dual task of assuring some eight miles of progress every day (though the deviating flocks might cover twice that distance) and of allowing the herds sufficient grazing for their long day's march. This spring, as Ghazan had foreseen from the light rainfall, pasture was scantier than usual, and the herds lagged. He thought of veering west, of striking up a parallel pass, then remembered that on his last patrol the stream there had shown signs of failing. At a pinch the horses could go three days without drinking, the donkeys five days, the camels several weeks. But every second night the two hundred thousand sheep and goats around him must drink their fill, to be able to quench the tribe's thirst with their milk. So they could not wander far from known deep streams until the Shiraz road was crossed. Beyond, in the higher mountains, they could travel almost at will and be sure of water. Besides, a diversion would take time. Once they were on the move and unprotected, Ghazan would allow no delays.

By mid-morning they had penetrated deep into hills thinly scattered with thorny jujubes and oaks, stunted and gnarled, so stony was the soil. They had met no living creature but occasional coveys of red-legged buff partridge, a thousand or more strong, and swooping blue bee-eaters; they had seen no habitation or sign of man. All the land they had traversed that morning belonged to Ghazan, and all—save a few villages—that the tribe would cross in the next few weeks was his: an ancestral heritage, a trust from God for his people's good. Yet he knew every part of this minor world: his brain was a relief map inscribed with each range, each fold in the ground, each underground watercourse. He could mark from one year to the next the erosion which had flattened this hilltop, the drought which had parched that fertile land to desert, slight rifts in a terrain which man altered even less than wind or varying climate. He had long since surveyed it, not with theodolite but with a loving eye, until now he knew the feel and character of every slope.

He called no halt that day. When the sun reached its zenith the herdsmen trooped to their pack-animals. The men wore strips of cloth bound across nose and mouth as protection from the suffocating dust and sand stirred up by their flocks. They and their women searched the baggage, while chickens slung behind cackled in protest, until they found dried balls of sour buttermilk prepared the previous night. Lowering their masks, the herdsmen ate the milk balls, still on the move. When they had returned to the heights, those women who carried infants uncovered their breasts and suckled them, still seated on horse or donkey or camel, still moving forward. More than one herdsman that day brought down a late lamb, too small to keep up with the flocks, to his wife, who laid it dangling across her lap, between herself and her child, while steadily the procession continued, unchallenged, through country in which nothing revealed the existence of man on earth.

As shadows began to lengthen, they too caught up in the movement, Ghazan hastened the pace. They rode beside a thin stream of water now, with green banks, its fertile power extending upwards too, hovering like mist in the form of grey willows and poplars tipped with buds. But all restrained their thirst till a halt should be called. Twice they swept through narrow gullies, where progress was in single file, then out to more level slopes where Ghazan considered the pasture adequate. With a wave of his left arm he signalled that camp should be pitched. The column of riders dispersed and in turn the herds were led to drink, their guards kneeling beside them and drinking no less deeply. The thirst of so many thousands gradually narrowed the stream to a trickle. One by one black tents were unrolled and set up, as the western heights flung their bulky shadow across the people, and the first day was done.

On fires of camel-thorn tea was made and food heated. Ghazan regained his own tent. The court lived under red, yellow or blue canvas, in shape like the tribesmen's tents but twice as large, measuring eight paces by ten, and supported by seven poles instead of four. Ghazan's tent was turquoise blue, traditional colour of the Khan. His tunic was also blue, whereas the tribesmen's tunics were fawn. In the tent all was set up as in the valley, the interior hung with multi-coloured woven clothes, the ground soft with carpets and cushions. Here Ghazan sat and was served with rice and partridge breast, followed by *mast* —fermented goat's milk. He ate in silence from a silver platter incised with bird and beast, using the fingers of his right hand, then stretched out on the cushions and stared across at the newly founded city, the city of a single night. In how many different valleys they had slept! Bronze bells-within-bells sounded on the necks of bull camels; songs and ballads mingled with bleating and whinnying; everywhere excitement that the long migration had begun.

Summoning his groom, Ghazan mounted once more and, making a wide circuit, ascertained that guards had been posted. The encampment could sleep secure: but for himself there would be no rest. He rode south-west, towards the Farrashband road. In that direction lay thirty times today's numbers, the remainder of his people, more than a hundred thousand waiting to be set in migration, each group following a different route to be sure of grass and water, yet still remaining close enough, one to another, to be under his protective command.

He reached the track linking Shiraz to Farrashband, half-way to the encampment of the Shalguli. This was one of twelve tribes which formed a loose federation under Ghazan's leadership. Each tribe took the name of its own chieftain, but as a collective group they called themselves by Ghazan's own family name, Falqani. Their loyalty was to Ghazan; the Falqani were his people.

The night was moonless and dark, but even in pitch darkness his horse would have known the way. Land and sky were composed of shades of black and grey, the mountains rising to obscure half the heavens. Far away, but prominent against the skyline, stood a long-abandoned gendarmerie post, a pile of stones in a circle. A tomb to his enemies' hopes: and Ghazan took pleasure in marking its crumbled perimeter.

He saw a spark ahead like a low star. He thought it was a form of Elmo's fire, very common in the plain. On thunderous nights sparks would fly from outstretched fingers to the tent they were about to touch. But this reddish glow above the stones swelled to a yellow pinpoint of light, then subsided. He turned off the road, within cover of rocks. Who could be smoking up there? A shepherd, a brigand newly escaped from Shiraz? Or a third alternative, too much the embodiment of his apprehensions to be named?

Using cover, he went directly to investigate. His horse, sensing Ghazan's caution, picked a way quietly among the boulders. A dark head and shoulders took shape against the grey sky. Ghazan continued to within hailing distance, then a loose stone turned and rattled down the slope. The figure jumped perceptibly, unslung a rifle and began to fire at random in all directions. Ghazan swerved and cantered back. He knew now who it was. Only a gendarme would be armed and take fright like that.

Gendarmes re-established along the Farrashband road—after fourteen years' absence. The discovery filled him with dismay. Not that they could shoot straight, but they had eyes to report tribal movements along or near the road. They were watchers—in the heart of his country; a challenge and an embodiment of the past.

The gendarmerie and the army which had swept him to power had been the instruments of Reza Shah's will. It was they who, some twenty-five years ago, had rounded up the Falqani during the autumn migration, confiscating the arms they carried to procure game and to protect their flocks. It was they who had enforced the new settled life, so contrary to the tribespeople's nature. From the beginning of time the Falqani had been wanderers, servants and handmaidens of their flocks in the quest for grass; now they became as disconsolate as captured ibexes, fretting in a corral. They were hungry, sick and exploited. A petition was made to the Government—to Reza Shah himself—asking for some relaxation of the more stringent regulations. Reza Shah's retort was to seize Ghazan's father, Khan of the Falqani, who had presented the petition, and throw him into prison. There he died from drinking a cup of poisoned coffee.

The tribes lost their unity and hope, for their Khan had been a father to them. Every year malaria decimated the settlers in the plain, pneumonia the settlers in the highlands, until the survivors knew they must move with the seasons or in a few years cease to exist. But they were disarmed and under military control, so they had to pay to live—with the very essentials of life, since they had none of the luxuries. All the officers of the hierarchy in each region had to receive suitable 'presents', so that the tribes, when they moved, were like fleeced sheep. But they considered no price too high to strike their tents, to be themselves once more. These movements were local and restricted, not the present great sweeping trek of three hundred miles: sorties of a few days into higher or lower ground to nourish their flocks. No one but the sun was deprived of the grass yet the army took every occasion of humiliating them on these journeys, fixing (and constantly changing) their departure date and their route, compelling them to return before the agreed time had elapsed. And against this injustice there was no redress, for the Shah had settled them, and his word was law.

Ghazan thought of those years of settlement in terms of one incident, by no means unusual. The army commandant in Farrashband had a mongrel bitch, something between pointer and greyhound, which he used for flushing partridges. This bitch died a week after producing a litter of three puppies. Fearing to lose them, the commandant ordered his batmen to collect two bowls of milk daily from suckling tribes-women and give them to his puppies—an order doubly outrageous, for dogs were regarded as unclean and Falqani women revered by their men to an extent unknown among settled Persians. One of the most sacred Falqani oaths was "By my mother's milk." But the order was enforced, and daily for a month two bowls of milk from Falqani mothers were lapped up by the three mongrel pups. Ghazan had seen it with his own eyes, had heard the deprived infants scream in hunger. He had never been able to forget those cries.

When the Khan had been murdered, Ghazan, his only son, was eight, living at Farrashband and Shiraz, a virtual prisoner of the army. At the age of fifteen he had been sent to school in Switzerland. It was his mother's way of saving him from his cousin Rohim's fate. Rohim attended school in Teheran and every morning before lessons suffered the humiliation of having to report to the police—he, a prince and the son of princes. For two years Ghazan dragged out an alien existence in Lausanne until the invasion of Persia in 1941. The much-vaunted army, on which money, equipment and privileges had been lavished, put up a timid three days' defence and was utterly discredited. Soon after Reza Shah's abdication Ghazan had returned to rejoin his people, who had hailed him with all the enthusiasm due to their rightful lord. Simultaneously his exile and their enslavement had ended. He led them once more to grass.

But always the ambiguity in his position had remained. As the son of a man whom the Government had feared enough to kill, he was suspect; he directly confronted the son of a tyrant whom he believed to be his father's murderer. As tribal Ilkhan he owed loyalty to the Shah, but had undisputed lordship over his own people. As long as he paid annual taxes for them and their flocks and provided men in time of war, the Government had no right to interfere with him. But the present Shah had never formally acknowledged Ghazan's khanship, and Ghazan had always presumed that he did not choose to recognize it. Frequent changes of government, the threat from Russia, oil nationalization and subsequent economic difficulties: these had worked in favour of the tribe's independence. An army brigade stationed in Shiraz continued to harass the tribe, rather from traditional enmity than as part of a well-directed plan from Teheran. Since the war, neither they nor gendarmes had ventured far into Falqani territory. Either no group in the capital had been powerful enough to challenge Ghazan's authority, or else they had decided to leave him and his people in peace. This armed figure within the circle of stones might mean only that the Government intended to control roads within tribal country; on the other hand, he might mean much more.

The wild shooting was not resumed. Choosing a way invisible to the sentry, Ghazan rode south. Before midnight he reached the Shalguli encampment, larger than the one he had left, glowing with the embers of many fires. He was escorted by servants to a well-furnished tent. Within an hour the leaders of federated tribes had gathered round him. They were dressed like Ghazan in every colour but blue; some wore leather jerkins; none was without the brown felt hat peculiar to the Falqani, with flaps turned up on itself, so that it resembled a crown. In turn they gave him their information: disposition of tents, state of their flocks and neighbouring streams, the pasture lands already cropped; then made known the more important reports of agents and spies. One had seen jeeps patrolling the Shiraz-Bushire road; another gave news of artillery arriving from the north; a third had been told of increased firing on the Shiraz practice-ranges; a fourth spoke of a larger army headquarters being built; others reported soldiers manning forts long deserted. Ghazan asked whether the units had been identified. Had a new brigade arrived? No one knew. But this spring there were more soldiers, of that they were certain.

Ghazan listened gravely. Even without interference the migration was a highly complicated and exacting struggle against the elements, taxing resources of man and beast to the limit. During two months the Falqani were balanced on the knife-edge of survival. For the last six years their troubles had been greatly increased by the army's harassing tactics as the tribe crossed the Guyum plain. South, near the Gulf, few passable tracks crossed the hills, and northwards the mountains were largely unmapped: in neither region would the army dare molest them.

Only in the wide Guyum plain, less than twenty miles from army head-quarters, traversed by the Shiraz-Ardakan road and unprotected by hills, were the tribe vulnerable. The reports, linked with his own discovery of the newly-manned gendarme post, suggested that this spring the army might try to prevent their crossing altogether. While his chieftains fell silent, Ghazan weighed his decision, then spoke briefly.

"The army have one hope of success—repetition of their tactics nine years ago. They'll try to pin us south of the Shiraz road, then drive us east to desert-country—wait for sun and thirst to do what their bullets can never do. Our people must cross on a single night. Two covering parties will guard them. All must move north at once—no matter their hunger and thirst. In eight days we cross—by night."

At the end of the tent rose a bullock of a man: broad-shouldered and stocky, almost fat. This was Tughril, Ghazan's maternal uncle, chieftain of the Shalguli, the most powerful of the federated tribes. Sweeping a forelock of thick hair, still dark, from his eyes, he thrust his big head forward aggressively.

"Skulking across by night!" he growled with scorn.

"So long as the tribe cross safely, what does it matter, day or night?"

"If you slink across by night, you admit you cannot move by day."

"I admit nothing," Ghazan retorted, then, less warmly, "I like this course no more than you, but it's the best I can find."

"Some subtle Swiss strategy, perhaps? Too subtle for Tughril. Tughril has read no foreign books. Tughril has only his experience to draw on, only the experience of ninety-six such crossings. Not once that I can remember have the Falqani crossed by night." He looked round with challenging eyes and added darkly, "I'm not sure I can convince the Shalguli to flit across like bats."

"What is your plan, then?"

"Plan?" he echoed, in a pained tone. "That is the Ilkhan's affair. But one thing Tughril knows: if soldiers block the route he and his fathers have taken for seven hundred years, he doesn't slip quietly past by night, doesn't let them live to block the route a second time."

"Attack, is that what you want? But how?"

Half-sneering, he replied, "I thought the Ilkhan would have framed a plan."

"I have, Tughril—only to reject it. First you must cut the road north and south. Then you must surround the fort. How long to starve out the fort?"

"Say seven days."

"Seven days. And how long can our flocks find grass and water, hidden for safety in the foothills?"

"If you're playing for safety!" he taunted.

"Answer the question, Tughril." His uncle scowled but said nothing. "I will answer for you. Three days at most. Then they will start to sicken and die. So that your plan, though excellent perhaps for a wet spring, now that the grass is dry and burnt would do us more harm than good."

Tughril flung up his hands. "Am I never to have my revenge?" he roared, so that the big tent billowed and shook.

Everyone knew what he meant. Tughril's hatred of the Shah's army was crystallized in one ineffaceable episode at which he never tired of hinting. It brought him even Ghazan's sympathy.

In the summer of 1933 the Teheran races had been held before a record crowd. As the horses of the four-thousand-metre race approached the winning post it could be seen that the two leading horses were ridden by a white-robed tribesman and an army officer. The tribesman lay half a length ahead and the officer was doing his best to ride off his opponent or force him on to the uneven ground at the side of the course. The other retaliated in the fashion usual to Persian races by trying to ward off the officer's attacks with his whip. In this he succeeded and he passed the post an easy winner.

As soon as he had dismounted, the tribesman, held between two orderlies, was conducted before Reza Shah. His Imperial Majesty, wearing army uniform—tall, moustached, severe—delivered a short lecture and then proceeded to kick Tughril in the stomach. When the royal wrath had abated, servants belaboured him with any weapon to hand. He was led away in a pitiable condition. The officer, who had been more to blame, was not even reprimanded.

That same tribesman now pointed an accusing finger at Ghazan. "Always you find ways to cheat me of revenge!"

"This plan is not designed to cheat you, Tughril: it's designed for the good of the tribe."

The big figure, who seemed to fill the tent, snorted contemptuously. "Fine words to cover weakness!"

29

The chieftains murmured in reproach; Ghazan struggled with his temper. "As you well know, Tughril, only a strong hand can rein in a proud horse."

"Why rein it in—year after year? Soon the horse will forget how to gallop, shy at a cracking twig. The touch of spurs, that's what is needed: your father knew how to press in his spurs! Doubtless now he is watching with shame!"

Ghazan's father had led life as a saga, himself the hero, quick to defend, in daredevil deeds, even the semblance of infringement of traditional tribal rights.

"I care for my people no less than he," Ghazan retorted coldly. "What shame, so long as the tribe is safe—and," he added pointedly, "so long as we hold together?"

Some of the chieftains shouted assent. "What harm in a crossing by night?" they cried.

Seeing the tide against him, Tughril shrugged. "Do as you like, then," he said knowingly. "But one day you'll admit Tughril was right. One day you will say, I should have attacked before the army built up its strength!"

He squatted down. This sudden withdrawal angered Ghazan but did not come as a surprise. Tughril longed to lead and play the leader. But he lacked any rallying-point in himself, and so lacked the leader's banner. He found his strength only against a set object of attack. Whatever the course, he opposed and raised doubts. He was difficult to pin down, unpredictable: a host of enemies in one.

When Ghazan had given each chieftain the route he should follow and the date of departure, in a dark mood the assembly dispersed.

CHAPTER TWO

NEXT morning Ghazan rode up to Shiraz. Every spring he went to the family house to inspect accounts and pay taxes, bring pedigree books up to date, sell wool and buy for his people at a favourable price sacks of sugar-loaves and chests of tea. After a full day's ride he circled the town at dusk and from the north-west outskirts approached Garden of the Pines.

The house, built by his grandfather, stood in the largest garden of Shiraz. It had thirty rooms in two storeys, with a wide columned balcony facing south on the upper floor. The lower part of its walls was faced in blue faience, on which poems of Hafiz were inscribed in white mosaic, so large they could be read by moonlight from the garden.

For Ghazan the house meant Nowruz. Here every spring of his childhood he had celebrated the vernal equinox. All those early holidays had merged in retrospect with the first he could remember. He had arrived from tribal tents with his father to find the usually deserted garden crowded with men of all ages, talking over water-pipes or admiring the trees, the violets and pansies. To all of them, during the next few days, he had been presented. The strange faces were animated by the same blood and so a part of him. Nothing in appearance or speech made it evident, but his father said so, and that settled it. They were gathered at the house of the head of the family, to enjoy his hospitality and reaffirm loyalty. Most were chieftains or their sons; those who had married Falqani girls were sometimes landowners.

Inside on a large table were laid out *mast*, eggs coloured red, yellow and chestnut, fresh cheese and the traditional seven objects beginning with the letter *sin*; apple, vinegar, fennel-flowers, garlic, sumac, jujube sweets and a bowl of sprouting green corn: esoteric symbols which no one could explain to him and which partly for that reason set Nowruz above all other days. On the table also stood a bowl of water in which swam a goldfish, for the earth rested on the horns of a bull, itself supported by a fish. And at the crucial moment, when the sun entered the sign of the Ram, this goldfish turned towards Mecca. That

31

was a signal for them all, in their new clothes, to eat together, to laugh and enjoy themselves, and to exchange presents.

One of those early presents still lay in the cupboard of his room: a red cotton kite, the shape of a flint arrow-head, but flat, with twelve yellow bows to its tail. His father had shown him how to fly it beside the pool in the rose garden: first running into the wind, gradually unrolling the string which always became fankled and coaxing it with a flick of his wrist until it soared almost out of sight. Then his father had cut pieces of square cardboard, the size of a letter, with a hole in the centre, on which they wrote messages—sometimes to the sun, sometimes to no definite destination—giving secret, important information and always asking a question. With eager fingers he had slipped the card on the string and watched it career upwards to the seventh heaven. After what seemed an eternal wait, the string was agitated and the card brought down to earth. Quickly his father removed it and showed him the answer to his question, written in a clear hand on the card. Once he had asked, How old is the oldest carp in the pool? And the answer came, Ninety years old. Another time he had asked where a lost ball was to be found. The answer said, Behind the donkey stables. And there he had retrieved the ball. On those days he learned that nature had a voice, and later the discovery that his father substituted unseen a second specially prepared card did not alter in any way the fundamental childhood truth.

Some relations visited Garden of the Pines for one day only; others, usually the poorer dressed, remained for the whole holiday. On the thirteenth day they would drive or ride out under the archway of the Teng-i-Allahu Akbar. This, too, had been a childhood wonder. It contained a Koran heavy as a block of granite from which a single leaf, if withdrawn, would equal in weight the whole volume. His mother had told him that, and he believed her. Truth then had been whatever swung imagination highest.

They had spent the thirteenth day in the fields, sitting beside a stream, listening to the spring-wild water. Throughout Persia villages, towns, cities were deserted on that day until dusk, when all returned fresh and revivified to the new year, having first thrown away the sprouting green corn, but not the earth in the bowl, so that the shoots would wither more quickly. With this feast of fruitfulness the Nowruz celebrations ended, and the family drifted away. For a few days he missed them, but liked to think that wherever he might be in Southern Persia, he had loyal friends, bound by the blood tie. Even, wandering through the Shiraz streets, if some face caught his eye, he would think, That man, too, may be my kinsman.

Later, Garden of the Pines had become his place of study. At Farrashband, with the Koran and Saadi's gnomic poem, the *Gulistan*, as his textbooks, he had learned to read and write. At thirteen his mother, a woman known for her piety, had sent him to Shiraz to study algebra, rhetoric, jurisprudence and scholastic theology under a saintly mullah named Mahdi. This man was a Sufi: that is to say, he believed that God is Pure Being, and the created world reflects His attributes, as a pool of water reflects the sun. He believed that God said to David, "I was a Hidden Treasure, and I wished to be known, so I created creation that I might be known." The Sufi's creed, mystical in practice, was liberal in dogma and freely admitted the value of other religions as "interpretations of a single dream". He preferred living religious experience to abstract theological formulæ and insisted that man must strip away selfish desires in order to be united to God. For two years— the most important of his life—Ghazan had studied under the mullah Mahdi. At the end of that time he was a convinced Sufi.

Islam held that religion was a matter between God and the individual. God admitted no intercessor, no priest. A few men had been elected as His prophets, to call mankind to Him. The Koran was evident proof that God speaks to man, and the Sufi was one who likewise strove to catch the sound of His voice. A passage in the second chapter of the Koran showed where he might listen:

"Truly, in the creation of the heavens and the earth, and the alternation of night and day, and in the ship that sails the sea with that which profits man, and in the water God sends down from heaven and therewith quickens the earth after its death, and spreads abroad all kinds of cattle, and in the shifting of the winds, and in the clouds that are pressed into service between heaven and earth, are signs to people who can understand."

The Sufi believed that, by reading such signs—to which he attached considerable importance—by following the example of wise and holy men, and by God's grace, it was possible, even in this life, to anticipate the joys of eternity. The mullah Mahdi favoured an ascetic method, whereby man renounced human pleasures, whittled away his own sensations to be more conscious of God's presence. Ghazan had striven to impose this view on himself. But by nature he was more inclined to believe that man could approach God no less through joy than through sorrow.

At Garden of the Pines Ghazan had studied Sufi doctrine, written his homework and committed phrases to memory. Not that he had been forced to learn the commentaries parrot-fashion—his master cared nothing for the cargo of glosses which submerged original texts—but certain passages from al-Ghazali and Avicenna and the poet Jami he had been urged to make his own. Submission, acceptance, renunciation, resignation to the inevitable: these key-words still echoed through the rooms.

His master had sometimes checked as vicious his passionate eagerness to learn. Curiosity about the least detail of all subjects he had inherited from his mother, a Falqani of the Shalguli tribe: a round-cheeked, laughing woman, her fingers forever at wool-shears or loom. She had given the Ilkhan only one child, and after his murder it was she who had held the settled tribe together, issuing wise, often cryptic orders from her tent, feared and respected even by the army. She had loved her son too well to keep him by her, and had made him excel—in the saddle or at school—by expecting from him, as from herself, only the very best. He had seen her seldom. Sometimes, on winter evenings, she would call him to her tent to tell him by the hour stories of past Falqani feats and sing tribal ballads, her voice cracked and feeble because in the lowlands she had contracted malaria. Every year the disease recurred, gouging away the round cheeks, but not her laughter, bending her straight back, but not her will. Last summer she had died: and during that last summer she had named Anahita for her son.

An Ilkhan's marriage presented difficulties. By tradition he could seek a bride only from the Madaleh or Shalguli clans or from his own family. Though Ghazan had never seen Anahita, a distant maternal cousin, he took it for granted that his mother had made a wise choice.

On this visit his betrothal with Anahita was to take place. With care Ghazan chose sugar, tea and sweets, a fine orange-coloured shawl and, from a jeweller who brought his gems specially to the house, a ring set with diamonds and a pair of gold earrings. These he arranged on six large trays. On his second last day in Shiraz he had them delivered to Garden of the Orange Grove, Anahita's house. Next morning the earrings were placed in her ears by a friend—the mother of many children—and so, without their having met, Anahita was betrothed to Ghazan.

The marriage was arranged for that autumn. Until then Ghazan did not expect to return to Shiraz, yet he wanted to meet this girl his mother had chosen for him. He asked if he might call at Garden of the Orange Grove, and because he was Ilkhan his request was granted.

In the late afternoon of the betrothal day, feeling a little stiff and unnatural in collar and tie and blue suit, Ghazan was driven in his car out of Shiraz by the Isfahan road, past the public garden and the mausoleum to Saadi, towards a hamlet which bore the poet's name. A closely knit family, living apart from the rest of the town, the mother a Falqani, the father that rare creature: a landowner who cared for his peasants. Anahita was seventeen; she had one brother, a year younger, at school in Teheran. She herself had not been to school; she had been given lessons by her mother. Ghazan supposed she would know how to sew and make her clothes, run a household and give orders that were obeyed. But for a girl the days were long in Shiraz. She could not go out unaccompanied: there were few distractions and fewer parties.

At the hamlet his car took a side road, through open gates, through an orange grove, to a two-storeyed house of buff brick under the first range of the Zagros. Ghazan was admitted by a servant and shown into a large room with mirror alcoves, a brown Hamadan carpet on the stone floor: well furnished but not luxuriously. The family was not very rich.

The mother rose to meet him: a sturdy, rather stout woman in black. The girl was sitting apart on a couch. Her face was hidden by a pale blue cloak, hanging from the brow. He noticed she was tall and slender.

The mother took his hand. "Peace be upon you."

"Peace on you and your family," answered Ghazan warmly.

With a smile she invited him to be seated. He chose a straight chair which allowed him to see the girl.

"This is a happy day, Ghazan. If only your dear mother were with us!"

"God keep fragrant her grave!"

"A happy day for us all. And happier still—God willing—the autumn."

35

For a moment they sat in silence with the future, smiling but both a little ill at ease.

"Tughril and his sons—are they all well?"

"In excellent health. And your husband?"

"I must apologize—he's away at Fasa."

"Still planting trees? How well he looks after his people!"

She looked at him in surprise, none too pleased. "Still spending good money on peasants. Pistachio groves: that is the latest. It is the second time he has planted them."

"The second time?" he inquired politely, then looked beyond at the girl. All but a pale brow was still hidden by the chador, a semicircle of cotton worn as a cloak from the back of the head to near the feet, and which could be drawn forward and held at the chin to cover part or all of the face.

"This winter what do you think the imbeciles did? Cut down every one of the precious saplings for firewood! Always trouble. And now this talk of dividing estates."

Ghazan liked the chador. Tribeswomen did not wear it—a hindrance in so active a life—so their eyes met a man's directly. Tribal children wore it sometimes. The chador made Anahita seem childlike, and remote. He felt he had entered a new world, of shadows and half-shadows.

Tea was served in glasses, held in enamelled blue containers, decorated with gazelle. These Ghazan admired.

The mother was delighted. "Anahita found them. She went herself to the Bazaar-i-Vakil."

He turned to the girl. "Already you hunt the wild gazelle!"

"There were lots to be had with roses, but I'd set my heart on these." He found her voice unexpectedly timid: the voice of a very young girl.

"I like the gazelle too," he said. "Some of my plate is engraved with running gazelle."

They sipped the milkless, very sweet tea in silence. Twice he felt her eyes on him. But when he turned his own, she lowered hers quickly, like a child caught.

"You saw the bare trees coming in?" her mother asked of Ghazan. "All this morning we've been gathering blossom, Anahita and I, to scent our winter cupboards and to make orange-water. I said to Anahita, 'This is the last time you gather blossom from these trees. Next

36

spring your servants will gather it for you at Garden of the Pines—for the wife of the Ilkhan of the Falqani." Her voice was touched with triumph.

"Only if spring is early," Ghazan corrected. "Anahita must be with her people."

The wife of a Falqani, from camel-herd to chieftain, lived at her husband's side. Their shared life was made doubly close because, whereas men of the plains had the right to take up to four wives, the Falqani were, by custom, strictly monogamous.

"Yes, yes," the mother said. "But all winter she'll be at Garden of the Pines. You're not going to steal her completely, Ghazan!"

She had stipulated that they must winter in Shiraz and, because Anahita was an only daughter, he had agreed.

He turned to Anahita. "Next spring you shall ride into the hills. I've chosen your white mare already: I'm training her myself."

"But I've never ridden," she said doubtfully.

"I shall teach you."

After a pause she asked, "On a donkey?"

"No, on a small horse with a leading-rein. When you've learned to manage that, you will mount the Arab—I call her Milk of the Moon —and ride at the head of the tribe. Already they look forward to welcoming you. They loved my mother: you too they will love, and serve well. They are a loyal people: loyal and strong and tender."

"My mother has told me."

He bowed to the mother, then turned again to Anahita. "But be prepared at first for disappointment. You will leave your home and find apparently nothing: bare earth and cloudless sky. Only later will you come to feel that the sky is your roof and the earth your house, washed clean by rain, dried by the wind, a house with a storey each for winter and summer, with seventy thousand different rooms. You will grow to love it so much that even a house as dear to you as this will seem superfluous, coming between you and the earth and the sky.

"This time next year you will be leaving your winter apartments— climbing the long wide staircase of the hills . . ."

Her mother was watching Anahita. "Six weeks you will ride," she broke in emphatically, "without coming to the limits of your land. Whole ranges of hills: all of them yours."

37

"You shall ride over the mountains until we pitch camp in the high grass. And there, in the uplands, before anything else, you will knot a rug."

Apologetically she said, "I don't know how to knot rugs."

Her mother added quickly, "She will learn in no time. You will find her wonderfully capable, Ghazan. Everything she turns her hand to, she does well."

Still to Anahita, Ghazan continued, "Dilbar will show you—the wife of my shepherd. She knots very well. She will teach you how to mar the pattern—for perfection attracts the evil eye—and to leave a space at the bottom for the spirit of the rug to come out. Your tasselled rug will bloom on the brown plains and the green hills. It will be the garden of our home."

"God willing," she said. Again the young voice: Ghazan made an effort to adapt himself.

"Up in the hills that look so bare my people will show you their treasure. Cranberries and pomegranates with a yellow skin; pistachios and the seeds of the wild pear, which roasted and salted are better than almonds. Up in the hills you will find hidden all sorts of food." He paused, wishing he could see her face, but it still lay in the chador's shadow. "What would you fancy most?"

"Most of all?" She thought a moment. "Ice-cream, I think. I love ice-cream," she added with feeling.

He was a little taken aback. After a space he said, "The Falqani have never eaten ice-cream. But there is a high mountain in summer quarters called the Dina. Its peak is always snow-tipped. With snow from the summit and the top of goat's milk we shall make you a supreme ice-cream: the best you have ever tasted."

"Flavoured with strawberry?"

In spite of himself, he smiled. "Strawberries shall be specially planted. Sherbets you shall have and strawberry ice-cream."

As the servant entered to remove the tea glasses, a long-haired white-and-black cat glided in and made directly for Anahita. He drew his coat back and forward along her legs, purring. She took him up firmly, in a single sweep, by the scruff of the neck, and held him on her knees, stroking him slowly.

"What's his name?" asked Ghazan.

"Black Shoes."

38

He saw black marks on all four paws, but they reached high. "Not Black Boots?"

"When he was a kitten he had only black shoes. They grew with him. Then it was too late to change."

"He looks a good mouser. Is he?"

"Let's ask him. Are you a good mouser?" She tickled him under the chin. The cat began to purr very loudly. She looked up at Ghazan. He had the impression of grey eyes, but her face still lay in the chador's shadow. "He says he's the best mouser in all Shiraz."

"You speak for him?"

"Interpret."

"And if he had miaowed?"

She considered, and a smile glittered in her eyes. "It depends. He has angry miaows and impatient miaows and hungry miaows. And some miaows that no one has ever been able to understand."

The sun had slipped behind the trees, and the room was now cool with shadow. He noticed there was no electric light. Anahita lifted a white shawl and drew it across her shoulders.

Her mother turned to Ghazan with a smile. "That shawl you gave Anahita—the orange one. Forgive me for saying so, but it didn't really suit her."

"I liked it, mother," the girl stated rather than protested.

"Orange is not your best colour," her mother said firmly and turned again to Ghazan. "I saw that it came from the Brothers Sardeh. I took it back this morning and changed it for a white one. You're sure you don't mind?"

He did mind, but hiding his feelings he said to the girl, "Your trees carry blossom and fruit at the same time: why shouldn't you? If your mother permits," he inclined his head formally, "I shall have the orange shawl delivered tomorrow."

Anahita thanked him. He thought her mother would be displeased, but no. "You can wear it with your yellow dress," she said. "That will give you one more set for spring."

Though the room was darkening, the mother did not call for a lamp. Guessing it was time, Ghazan asked permission to leave and she, as custom ruled, said that it was early and prayed him to remain.

He turned to Anahita. "Next year, if you like, you can do as Falqani women: weave your own shawl and pick your own dyes on the hillside:

39

larkspur, madder and buckthorn. So that, moving across the green slopes, you will really belong to the hills."

"I should like that," she said and, after a pause, "But up on the hills aren't there many jackals?"

"Yes, there are many," he had to admit.

"I hear them on winter nights through my bedroom window. That angry, howling cry!"

He tried to reassure her. "We have many rifles to keep them at bay."

"The wolves, too?"

"All the wild animals. I have shot them all many times." Then he corrected himself. "Or rather, all except one."

"Which is that?"

"The snow leopard."

"The snow leopard?" she repeated, surprised. "I've never even heard the name."

He smiled. "And I've never even seen the beast, it's so rare. It lives on the highest mountains and prowls by night. Some of the older tribesmen have seen it and told me about its ways. All my life I've wanted to find a snow leopard." Then, almost to himself, he said, "I wonder whether I ever shall."

After talking a little longer, again he asked permission to leave, and the mother rose. He bowed to Anahita, who remained seated.

The mother came with him to the door. "May the days lengthen and shorten soon, and bring you safely back."

More formally he answered, "May your shadow never grow less."

He walked back to his car and was driven away. He thought, Anahita's still a stranger, but already I like her. He tried to give himself a reason. The way she had spoken of the cat: was that it? He pondered the question, riding back to his people. Every spring he had watched the migrating birds fly north across the blue sky: white, wide-winged herons and pink-legged storks; short-tailed coots and marble-headed duck, two by two in arrow-shaped flights; and as they called to each other with keen cries, lovers below joined hands in their march, but he rode on alone. And when the dew lighted on the grass, to the hoots of owls he entered the shadow of his blue tent alone. But now he was glad to feel the earth turn in its sleep, stir like a brown bear waking from winter. The dawn chorus was a particular announcement to him.

40

He felt himself a ballad which had glimpsed its music, a word which had found its rhyme.

In the extreme south, where a hundred men remained behind in one of the few arable districts to harvest a spring crop of barley and store it underground against the tribe's autumn return, Ghazan watched the young men take leave of their families and stayed specially to hear them bid farewell to the girls they loved in a traditional song:

> Spring lifts the myrtle leaf,
> Lambs and kids are bleating,
> Shear the sheep and pound the wool.
>
> "Gah-gah, gah-gah"
> Red-legged partridge cry:
> Here they fly and now are gone.
>
> Alone I thresh the yellow grain,
> Long is my outstretched arm,
> "Soon return" my flail calls.

This song in his ears, Ghazan herded men and beasts north. Messengers arrived reporting delays, asking his advice, calling him to one section stranded far from water, to another which had clashed with the Arabic-speaking Khamseh. Almost every spring these neighbours encroached on Falqani grazing-land and Ghazan had to go in person to settle the dispute. Seldom had he had to deal with so many problems, take so many decisions. In the week before the crossing he had only one full night's sleep.

On the eve of the crossing the chieftains again gathered for final instructions. Their bronzed faces also bore lines of sleeplessness, their clothes were sour with sweat. They spoke curtly and to the point. Only Tughril stood aloof and silent, as though waiting to see Ghazan's plan go awry. The moon would rise soon after midnight: Ghazan said they could start to move as darkness fell, about eight. Four hours would allow just sufficient time.

As the leaders left, Ghazan called "Rohim" and the youngest man returned. He had the same cast of face as the Ilkhan, but the eyes were hard-set, never wandering like his cousin's, his body a shade less tall but broader-shouldered, with a suggestion of density absent in Ghazan.

41

He was Tughril's son, not himself a chieftain, but as the Ilkhan's cousin and most intimate friend he sometimes took part in assemblies.

Ghazan laid a hand on Rohim's shoulder. "I'll lead one of the covering groups. You take the other. Choose fifty Shalgulis."

"Give me a hundred, Ghazan, and I'll capture Shiraz."

Rohim's muscles swelled, stirring his tunic, and he made his eyes glint like onyx, a gesture he knew was impressive. Ghazan looked him up and down, amusement mingled with annoyance. Always he had to rein his cousin in. Whereas the father's desire to tilt at the army arose from rancour and personal discontent, the son's was the direct expression of his own physical strength and the assertion of a proud, independent nature.

"What would you do with Shiraz?" he laughed.

The question took Rohim aback.

"Why, anything you say. And the glory, Ghazan! The glory!"

"As if we were lacking in that! No, we take no risks." And Ghazan began to explain his plan in detail. Rohim listened without protest. Admiration for Ghazan's energetic leadership was reinforced by scrupulous loyalty, itself a form of reaction against an overbearing father.

Together the two cousins rode to take up position on bluffs overlooking the Guyum plain. This was cut by the road and dominated by a small fort, no more than a black square patch in the twilight. They watched the sun sink from a cloudless sky and as soon as the grey, brown and black of the flocks were indistinguishable one from another, Ghazan sent his runner down from the heights to set the crossing in motion.

A few minutes later the first riders, the first bleating flocks began to issue from the mountainside like a volcanic stream, harness-pieces and copper pots glistening in the starlight, young boys calling softly to the leading rams and he-goats, hurrying them along. This first group, the Madaleh, was composed of Ghazan's own personal following, the column he had led eight days before from winter quarters. Beyond came another, the Shalguli, whose chieftains had for centuries been related by marriage to his own family. Most of the Shalguli pack-animals were camels, and their humped backs lurched across the horizon like a line of moving hills. For half a mile, the limit of road protected by their rifles, the mass of humans and animals extended.

42

Two groups by two they followed: the Adashuri, renowned for their swift horses, the Pardalun, hunters of ibex: each one Ghazan recognized in the dark by some characteristic of form or movement, like the women of a harem. With growing relief he watched eleven groups cross: ninety thousand tribespeople safe. But one was still missing: the Galanzi. Meanwhile the eastern horizon grew pale. The plain stretched empty of men. Perhaps lack of water had delayed them. Ghazan began to feel anxious. To postpone their crossing a day was out of the question: the army would rush reserves to isolate the Galanzi permanently from the main body. However late the Galanzi arrived, they would have to join the others, exposed to fire from the fort.

A bright crescent moon rose to reveal a squat mud-walled building in the centre of the plain: alongside the road and a little apart from a small village. On either side of closed wooden gates stood a sentry box. Above waved a tattered flag, its colours merely three shades of grey. Usually the fort was manned by four soldiers, but Ghazan counted more than twenty stirring on the raised walls between the embrasures.

Soon after the moon slipped free of the hills, the first section of Galanzi appeared, women and children in the centre with their flocks, men mounted or on foot along the vulnerable flank. As they flooded out across the plain, a blast, as though from an eruption, rent and rang round the rim of hills. Rifles from the fort had opened fire. Ghazan ordered his men to reply; Rohim did the same. Not very effectively, for the range was above five hundred paces and the embrasures lent excellent cover. But neither was the army fire effective. The soldiers seemed to be playing with the idea of attack. Ghazan could not understand it. They fired spasmodically, as though short of ammunition— but that was highly unlikely—and he saw none of the moving figures fall.

Whining bullets panicked and scattered the flocks. The tribespeople on foot started to run, those mounted to trot across the plain. Despite the danger, they kept together. The dust they raised helped to obscure them. Ghazan held his breath, fearing a leading ram would turn back. Then, despite their shepherds, a whole herd would follow, and for many months the Galanzi would go hungry. A small troop of goats did seek shelter in the bluffs below Ghazan, but the main body crossed together under continued intermittent fire which the Falqani tried in vain to silence. It was so uncontrolled that Ghazan decided the officer

43

in command had issued orders not to shoot; but that one or two soldiers could not resist the easy targets. Such cases of disobedience were not exceptional.

In less than an hour the last Galanzi disappeared behind the foothills. Shooting stopped. Slinging their rifles with care, for the metal parts were burning hot, Ghazan and his men, followed by Rohim's group, rode across the plain unchallenged. Ghazan at once went to the Galanzi chieftain to learn his losses. One man had a bullet-wound in the arm, a dozen sheep and goats had been killed; fifty goats had turned back and were lost. They had escaped incredibly lightly. For some reason he did not know, the army was withholding its new strength.

"Glory to God the merciful and compassionate," he said aloud, then rode ahead to look after the wounded tribesman, wondering and not quite peaceful at such an easy triumph.

CHAPTER THREE

At dawn the tribe, after three hours' encampment, was again on the move, split into component groups which gradually became strung apart. Once more the migration was taking its normal course.

Towards evening Ghazan, having rejoined the Madaleh some four miles north of the road, was informed that two officers were approaching on horseback, guarded by no less than fifty soldiers on foot. The officers sent a message, asking if Ghazan Khan would receive them. He gave orders that precautions should be taken and the officers escorted to his tent.

They arrived half an hour later, unarmed, in full-dress khaki with red tabs on their collars and peaked hats: a major and a captain.

"Peace be upon you," Ghazan said, welcoming them into one of the court tents and indicating cushions.

"Peace be upon Your Highness."

He ordered tea and sat watching them suck it through a lump of sugar held in the mouth. The Major was a thin man, his gaunt face marked by smallpox, his lips never still; the Captain was small and jovial, with a cast in his eye: a certain Ali Morteza, who as aide-de-camp had visited Ghazan more than once. Had they had a satisfactory journey; were they treated with courtesy by his men? Yes, they replied, not tripping over themselves to be polite. He was surprised at their self-assurance, at their steady fingers.

"To what do I owe this honour?" he asked, when the full time for compliments had been allowed.

The Major answered, "We have come on behalf of General Bahrami, Your Highness."

"General Bahrami?"

"The new commander of Fars district."

Most of Persia had for years been under martial law, and Fars, though nominally subject to a governor, was actually ruled by the military commandant. The name meant nothing to Ghazan. As for the change, it might or might not mean a reversal of policy. The post, notoriously, was given to the highest bidder.

"He wished you to bring some message?" Ghazan suggested.

"He expressed the desire, Your Highness, that a return might be made to conditions of order and good will. He particularly wishes that past acrimonies be forgotten."

A string of lies, thought Ghazan, but why these particular lies? Like the boxes of foreign paper handkerchiefs in the Shiraz bazaars, flourished but never put to use, terms such as order and good will were now fashionable but in no way corresponded to the realities of Persia, which remained a loosely knit state with no internal security, where strength alone was respected.

"Your general shows the feelings of a man of peace," said Ghazan, with a trace of irony.

"For this reason, Your Highness, he has ordered his officers to show the greatest forbearance. He hopes you will do likewise."

The Major was studying him carefully, and Ghazan showed suitable pleasure.

"Such news has seldom come my way or the way of my fathers before me," he said.

He saw the officers were pleased and were memorizing his reply for their report. Then they began to look round the tent, appraising the rich hangings and carpets. Their glances showed a shade too much freedom. Ghazan remembered that on his last visit two years before Captain Morteza had kept his eyes fixed firmly on the ground.

"Am I to thank General Bahrami for this change?" he continued, hoping to learn more.

"A new directive from the Chief of Staff ..." began Captain Morteza.

With a glower at his subordinate, the Major cut in, "General Bahrami has a free hand in Fars."

Ghazan made a placating gesture. "Naturally."

"The General told us himself . . ."

"That will be all, Captain Morteza," snapped the Major. Turning back to Ghazan, he ran thin, nervous fingers along neatly pressed trousers. "Like his predecessors, General Bahrami maintains the closest liaison with Teheran."

For a time they sipped tea in silence, while the officers stuffed themselves with the sticky green tamarisk nougat called *gaz*, which lay heaped in two silver bowls.

"Good," the Captain said approvingly. "Very good." Then, with a heavy attempt at bonhomie, he asked:

"Is it true you're to marry this autumn?"

His title had been dropped, perhaps by mistake, and if so, the slip was even more ominous. Ghazan thought, For the first time I can remember army officers are lacking in respect. He held the Captain's eye.

"Were you addressing me?"

His tone caused Captain Morteza to gulp down his *gaz*. "I asked whether Your Highness is to marry this autumn?"

"Yes, I am to marry."

"Your Highness does well to ensure the succession," said the captain, soothingly.

Then the Major started lulling him again. "General Bahrami also says that should Your Highness have any complaint of the army's behaviour, you are to let him know."

Was there the hint of a scoff? Ghazan could not tell.

"Incidents have not been infrequent: with 'good will' on both sides they may grow fewer."

"Of Your Highness's own good will we have no doubts. But Your Highness leads eleven allied tribes."

"The path I choose they follow."

"If they should find what seems a better way?"

"The path I choose they follow."

"Even Tughril?"

"Is Tughril not a Falqani."

"A month ago Tughril visited the Khamseh."

Ghazan hid his surprise with a shrug. "Neighbours pay visits."

"From one of the Khamseh leaders we learned that Tughril still dreams of a rising by all the tribes to gain control of Fars."

Ghazan had often heard this from Tughril's own lips. Governors and government officials from the capital, in order to supplement inadequate pay, exploited, extorted and embezzled during their term of office, but provincials usually lacked the influence to get redress. Tughril believed that only a rising could enforce the often-repeated demand for the appointment of local men only in Fars.

"I have no such dream," he said quietly, but he did not like the trend of their words.

"Tughril's dream makes us uneasy, Your Highness. This visit may

47

be only one part of a well-developed plan. In short, we should take it as proof of the new era in our relations if . . ." The Major paused and looked, as though for support, at his colleague. "If you could place Tughril in our hands—simply as a hostage. He will be well treated and his safety guaranteed."

His life would be easier without his uncle: they were playing on that. With an effort Ghazan checked his anger.

"What wild talk is this? Do you ask the head to sacrifice hand or foot in its own interests? You mistake your man."

"More than mere interests are at stake. Your Highness marries this autumn. Until a son is born, who would succeed as Ilkhan?"

"You know very well: Tughril."

"So that if between now and autumn anything were to happen to you . . ." he revolved his lips nervously. "Say a hunting accident: you hunt a lot together . . ."

Through clenched teeth Ghazan demanded, "Go on."

The Major spread bony hands. "Then Tughril would be free to fulfil his dream."

Ghazan's anger broke. "You dare to crawl here," he cried, "and dart out your little forked tongues. You fill me with disgust and pity. A building like ours, where the stones have been carefully cut and matched, is not overthrown by lizards."

They drew back, outraged.

"An insult to our uniform," cried the Major.

"Insult! It was you who invited me to betray my own blood. What greater insult than that? You come like tale-telling, mischief-making children. You expect me to stroke your hair and say, 'Yes, yes, yes.' In the name of what? Good will! But what good will can there be with men who seek only to divide?" In his anger he had risen and now stood over them. "You are my guests, and continue so as long as you choose. But I do not remain with enemies of my own blood."

The Major hastened to repair the damage: it was merely a suggestion, he said. But Ghazan strode out of the tent. Apologies were followed by a farewell—"May Your Highness's shadow never grow less"—then by the jar of bickering and mutual reproach.

Shortly afterwards the officers left the encampment with their heavy guard.

.   .   .

48

Soon after sunrise next morning Ghazan gave the order for camp to be struck and the upward trek resumed. Grass, scattered now with blue hyacinths and wild irises, grew higher and more succulent. Pasturage proved easy and, less intent on his tribe's survival, Ghazan rode along the heights, watching, far away, herds of wild gazelle and antelope furtively moving up with the nomads. Hidden he knew that jackals and leopards were following. Flights of birds, quail and francolin, were winging north, as surely as the sap rising in the grass, and they too were followed by predatory species: hawks and vultures. An undeniable movement of creatures compelled by forces beyond themselves, a tide of flesh and blood.

Already the air had become thinner and cooler: it was veined with scents that excited desires. In breathing it the tribe seemed to come under a spell which drew them upward, in spite of themselves, as though to its source. The sun shone brightly from a turquoise sky on the reds, yellows and oranges of the women's clothes, on the fawn camels and an occasional white calf camel. The flocks extended as far as Ghazan could see, creeping like a swarm of flies along the flanks of the patient mountains.

Mile after mile the country remained a uniform dusty-brown, its veil of green blotched with the dark-green, almost black of occasional camel-thorn bushes, each one perfectly distinct, in the clear dry air, to the far horizon. In this colour-scheme, without disturbing it, were blended the occasional villages the tribe passed from afar, nearly always snuggling against the base of mountains, nuzzling there like the young of the mountain, to catch each drop of frothy water. Most were surrounded by an earthen wall, higher than a man, to protect the villagers and their cattle from marauding jackals and their gardens from wind-swept sand. Above the wall rose the green of apricot and pistachio trees, of willow and plane. Fortresses, each one of them, where the gates were locked every night, and beyond the outlying fields of which the villagers scarcely stirred in a lifetime. There lay the other Persia, the bulk of her people. His tribe had as little in common with them as seafarers with the coast-dwellers whose lights they distinguish from afar by night. At intervals tribesmen would enter a village to barter their milk and cheese for barley and dates, or even to sell them outright. But they exchanged few words with their goods, and there remained fixed between them a deep gulf. This was partly in the nature of things—the lark's avoidance of a caged bird, the gazelle's stealthy approach to dangerous waters—partly in their own nature, for Ghazan's people sprang from different stock. Though most of the men could speak Persian, their native tongue was Turki, a relic of their original home in Turkestan, and this gave a clangorous, wild tang to their speech. That and their roaming life made them half-scorned, half-feared. Any damage to crops near the migration routes was attributed to the tribes, as though they shared the attributes of a swarm of locusts or a searing wind. This particular charge was unjust, a heritage of past centuries, when invading peoples had indeed burned and looted. For many years now the Falqani had refrained from raiding: they preferred peaceful relations indispensable for trade.

Forward and upward the Falqani advanced. At the end of the seventh week they were camped on the slopes of snow-tipped peaks, huddled at night with their beasts, fingers outstretched to camel-thorn fires. These high ranges, which lay like a barrier between them and their upland pastures, were crossed by a narrow pass, with a deep gulf on either hand. Hell and Heaven they called it, in allusion to the razor-edged bridge of Sirat, by which the faithful have to cross the infernal abysses into Paradise. That spring the Falqani were surprised at the approaches to the pass by a blizzard and, to save their flocks from drifts, were obliged—men, women and children—to march eight hours by night into cutting snow.

Only the drive of spring in their steps brought the Falqani safely across the steep mountains and, in the eighth week, to summer quarters, over six thousand feet high, the promised land of thick grass, of warm days and cool nights. From the snow-tipped peaks a cleansing wind blew the scent of juniper and cranberry along broad valleys. Black tents were stretched like bats' wings on the slopes, and the people rested. But since they moved to the cycle of nature, this was a pause rather than an ending.

Around every fire on the first night after their arrival the tribe talked of their journey and compared experiences. Beside one, more blazing than the rest, its fuel being two heaps of camel-thorn combined, sat two Falqani. One was a strongly, stockily built man of forty, with deep chest and broad shoulders, hair ruffled above a round, frank face, tunic so loose it billowed from its sash in the slightest breeze. Ahmad was the Ilkhan's shepherd and personal servant. Apart from this hereditary privilege, he stood out from his fellow-tribesmen in one other respect: he was a recognized story-teller. Most Falqani could tell a good tale, but certain men, for their expressive voices, retentive memory and powers of invention, had a faithful audience, to whom once or twice a week they narrated, with gusto and gestures, a traditional tribal story or an episode from the national poet-historian Firdowsi.

The other Falqani was Ahmad's best friend: a smaller man of about the same age, with lean face and sunken eyes. His woollen jerkin was thinner but cleaner and tidier: many patches had been neatly sewn in it by his wife Mahin, an industrious, plain-faced woman who had borne her husband four children.

With a flourish Ahmad had just hung his kettle on the tripod, and sat watching the flames lick round it.

"How far it seems now, Sanjar, yet this was the worst blizzard the Falqani had ever faced." His voice boomed with conviction. Sanjar's, when he replied, was softer and more even.

"Not the worst. The wind was high, but the snow piled only calf-deep."

"The worst without exception. Manuchehr the elder said so."

"Worst or not," Sanjar sighed, "it was bad enough. Mahin's shoes ripped to pieces: two of my best goats caught in drifts."

Ahmad cut short his friend's lament. "God be praised, I lost no lambs—and I gained a son."

Sanjar had already heard the news. "One of those goats . . ."

"Listen, about my son."

"That goat, I tell you . . ."

Ahmad showed mild reproof. "Sanjar, which is more important, your dead goat, or my son? . . . It happened five nights ago. We were all dismounted: Ghazan at the head of the column, leading us over the Kuh-i-Kalar. I was beside him. We had climbed high and were breathing fast. We could just see the cloud of our breath in the dark, and the spinning white flakes. 'It can't be now, Ghazan Khan,' I shouted—I had to shout for the wind—'Not her first child, not in a blizzard.' He kept encouraging me. 'Cold delays a birth,' he said, and so on. But we didn't speak much, else the snowflakes filled our mouths." Ahmad paused dramatically, and noticed with approval that Sanjar was looking agog. "Then her mother hurries up. We'd agreed she'd come when Dilbar had to stop. I didn't know what to do. In the howling wind I couldn't raise a tent. I couldn't even light a pitch-flare or a fire. But Ghazan Khan strides back down the long line of moving figures, to where Dilbar is. I follow, stumbling through the snow. The Khan stops a man. 'I need your horses,' he says, and the man gives him them. From their packs he lifts bedding and blankets, and flings them to me. 'Spread these,' he shouts, then leads the horses to windward of Dilbar. I tug at the cords, but in the dark and cold I can't undo them."

Sanjar nodded knowingly. "You were frightened, I daresay, and who's to blame you? Your fingers were doubtless trembling."

"With cold more than anything," said Ahmad easily. "I even tried my teeth on the knot, but they were chattering so, they wouldn't grip. Then the Ilkhan comes back, unknots the cords and with her mother spreads the bedding for Dilbar. He joins me and the horses: we stand there to windward in the dark, sheltering Dilbar from the snow. Ages it seemed, my whole body shaking with cold, snow in my eyes. Terrible things I thought there: of what might be happening. Then through the wind I hear a thin cry. So thin it seemed a girl's cry. Fatima the astrologer is right, I thought—she predicted a girl. I didn't want to look. But Ghazan Khan—he goes and a moment later returns. 'A son, Ahmad: a hefty son.' 'A son?' I shout, still thinking of Fatima's words. 'A brave one,' laughs the Ilkhan. 'He didn't want to miss the blizzard.' He looks up at the sky. 'If we get through this,' he says, 'you shall have a lamb to celebrate.'

"Not once did Dilbar complain. You'd have thought the snow had been white linen sheets. A woman to load with bracelets! . . . But I'm thinking, Sanjar, this son of hers will be a very special boy."

"What makes you say that?"

"Born in a storm. He'll be brave, as the Ilkhan warrants; he'll ride his horse fast as the driving wind—and he'll have fat flocks, for snow makes the grass tall."

"Maybe," Sanjar conceded, and added with regret, "Not everyone's lucky enough to be born under such a sign."

For a few moments they looked at the flames in silence.

Very casually Ahmad said, "I was born in a storm, Sanjar."

His friend looked up in surprise. "You never told me that."

"This birth reminded me."

"Not in a blizzard?" asked Sanjar doubtfully.

"Worse. Thunder and lightning-flashes. One of the tents was

struck: it went up in smoke and big orange flames like these, but high as an oak. Even the rain didn't damp them."

"You talk as though you had seen it all," mocked Sanjar.

"I did. I was born at the most dangerous moment. My mother and father were terrified, seeing the flames, hearing the thunder crack, and hail slashing the tent-skirts."

"Hail as well as rain?"

"Hailstones like hen's eggs."

Sanjar nodded. "I thought they'd be big for your birth."

Ahmad ignored the thrust. "The tribe were in panic. I was the only one absolutely calm. Do you know, Sanjar, I actually smiled that very night. Not that I knew it then: but my mother told me."

"Every mother has some such fancy."

"It's true, I tell you."

"A sort of twist to your lips before you started to cry."

"Not at all: a smile: almost a laugh. Unmistakable. My mother used to point me out to her friends: 'This is the one who smiled the day he was born.'"

"And now," remarked Sanjar dryly, "it's your friends who smile at you, when you start with your wild stories."

Ahmad dismissed the taunt with a wave of his hand. "You have only to ask my mother. After all, she should know. And now, if that tea's stewed, I must take it to Dilbar."

He lifted the kettle off the tripod with a stick and, folding part of his tunic round his fingers, grasped the hot, sooty handle. With a gesture of farewell to Sanjar he strode away to his own tent.

A mutton-fat lamp cast a yellow glow on a large red-and-yellow tasselled rug. Carpet bags stuffed with barley held down the tent-skirts. Along one side lay bedding with plaid blankets, and an oak-branch cradle Ahmad had made that winter. Clothes and belongings lay neatly arranged in the far corner.

Kneeling in the centre was a slender, full-breasted girl, half Ahmad's age. Striking long brown eyes, set wide apart, shone from shadows of kohl; high-boned cheeks were touched with red and white fard; black hair, washed in indigo, gleamed like a cock's tail-feathers. In one hand she held a lamb, a nimble finger of the other she dipped into a bowl of milk and gave it to suck.

Ahmad looked first at his sleeping son, then went to a tin box where

53

glasses were packed in hay. Taking out two, he cut off three slivers from a sugar loaf into each glass, which he filled with tea from the kettle. Stooping from behind he placed one in front of his wife. She gave a little cry of surprise and turned.

"You shouldn't have, Ahmad."

"Why not? It's now you need it."

"There's so little left."

He smiled easily. "Ahmad will buy you more."

They sat opposite each other on the rug, sipping their tea. The cosset, neglected, began to bleat. Ahmad watched his wife dip her finger again and give it to suck.

"That reminds me, Dilbar. We must think about Jahan." He saw her questioning look. "Of course, you wouldn't have seen. Jahan lost most of his flock coming down the Kalar mountain. A silly thing. The leading sheep stumbles in a dip in front of boulders, hidden by the snow. The rest are going so fast they can't stop. One on top of the other they pile up in the dip. Before anyone can drag them out, they're dead of suffocation."

"Always in trouble, that poor Jahan."

"He's an idiot. Remember last summer he shot my uncle's dog? Thought it was a jackal. A jackal! If there were one qanat hole in the entire Marvdasht plain, Jahan would be sure to fall down it." Ahmad brooded a moment. "And yet, even if he's chicken-brained, he's still a Falqani and must be helped."

Dilbar clasped the lamb protectively and shifted her position. "With the child, we can't afford to give much."

"Cannot afford to help our friends!"

Doubtfully she suggested, "Perhaps one ewe then."

Her husband gave her a lordly look. "Ahmad is not the one to skimp. Besides, Ghazan Khan has promised us a lamb."

"Because the Ilkhan plays high notes, you think the Ilkhan's shepherd must pipe the same tune."

"Nothing to do with it. Jahan has five children to feed and a widowed mother, not to mention a maternal aunt who's always dropping in, quite by chance, at mealtimes." He paused and announced dramatically: "Three ewes we shall give him—no less."

"Three ewes!" she protested. "When he won't expect more than one."

54

"Ahmad doesn't do things by halves."

She pouted. "It's just to show off."

"How so?"

"We cannot afford three ewes. You want your flock to seem larger than it really is."

"And how could I seem to have more, by giving three instead of one? That's a woman talking." He began to tap his chin thoughtfully. "Which shall I choose? There's Ebon Ears: I cannot give her without giving Wanderer. They graze together; to part them now would make Wanderer thin. I can't risk that with twin lambs at her udder. Nor Drooptail: she'd never thrive with Jahan. Such a silly way to lose a flock. I wouldn't have minded so much if they'd tumbled over a precipice."

"Surely they'd be dead just the same."

"That would have been a sight worth seeing and talking about. But this! Suffocated!"

With a snort he continued his choosing.

That evening the men of Jahan's section—also the personal following of the Ilkhan—assembled round Ghazan's fire. He sat in the centre, beside a rush-work pen, with Jahan, a large-boned, gawky shepherd of Ahmad's age.

Ghazan, as the custom was, explained the loss, though all the men knew. Then, one by one, beginning by the eldest, the tribesmen came up to Ghazan, and laid sheep or lamb, one or many, at his feet.

"This is for Jahan, Ghazan Khan, that his family may not go hungry." Taking the animal from Ghazan and lifting it into the fold, Jahan said:

"Praise be to God, and may He bless you."

The gift came from above; the tribesmen were merely the means of bounty. And at the end of the evening Jahan owned a flock as large as that he had lost.

This redressment was not peculiar to the Ilkhan's following. In each section the headman called an assembly; those who through no fault had lost beasts during the migration, and stood in danger of going hungry, were helped by their fellows, each giving according to his means.

After the assembly Ahmad attended to business of his own, then fed the Ilkhan's mare its measure of barley.

55

When he returned to his tent, Dilbar gave him a reproachful look. "Mahin's been to see me."

Ahmad finished the tune he was humming. "What did she have to say?"

"Sanjar told her you gave Jahan only one ewe."

"Isn't that what you wanted?"

"I thought we decided on three."

He smiled. "There's our son to think of now."

"All the same, Jahan has five children and a widowed mother to feed."

He put his arm round her. "Then why did you argue against me? It's true I gave him only one ewe in the assembly. But I went to his tent afterwards—when he thought there were no more coming. I gave him the two others then. Surprised—you should have seen his big ram's eyes!"

"You and your surprises," she said, softening.

"Dumb as a stork he stood, but I could tell he was pleased. He rubbed his hands along their heavy tails and fat briskets—staring, as though he couldn't believe they were sheep. And it's a fact, Ahmad's ewes are twice as big as those skinny pieces of gristle Jahan lost in the snow."

CHAPTER FOUR

As soon as the federated tribes had arrived, Ghazan assigned grazing pastures and a little arable land to tribal chieftains, who in turn would apportion shares between their men. A rich shepherd would receive forty acres of summer grazing land: on this he paid no pasture dues. In addition, he might rent two acres of farm land at a low price. This money was set aside by the Ilkhan against years of famine. In theory the system meant that all land, the Ilkhan's property, was graciously assigned to his dependants; in times of disunity a too-powerful leader could be curbed by assigning him stony ground. Now it had become a formality, though one which most of the chieftains respected and would not wish discontinued. They liked to show their loyalty in outward forms.

A crop of barley was sown, to be harvested in autumn. A smaller crop, sown the previous autumn, had lain under the winter snow and would be ripe for harvesting in six weeks' time.

Upland life began. Men plaited goat-hair ropes, tanned sheepskins, pastured their herds and sought fuel, in the evening driving back donkeys laden on either side to the ground with twisted branches of camel-thorn. Women helped shear their sheep, washed the wool in the nearest stream, carded it on long-toothed combs, then spun it on a distaff whirled by hand. Setting up wooden looms, they wove cloth for their families' winter clothes, as well as blankets to furnish the tents. Cooking took some of their time and the making of cheese. Goat's milk was left to sour in an open bowl containing rennet, then packed in a cloth, which was twisted to force out moisture and left in a running stream. After a few hours the curd was dried and divided into small cakes.

In all these activities Ghazan took a personal interest. Their life was his life: his rugs and the hangings of his tent were made in the same pattern and from the same materials as those of the poorest; his flocks shared the same fodder, he ate as his men ate, for they would not accept a leader who did not live level with them. And now, as every spring, he was swept up in that circling dance within the annual cycle: sun and rain acting on the brown earth, the earth yielding its grass, which formed the staple of their food: milk in all its forms, cheese, unsweetened *mast* and *dugh*, which was curds mixed with water and boiled; sometimes a little barley and meat. The grass too became skin for jerkins, saddles and bridles, wool for clothes and coverings; even, in the form of goat-hair strips stitched together, their homes. And the grass went back into the earth, to respond once more to the touch of sun and rain.

The milk that made Falqani bodies tall, lean and strong bound them to earth. The keen air swelling their deep chests bound them anew to the sky. Their strength depended on earth and sky. Their red blood a tributary of the grass's sap, flowed in unison with the sap's tide. Their strength waxed and waned with the seasons. Their well-being, the gleam on the flashing horseshoes of action, blazed at its brightest now under the spring sun.

Towards the end of the first week the pattern of their life was interrupted by visitors.

"We have come in a metal bird from a great country beyond the seas to bring you knowledge, to improve your herds, to help you care for your sick."

A Persian translated the words as they were spoken by a prim, tight-lipped little man, who peered out rather solemnly from under a long-peaked canvas cap.

To hide his smile, Ghazan bowed.

"Consider yourselves my guests. I shall gladly give you all the help I can."

Another mission of inquiry had arrived. Four men, three foreigners and their interpreter, had driven in jeeps from Isfahan as far as the nearest village, where they had hired asses to ride into the hills. Ghazan had experience of many such missions, national and international, which occasionally came to view his "backward" people. These visits had started only five years before. After the war successive Governments had refused to let foreigners see anything but the "new" Persia, that is, all that was modelled on the West. But as foreign influence increased in Teheran, the Government could no longer keep up a pretence of perfection. It was pointed out, also, that if a nation were to be progressive, she must have no secrets. She had to allow teams to circulate, speak to ill-housed peasants and beggars debilitated by opium.

Only so could she justify the flow of foreign money for development. But she saw to it that members of these teams were rather less than brilliant, and that each report was matched by a second, making contrary recommendations.

This mission Ghazan distinguished from others by the bulk of its equipment. No less than six pack-asses carried not only sleeping-bags, food, water-purifiers and medical chests but a collection of unidentified bales and crates. The members presented themselves through their interpreter: the strange names Ghazan soon forgot and he remembered only their appearances and functions: their leader, an educational authority and by profession a teacher; a hulking, loose-limbed young fellow referred to as an authority on stock-breeding; and a fat, bald man, wearing ordinary spectacles under his dark glasses, who was an authority on hygiene. All wore very large dark glasses and, despite the heat, highly polished riding-boots. As their interpreter, an Isfahani, spoke only a little Turki, conversation was conducted in Persian.

After receiving their credentials—they were authorized and commended by no less than eight international organizations, committees and associations, and had arrived in Persia two weeks before on a three-weeks detailed visit—Ghazan invited them to his tent for tea. Impossible, their leader said: their time was strictly limited to four hours in the encampment. So it was decided that each authority in turn should speak with Ghazan Khan concerning his special subject, while the others toured the camp on their own.

The educational authority stayed with the Ilkhan. He seemed pleasantly surprised to find a primitive tribesman educated and courteous to a degree, though a shade disappointed that his "metal bird" had fallen flat. He wasted no time. Through his interpreter he asked Ghazan kindly to sum up in five minutes the educational system among his people—and glanced at his watch.

"As we are wanderers," Ghazan said, "we can carry only what is necessary for life. Books, unless it be a Koran, are too heavy: we must keep our learning in our heads. So it has to be essential, usually in verse, for that is most easily memorized. Chieftains and the scribes who keep accounts are educated in neighbouring villages. Each group has a number of elders, men trained by mullahs in the Koran and who have won general respect. They guide the policy of tribal chieftains, and see that the people lead a life which will win them salvation."

"And your schools?"

"We have no schools."

"But every ethnico-social group—no matter how primitive—has some form of school."

"Then we cannot be an ethnico-social group," said Ghazan humbly.

"You mean most of your people are illiterate?"

"Nearly all."

As the teacher seemed exceedingly upset, Ghazan added in all seriousness:

"Does it really matter? My men are wiser than any in the plains, and wisdom surely is the aim of education?" The teacher seemed to think himself mocked. Noticing him tighten further his tight lips, Ghazan added amiably, "Don't take my word, you shall see for yourself."

Ghazan led the way out of the court tent. After a few minutes' walk they met a cameleer sitting beside his beasts, carving the head of a stick. His camels wore red scarves round the neck, ornamented with blue beads and dangling tassels. They were cropping quick, full mouthfuls of grass: now was the season when they laid up grease in their humps. The cameleer rose and bowed before the visitors: tall, with the slow dignified movements of one in tune with a natural rhythm.

"This is Mansur," Ghazan said. "One of the poorest Falqani. I'm sure he will gladly answer your questions."

"Can you read, Mansur?"

"I am trying, sir, but I am a foolish man and learn slowly."

"What book are you reading?"

The cameleer turned puzzled brown eyes on Ghazan.

"No book, sir. I am learning to read the signs of earth and sky, the phases of the moon, of the seasons, the wind that blows now hot, now cold."

The teacher wrote in a notebook.

"Why do you study these things, Mansur?"

The cameleer looked down at the teacher, bewildered. He stumbled to find words, but the answer was too self-evident to come easily. Ghazan spoke for him.

"So that he may know where to pasture and water his camels, when to mate them and take the young from their mothers. And also because he likes studying them. They are beautiful. The outward beauty demands an inward beauty from him."

60

"Surely a little far-fetched," said the teacher drily.

"I assure you it is true. I have spent my life with these men. That concord they prize very highly."

The teacher turned back to the cameleer.

"Can you count, Mansur?"

The question delighted him. Proudly he answered, "I can count all my camels. Fourteen."

"No higher?"

"I can count the twenty-eight days of Ramadan, and the beads in my bull camel's necklace."

This the teacher examined. As he took more and more copious notes, the cameleer looked anxiously at Ghazan.

"Don't fret," Ghazan reassured him in Turki. "The stranger has come to learn from you." Then he explained, "Mansur can probably count to a hundred. Some Falqani can count to a thousand. But no further. Beyond lies Iblis, the devil."

For some reason this seemed to annoy the teacher.

"Rank superstition," he exclaimed. "In my country every adult here would be put in prison."

Ghazan decided to treat this lightly. "I have heard that a man may acquire great wisdom in prison."

"Not to be educated—to be punished."

"Why?"

"For neglecting their children."

"But they do not neglect them. They love them. And teach them, too. What did your parents teach you?" he asked the cameleer.

The answer came slowly with a lift of pride.

"They taught me to ride, to shoot and to speak the truth. They taught me the history of the old kings in Firdowsi's poetry, the battles we have won, the famines and droughts we have suffered. They taught me the ninety-nine names of God. They taught me my prayers and much poetry."

"Poetry! What use is that to a man like you?"

The bronzed face broke in a smile.

"Without poetry how should I have won my wife?"

The conversation was taking unscientific lines.

"Did you learn no geography, no mathematics, no physics?" How far away is Teheran?"

After some thought, Mansur replied, "I am an ignorant man. Certainly it lies very far. But since I do not wish to make the journey, is there need to reckon the days' provisions?"

The teacher entered this in his notebook.

"Even by your standards Mansur is not a dunce," Ghazan added with a touch of malice. "Like most of my men, he can speak two languages, Turki and Persian. Three even, for they all have a special way of addressing their beasts. And look at that camel-stick." Mansur was carving the top into a lion's head. "You can almost hear it roar. Nowhere in the towns will you find such careful workmanship."

The teacher took the camel-stick, admired it, then handed it back with a word of praise.

"And that is not all. Mansur is an expert at the difficult art of blood-letting. He can cut the jugular artery to draw out a congestion of blood in his camels' heads—an extremely skilled operation which I doubt any other people in the world can perform."

"All the same, this man is illiterate. He is therefore not a good citizen. He cannot play his part as a member of the community."

"Let us leave the abstract," Ghazan replied. "I have been schooled; I am, I suppose, educated in your sense. But am I a better citizen than Mansur? Not a bit. I have been exposed to a hundred false and pernicious theories as well as to the truth; every decision I take has to be fought for, and even then I am by no means sure it is right. But Mansur, who has never read a word in a book, chooses the right course almost instinctively: he imbibed his culture—and it is a culture, though different from yours—with his mother's milk. In the whole world you will not find men more loyal, more brave, more ready to help one another. They do their work well, they do not meddle. Can all our schooling impart those virtues?"

Instead of answering, the teacher turned to the cameleer.

"Don't you want to learn to read books, Mansur?"

"I am growing old, sir. Books are for scribes and elders. They would be wasted on me."

"But your sons, don't you want them to read—to go to school?"

Mansur thought a moment before replying.

"The best man I ever knew was my father. He had no schooling at all. I have known men in the towns and in the army who could read and write. Some stole from me, others cheated in the bazaar. No, I do not want my sons to learn what is taught in the towns."

"Schooling is impossible for a nomad people," added Ghazan. "And they are well contented without it. Let us leave them as they are. We have a proverb," he added with a smile: "'It takes ten pounds of common sense to carry one pound of learning.' I think there's much truth in that proverb."

The first hour ended. The teacher blew a whistle and yielded his place to the expert on hygiene, who was less indignant than excited at the extraordinary things he had seen. His brow gleamed with sweat, and he brandished an atomizer. "Milking sheep from behind!" he cried. "By all the laws of medical hygiene there should not be a single Falqani alive."

"A little dirt spices the milk," said Ghazan lightly.

"I have taken one or two samples. I hope to get a record count of tubercular bacilli." He checked a list in his hand. "Now for clothing. I have seen the men's. Could I have a look at the women's? Not everyone knows it, but the right dress is essential to hygiene."

Ghazan led him to a group of eight women, working at a carpet loom. They broke off their gossiping to greet the stranger with smiles. Dilbar happened to be among them, her infant wrapped on her back in a shawl. She wore a dark blue cotton shift over a wide, pleated skirt of the same colour, a length of pale blue cotton bound high round her hair and covering the top of her forehead. Ghazan knew she possessed a second outfit of clothing and asked her to fetch it. She came back, her arms piled high with a bundle which she laid in front of the stranger, while her friends crowded round in a circle. From the top of the bundle the hygienist lifted a pair of shoes.

"Where did you buy these?"

"I made them, sir."

Shyly she explained how she stitched uppers of woollen cord on to strips of sheep's hide tanned hard as wood, how they were kept white with pipeclay. As the interpreter translated, the hygienist nodded and seemed satisfied. But he was less pleased when Dilbar added that one was made slightly larger than the other to avoid the disastrous consequences of perfection.

"And what is this?" he next asked, lifting a large piece of orange cotton.

63

"A skirt, sir."

The women began to chatter and shake their heads as he stretched it out on the ground. It curved to form almost a full orange circle.

"Extremely large for a skirt."

Dilbar was gaining confidence.

"You fold it like this," and she showed how her dark blue skirt had been bustled. "Then it swings."

"But it's very awkward."

"We love swinging skirts, and our men love them too."

"La la," said the women, laughing, trying to catch the stranger's eye. But he seemed interested only in the clothes.

"And this?" He lifted a piece of red cotton from the bundle.

"Another skirt."

"Ah yes. For a holiday."

"No, for the same day. I wear it underneath the orange."

He considered this in silence, then picked up the next piece of clothing. This too was a red skirt.

Ghazan explained that except for cotton trousers, a shift and head-dress the bundle was made up of skirts. One by one he lifted the coloured cottons and counted them.

"Seven. You don't mean you're wearing seven skirts now?"

"Yes, sir."

"Do you all wear seven skirts?"

"Yes, yes," they said and, seeing his astonishment, laughed again.

"Why not only one?"

"We have fat flocks. Only poor women wear one skirt."

"Seven skirts. Say each has seven yards of material, when two would do." He turned to Ghazan. "And there are how many Falqani women?"

"About fifty thousand."

He made a rough calculation.

"Nearly two million yards of wasted material!"

"Not quite wasted," Ghazan protested. "These skirts are a woman's pride, and her husband's too."

"But seven skirts at a time—that's most unhealthy."

"It keeps them warm on cold nights."

"In my report I shall recommend a change," said the hygienist firmly.

64

"Wild tigers couldn't make them yield even one of their skirts," laughed Ghazan.

But the hygienist considered the matter closed. He sprayed Dilbar's clothes with D.D.T. and asked Ghazan if he might take one of the skirts with him as a specimen. Ghazan told Dilbar he would make good the loss, and obtained her consent. Then the hygienist asked Dilbar about her baby. No, she had been attended neither by doctor nor midwife. Usually women were back at work within a day.

"What is your percentage of doctors?" he asked Ghazan.

"A difficult question. Is zero a percentage?"

"No doctors at all?"

"Say, rather, no sick. No permanent sick."

"No sick?"

"Not unnatural, surely. Have you seen a flagging hawk or an ailing ibex?"

"True enough," the hygienist admitted. "But what protection have your people against epidemic?"

"Only their hardy physique, herbal remedies and, in danger of death, the Koran."

"The Koran?"

Ghazan unbuttoned his blouse and took out a square, flat object the size of his palm. Two sides were of silver inlaid with turquoise and it hung from his neck by a silver chain.

"This is a Koran written in tiny characters. Many of my men wear one just like it. In case of severe illness they go to a special scribe— usually a woman—who copies a chapter cabalistically. Then they roll the paper tight and swallow it as a pellet."

"A form of magic," decided the hygienist.

"No, of religion. Magic, surely, is a tricking of nature. I know what you think," he continued, "that we should be better off in villages. You think that because births are registered, children will live. Listen, please, to one example of 'law and order' in our country, and tell me whether the nomads are not well off.

"Last winter one of the Bakhtiari khans was staying with me. The Bakhtiari are our northern neighbours. He told me of a recent incident in Shush where some of his tribe had remained settled since the days of Reza Shah. One evening a mad dog bit thirty-seven men. You may not know, but our small towns have no medical facilities. Fortunately an archæological expedition happened to be there, excavating the Persian and Elamite capital of Susa. One of the members was a doctor and he immediately telegraphed to the Pasteur Laboratory in Teheran. After some delay a reply came, ordering the police to put all those who had been bitten on the next train north."

"A train in tribal country?"

"Shush, I should have said, lies almost two hundred miles from here on the Trans-Iranian railway. None of the men had ever visited Teheran; few had ever left the protection of family and friends; all were terrified of trains. The police visited the sick in turn, telling them to pack their belongings, sympathizing a little the better to prey on their panic. Anything, they said, would be better than to be put on the death-train. They hinted at unspeakable horrors. Still, they had to do their duty. The sick men implored the police to let them stay, their women wailed. The police replied, 'What can we do? Orders from Teheran cannot be waived. At least, not from friendship alone.' Money would have to change hands: twenty tumans. For them a huge sum— a man's labour for three weeks. However, loans were secured, friends and each member of the family contributed. By the time the train was due, thirty had bribed the police to remain. The other seven could not find the money. Despite appeals and protest, only these seven were put on the dread train and spirited away."

"What was the doctor doing?"

"Raising heaven and earth to get them all to Teheran. But the police said he had miscalculated, that some had already died and others had fled the town in terror.

"The thirty men with rabies breathed a sigh of relief. They fêted the police and one by one they died off. They were mourned, but everyone agreed that a far worse fate must have overtaken those on the train.

"Several weeks later the seven men returned from Teheran, cured of rabies, in excellent health. They were welcomed as though from the dead. Amid the music and feasting that night, the police came round. 'Don't forget your friends,' they whispered. 'We made you get on the train. Had it not been for us you would have died like the other thirty.' From each of the seven they extracted twenty tumans."

"Scandalous," the hygienist said. "I shall mention it in my report. And I see a moral there. I shall spray a dozen or so tents with D.D.T. I notice most of the villages have been sprayed."

66

"If you like, but remember this. We leave our refuse behind every day or every few days. A dry wind blows. You will find no flies and few vermin."

"All the same," the hygienist said, "spraying would prove beneficial."

"One last point," he added. "How many tents to the acre?"

Ghazan was unable to tell him.

"They will know in Teheran."

With a smile Ghazan agreed. Five years ago the first teams had asked the ministries for statistics. After their first surprise, officials had compiled and provided them—purely imaginary censuses—and surveys and tax returns, poems in numbers. These delighted the foreigners; demand and supply had increased until now they were the mainstay of several international publications.

At the end of the hour, again the whistle blew. While waiting for his next critic, Ghazan thought over the last two hours. It was natural, after all, that the teacher and hygienist should not admit defeat. The tribe's way of life was a denial of all their presuppositions: if the tribe were not proved wrong, then they were charlatans, idiots. It was a case of establishing their sanity.

Similar scenes in the past had shown Ghazan that he was in radical conflict not only with welfare missions, but with opinion at Teheran. Number, it seemed to him, was becoming the new truth—it towered over and humiliated the Prophet's word. Faced with a people without history and written records and measurable habitation, science stood abashed. Forever in movement, the Falqani could not be counted and tabulated, inoculated and hospitalized. And so they must be changed: in a man-made future all change was necessarily for the better.

The third member, the stock-breeder, Ghazan took to at once. Perhaps because he tried to change animals only, or, more simply, because he started off by praising the horses.

"The Bakhtiari import Arab blood from Khuzistan," Ghazan explained, "and sell to us. We breed our own and pride ourselves on the finest in Persia."

"That I can well believe. But quite frankly, your goats and sheep could do with a lot of improvement."

Now it happened that Ghazan had devoted many years and much of his own money to perfecting his people's flocks and he was convinced they were as good as it was possible to make them. From Syria he had imported long-woolled rams; from Africa the Angola sheep with slender legs and muscular shanks; he had bred from wild Argali, which stood three feet high at the withers, and from the Wallachina, to ensure a silky fleece.

"Supposing I were to tell you," the stock-breeder continued solemnly, "that with modern methods you could obtain sheep and goats *double* the present size?"

"That would be ruinous. There is too little grass to feed a larger strain."

"You would need only a little more. And fewer beasts."

"It would make no real difference, then?"

The stock-breeder pondered this. He seemed disappointed. Ghazan explained how delicate was the balance between grass and stock, how sturdiness, thick coats and milk-yield were combined in the Falqani sheep: level back and belly, rounded carcass and light small leg, large head black even to the spiral, wrinkled horns.

"All the same, a big animal is better than a small one. Take the Merino. More sturdy . . ." His voice tailed off.

Ghazan felt slightly sorry for him.

"Try breeding if you like. Take back a couple of my ewes."

"You mean it? But I can do everything here."

"With your asses?"

"Artificially."

He explained his technique.

"But this isn't mating time," Ghazan objected. Rams were given to ewes for six weeks, covering three oestrus periods, in late autumn, so that lambs should be dropped in early spring.

"Never mind that."

He asked that a man should drive the ewes up to his baggage. Ghazan said that was impossible: the shepherd would be profoundly shocked: indeed no one else must see. So they walked up to unpack the apparatus. Ghazan summoned Ahmad, told him to corral a herd, and then dismissed him.

On the way to the baggage they met a group of children playing a game peculiar to the Falqani. The stock-breeder stopped to watch. He had two sons, he said, and was fond of children.

One boy lay hidden in a pile of goatskin tent-strips, holding a cord. The other end was tied to the waist of his partner, so that he could turn in a limited space round the pile. Three others were armed with compact bundles of sheepskins at the end of a short cord. According to the rules, they had to keep a certain distance. The idea was to elude the defender and catapult their bundles onto the central pile.

Ghazan and his visitor watched this several times, until the attackers hit their goal. Then the stock-breeder took chocolate bars from his pocket and distributed them. He showed the boys how to unwrap the silver paper and coaxed them to eat. Gingerly they nibbled, turned the chocolate over in their mouths, hesitated a moment, then spat it out with wry faces. A watching mother hurried up in alarm. She shouted and gesticulated. Ghazan had to calm her: No, the foreigner was not trying to poison the boys. To the stock-breeder he explained that tribal children were not used to sweet food: as well offer his own sons sour cheese when they expected chocolate. Ghazan laughed the incident off but his guest seemed hurt.

Having unpacked his supplies from a small portable refrigerator, the stock-breeder put on rubber gloves and a gleaming white apron. A pipette in his pocket, he entered the wicker corral, where some twenty grey-white wethers and ewes stood eyeing him. He grabbed at a ewe and seized it adroitly by the rear legs. It bleated like ten, evidently terrified by the white apron. Ghazan saw him pinion the animal to the ground and very efficiently carry out his work. A second time, with growing admiration, he watched the stock-breeder skilfully capture and pinion another ewe.

Looking well-contented, he came out of the pen. "In five months you'll have a finer pair of lambs than any in your herd. Perhaps more: my Merino ram is a twin-getter." He began to remove his gloves and apron. "The trouble is, this thin grass. My advice would be, move, as soon as you can, to richer pasture. Fars province isn't fit for scorpions."

Nothing that day astonished Ghazan more than this view of the earth as something alien, to be rejected at will. It had always been his definition of man that he was one with the earth, that even his mind must be woven like one gold thread into the green carpet.

To enter the mating in the Ilkhan's herd-book, they walked to Ghazan's tent. In one corner stood an oak-branch loom, an arm's length wide, white woollen warp strung tightly to the top, the almost finished rug wound on a wooden roller at the bottom. The stock-breeder seemed interested. He felt the velvety pile and smoothed the

69

nap with the back of his hand. His wife, he said, had told him to bring back a rug from Persia.

Ghazan turned the roller to reveal the pattern: a yellow pole medallion forming three linked diamonds, within a red medallion containing perched yellow birds. The violet field outside was enclosed in four wine-and-yellow border strips. Small tassels of wool decorated the side-edging, and Ghazan explained that the warp threads at each end would be braided into long tassels.

"I've looked at rugs from Kerman to Kermanshah," said the stock-breeder, "but I've never seen one like this nor half as fine."

"A rug's something of a mirror," Ghazan replied. "Ours have more birds and animals, but fewer flowers. They're not convoluted, but geometric. We brought the pattern from Turkestan—you find much the same in Caucasian rugs. It's been handed down from mother to daughter, never put in writing and never influenced by rugs of the plains."

The stock-breeder nodded. "The colours impress me most. I've never seen colours so vivid." He pointed to the outer medallion. "That red, for instance."

Ghazan bent to examine it. "A specially bright one. For this," he laughed, "we melt down rubies." More seriously, he continued, "This rug is being made by the wife of my shepherd. Last summer he was lucky enough to find a swarm of coccus on a clump of oaks. He collected the females, then dried and crushed them to make the red dye we call kermes."

"And if he hadn't been lucky?"

"He'd have used Indian red, onion skins or even sheep's blood. Blue comes from indigo applied over madder, brown from valonia and the green husks of walnuts, yellow from a fungus on the mulberry, from turmeric and saffron."

It seemed to Ghazan important to impress this critical foreigner with his people's skill. He explained how the wool was treated with sheep's dung, the albumen in which retained a dye longer and made it more brilliant. But townspeople found it too much trouble to collect natural dyes. They substituted synthetic anilines, very garish, which they toned down by washing in wood-ash. The result faded in a generation.

"Compare the best Tabriz or Kashan rug now being made," he continued, "with the masterpieces of three hundred years ago. Loose and

70

dull as sacking they seem. But over the years Falqani rugs have improved. I've got rugs which belonged to my great-great-grandfather—handed down as heirlooms—far inferior to this one here. Though it's true," he conceded, "the woman who knotted this is especially gifted."

"I've seen them being made," said the stock-breeder. "Six children to a loom, with the pattern hung in front."

"Somewhere in the plains?"

"In Isfahan. I was told at the age of ten they're dismissed. Fingers no longer nimble enough. That made me feel a greyhead, though I'm only thirty-five."

"At that age Falqani women still knot well. But there's a world of difference between our technique and that in the towns."

He turned over part of the rug and, pointing to the knots, explained how, beginning at the bottom and working towards the right, the wool yarn, which would go to form the pile, was looped around the warp-threads by the aid of blunt needles and then tied in such a way that each knotting bound two of the warp-threads. Most Persian weavers used a knot common to Turkish rugs, whereby these two threads were bound side by side. But the Falqani retained the Sehna knot, of Far Eastern origin. At Garden of the Pines he himself had a Chinese rug with the very same Sehna knot, whereby one thread was bound in front of the other. After each row of knots one or more weft-thread was passed through between the warp-threads and beaten down with a metal comb. The pile was then trimmed off with a knife.

"Intricate, delicate work," he concluded. "The finished rug is a harvest from a hundred different soils. When you think that looms are carried with us, wherever we go, set up now in the valleys, now in the hills, exposed to heat and damp, you realize what pride a Falqani takes in his rug and what it means to him."

"A sort of flag," suggested the stock-breeder.

"More even than a flag. When he returns from the bare hills, exhausted, covered in dust, his feet bruised by rock and stone, his soft rug is a glimpse of paradise." He had been carefully watching the stock-breeder's expression. "Since you're looking for a rug, why not one of ours? I see you admire the design. No, I won't accept money. But treat it lovingly, won't you." He promised to have one folded and corded, ready for the stock-breeder's departure.

They rejoined the other visitors in the court tent. The team held a ten-minute conference; then the teacher, as leader, gave a brief report to Ghazan on what they had seen.

"Frankly," he said, "my colleagues and I are horrified. It is nothing less than scandalous to find men, women and children living as though in Biblical times. Unbalanced diet, no dental care, poor shelter, small, underdeveloped livestock—there is no end to your evils: classic cases which will doubtless figure in future text-books." After considering possible remedies the teacher concluded, "You live far from doctors: you yourself have admitted that schooling is impossible for nomads. We shall therefore propose you be settled. That will solve your most urgent problems."

The bluntness and lack of tact astonished Ghazan, even making allowance for foreign manners. But he overlooked these and went to the point.

"You may be right in theory," he conceded, "but are you right for us, here and now? Persia is one of the world's poorest countries. The kind of education you envisage would be a luxury beyond our means. Suppose the Falqani were settled in villages. Villages here are barely self-subsisting: none can possibly afford a qualified teacher. Only our large towns have schools, and even there teachers are so ill-paid they must have other occupations. The standard is very low indeed. In two or three hundred years perhaps there will be schools ready for us—then the question may be worth discussing—but at present it does not even arise."

He paused while the interpreter translated.

"I know my people have their faults," he continued. "But settlement won't change them—and it certainly will bring many evils. Why do you want to rush so fast?"

"You seem to oppose all change," the teacher said drily.

"Persia can be changed in one way only—by a wetter climate. And that will be an act of God. I think we had it once. You'll find ruined dams in Baluchistan which now regulate only desert mirages."

The teacher returned to his notes.

"As I said, we shall advocate settlement. Our good friend the Minister of the Interior may, of course, point out obstacles of which we know nothing. It will take time. Meanwhile I suggest you keep your numbers down. There are about ten thousand too many of you for a decent standard of living."

72

Ghazan was so taken aback he could think of no adequate rejoinder He simply glared, clenching and unclenching his fists.

"I understand," the teacher continued, "that you reckon your date from the birth of Mohammed. Am I correct?"

"From the time of his flight to Medina," said Ghazan dully. He guessed what was coming. Almost every team of inquiry had made the same joke.

"So that you are now living in the year 1332. That's just about right according to our Gregorian calendar. More than six hundred years behind!"

The teacher undid the string on a packet which had been unloaded from one of the asses and handed the contents to Ghazan.

"Here are some coloured diagrams which should be distributed. They will help improve personal hygiene. In conclusion, I may say that it is very fortunate we decided to make our visit. This state of affairs might have continued unnoticed for years. It only remains for me to thank you on behalf of our team for your friendly co-operation."

The visitors had time only for a quick meal. Ghazan had ordered a special lamb pilav, spiced with cummin, but they would not touch it. They produced their own tinned food from a picnic basket and ate it with knives and forks. Then they unpacked the crates, which contained cotton-wool, bandages, aureomycin eye-ointment for trachoma, the endemic disease, and vitamin tablets. Collecting their notes and the promised rug, they mounted and rode away. They were most anxious to regain the village that night.

After watching them out of sight, Ghazan looked at the coloured pictures: each was a piece of bright red paper two palms high and four long, divided into three. In the first part a miserable, dirty child was swarming with flies; in the second its mother was bathing it in a neat white basin full of clean water, a large piece of soap in her hand; in the third the child, clean and well dressed, smiled up at its mother. Ghazan gave them to a servant with instructions to deliver one at each neighbouring tent. He wondered what his women would make of them, especially of the soap. The only soap they knew was the dried and powdered leaves of the jujube tree.

Later, on his tour of the camp, he looked about for these leaflets. Only in two tents did he discover the use to which they had been put. One

73

woman was boiling the paper to get a red dye for her hair; Dilbar had wheedled more than her share and set two sideways, two upside down to form an abstract pattern on the skirt of her tent.

"See how pretty it is!" she said to Ghazan.

To tease her, he asked whether she intended to copy the pattern into her rug.

She cocked her head and considered the question seriously. "No," she decided. "My little yellow birds would be frightened."

But the new motif Ghazan was unable to dismiss to easily. He could smile at the visitors bound in their narrow prejudices, but underneath felt anxious. Good will in union with common sense—he supposed that was their ideal, but could sense be common to two such different peoples? They seemed to challenge him. Without admitting the team were right, might not he be wrong? Could he claim a breadth of vision they lacked? Or were there two incompatible truths, one of rich green fields and the other, his own, of bare treeless hills?

That evening he discussed some of the *contretemps* with Rohim and Manuchehr, one of the elders: a greybeard—but, since beards were out of fashion, his face was shaven. Manuchehr was a Madaleh of noble birth, formerly the best rider and huntsman of his generation. A bullet-wound in the hip during the First World War had crippled his body (he could walk only with a stick) and turned his mind to the chase of wisdom. He had learned by heart Persian and Falqani poets and the entire Koran, of which he could still recite half the surahs. He had also learned to control a particularly fiery temper. A trusted adviser of Ghazan's mother, he had played an important part in restraining the old Khan's chief weakness: infatuation with the occult. Now he was shrunken and wizened as an apple in March—as a russet which has improved the flavour of summer—somewhat deaf, but still a favourite in the court tents.

Rohim had overheard the leader say: "Replace every Koran by a technical manual, in fifty years they will be civilized." His voice sharp with indignation, Rohim heaped abuse and scorn on the idea.

Manuchehr held up a calming hand. "Such idiocies are inevitable, for these strangers have not found the true religion. They are still seeking, discontented. They think civilization means cities and things made in cities. But we who have been given the Message know it is the way of life which best allows man a vision of God."

74

Rohim nodded, but this sort of religious dogmatism jarred on Ghazan. He turned the conversation, and began to rail against the age they lived in, against this new conflict which had not plagued their forefathers.

"It is less new than you think," Manuchehr said. "Were you never taught Rumi's story of the grammarian?"

Rumi was a poet of the thirteenth century. Ghazan knew his works, but this particular story he said he did not remember.

"It goes like this. A conceited grammarian once boarded a boat and, turning to the boatman, said, 'Have you ever studied grammar?' 'No,' replied the boatman. 'Half your life has been lost,' said the scholar. 'Grammar is the keystone of knowledge.' The boatman was too humiliated to reply.

"Later a wind rose and sent the boat scudding towards a whirlpool. The boatman shouted to the grammarian, 'Tell me, do you know how to swim?' In a friendlier tone the grammarian answered, 'No.' 'O grammarian,' said the boatman, 'your whole life is lost. This whirlpool is sinking our boat.'"

The cousins laughed and Manuchehr continued.

"Rumi points his moral. Self-denial, not grammar, is needed; if you are dead to self, plunge into the sea without peril; the water of the sea will cause you to float to the surface; but if you be living, how shall you escape from the sea? But there's also a simpler moral. Concern yourself first with essentials: learn to live before teaching others. If they hadn't been our guests I think I should have told them that."

Ghazan agreed, but not wholeheartedly. He saw the other point of view too well. He wished sometimes he sympathized less readily, could play life like a game of backgammon, his own white pieces against everyone else's black. He believed, too, that the mission's report might rouse Teherani opinion actively in favour of tribal settlement.

Manuchehr disagreed.

"The Government will give a dinner, flatter them, say their report is invaluable, then toss it into a well-heaped cupboard to gather dust."

"I wish I could believe that."

"You take this visit too much to heart, Ghazan. Think of our country as a peasant who has stumbled on a long-buried treasure. He is spending it as fast as he can. He gives himself airs and despises his former occupation. He goes off to town, builds a fine house and mixes with wealthy new friends. But soon the last gold coin will be unearthed and spent. Then what will he do?"

"Take service with the highest bidder?"

"Not at all. He will return to the soil and live like his ancestors. Foreign influence—what has it amounted to in the past? What remains of Alexander's Hellenism? You know as well as I, nothing lasts here but the land itself."

Yes, thought Ghazan, the land, the sky and things which hovered between—metaphysics, religion or poetry. Those were exempt from foreign influence.

"And their new notions!" continued Manuchehr. "Artificial insemination is neither theirs nor new."

"Surely it is!" the cousins exclaimed.

"Five centuries ago, when Europe was benighted, the Arabs brought it to perfection."

"And the West learned from the Arabs?"

"Very likely. So you see, Ghazan, the new is really old, and with the old we have come to terms. There's nothing to make you fret."

When he returned to his own tent, Ghazan found Ahmad making up his bed in a state of high excitement.

"Have they gone now?" he asked. "Gone back to Hindustan?"

Hindustan was the foreign country *par excellence* of tribal stories.

"To a land beyond Hindustan," Ghazan replied—"by the Isfahan trail."

Ahmad pondered this. "The man with the peaked cap wrote many numbers."

Ghazan wrinkled his brow. The teacher had seemed the one least interested in figures.

"What makes you think so?"

"He wrote from left to right."

Ghazan nodded. Though Ahmad could not write, he must have seen scribes write in the opposite direction. Only Persian figures—Arabic numerals of Indian origin—were written from left to right.

"It is true," said Ghazan. "They all wrote many numbers."

"You saw how they ate, Ghazan Khan? With pieces of iron."

"That is the custom beyond Hindustan."

"How clumsy their fingers must be!" He paused as though recalling

76

something. "And the watch! Did you see the watch of the man with the peaked cap?"

Ghazan had noticed it—a complicated chronometer-style instrument. "It had three sets of hands. Now why is that?" He was pleased rather than disappointed when Ghazan could not explain. "There's some secret there," he murmured darkly.

Squatting down, he began to polish Ghazan's riding boots. "Theirs were new, but not as strong as yours. They sat hunched in their saddles, and," he added, with a touch of pity, "they all have poor eyesight. You noticed their black glasses? When you wear those, the sun is like the moon and daylight like evening. Everything is gloomy and sombre. That's why they did not laugh."

Ghazan looked into Ahmad's eyes, amused and suddenly very pleased. He and his shepherd saw the same world, the same at least in all essentials: and now, in one day, he had become aware that this was not an inevitable consequence of their manhood, but a blessing. Yes, it was something to be thankful for that they had been made—the two of them, all the Falqani—from a single heap of dust.

CHAPTER FIVE

LATER that night Ahmad united his closest friends outside his tent. Dilbar had rubbed her child's joints with antimony and prepared a strong syrupy tea. While this was being sipped, each fondled the infant, admired his long legs or tenacious grip, but with qualifications, lest he excite the evil eye. Before passing it to his neighbour, he would say, "God preserve this child." Paternal relatives declared the boy the image of its father; at this Dilbar's family threw up their hands in derision. Anyone, they said, could see the child had its mother's eyes and nose and colouring.

Last of all Ahmad took his son in his arms. Those gathered for the naming were not surprised that Ahmad kissed and fondled him with inordinate affection.

"No one shall take this one from me," he murmured.

The boy's birth had ended fourteen years of mourning. Dilbar was Ahmad's second wife. He had married first as a youth and soon after the tribe's settlement his wife had died from the bite of a copperhead snake, leaving him an only daughter called Laila. This girl lived up to her name, which betokened all the charms of Persian womanhood. She had almond-shaped eyes and long black curls; her figure was slender, her arms were strong. In her pink cotton cloak with white flowers she looked like a sprig of apple-blossom and Ahmad would proudly say, "How can this be my daughter—surely she must be a princess."

One summer's day, when Laila was fourteen, Ahmad's section were accused of failure to pay their taxes. This was a trumped-up accusation: for once, a wet spring had enabled them to pay in full, as well as the commission demanded by the collectors for not overcharging. The usual reprisals were taken. Hostages—among them Ahmad—were seized from the section, rounded up for a few days until they or their family produced a sum equivalent to the value of a lamb. This money went into the pockets of local army officers.

When Ahmad returned after four days' absence, Laila, who kept house for him, was gone. Neighbours told him a party of soldiers had ridden over one night and carried her away.

"What could we do?" they said. "It was dark and we have no weapons."

Ahmad, wild with grief, at once went off to the nearest villages, where troops were stationed, seeking news of Laila. This proved difficult, for the tribespeople feared reprisals if they gave information. For two weeks Ahmad visited on foot all the surrounding country. At last from a shepherd boy, too young to know about reprisals, he had news. He found her body, used by the soldiery, thrown down a stagnant well. With ropes he succeeded in raising her and took her home on a borrowed donkey for burial. Ahmad never discovered who exactly were to blame. The Falqani had no rights and were fair game for lust or greed. But he went to the local Commandant and told what had happened.

"That's all you Turki scum are good for," the officer said and laughed in his face when he demanded justice.

The naming ceremony brought this death back to Ghazan. He watched Ahmad's happiness with a new sense of responsibility. He was guardian of this man's freedom and welfare multiplied a hundred thousand times. Was he doing all in his power to protect him? In all frankness he could answer yes. He had set his face against raiding and provocation. Army reinforcements, the team's recommendations— these were worrying but could not be prevented. Meanwhile his strength and his people's strength lay in scrupulously holding to their way of life, in such moments as this.

Ahmad had chosen five names which Ghazan had written down on slips of paper. These were inserted by one of the guests in Ahmad's Koran. Having recited the first chapter, Ahmad drew out one of the slips by chance. Handing it to Ghazan, he asked him please to read it.

Ghazan took the paper and announced the name:

"Hussein."

"By the will of God," the company added.

In this way, among the Falqani tribesmen, important decisions were taken.

The guests looked at the child and repeated the name, until the two became one, and it seemed there had never been a moment when Ahmad's child was not Hussein. An excellent, altogether appropriate name, they decided, and one for so fine a boy to live up to: Hussein with his brother Hassan being among Persia's holiest saints.

When they had exhausted all the overtones and advantages of the new name, Hussein was laid in his home-made oak-branch cradle, and the roasted lamb given by Ghazan, which Dilbar brought steaming from the fire, became the centre of no less attentive interest.

As the guests began to leave, one of them—Sanjar—invited Ahmad to his tent for a game of cards. From a sheepskin satchel he took a coloured pack made of stout wood, with five denominations: ace, shah, queen, warrior and dancing girl. They seated themselves on the rug. Sanjar dealt, slowly and methodically. They took up their hands and began to play a game of Aces, the object being to take tricks and to make flushes and royal flushes.

"How her eyes shone tonight!" said Ahmad with feeling.

"Whose eyes?"

"Why, Dilbar's of course. Oh, I'm in love with that woman."

Sanjar shrugged. "After a year?"

"More than the day we were married," said Ahmad with conviction.

His friend smiled. "You like thinking you're in love."

"You don't believe me? But, after all, why should you? I've done nothing to prove it. Look at Rustam—he killed thousands in battle. Look at Majnun—for love of Laila he roamed the wilderness and went out of his mind. Every week I tell of lovers who kill dragons and giants, of husbands who save their wives from monsters and jinns. And I—what do I do for Dilbar? Nothing. Nothing but lay an occasional partridge at her feet and win a game of Aces."

"So far you have lost every trick."

"I'll catch up," said Ahmad easily, but his attention soon wandered from the cards. "When I tell of the Princess Budur, I think of Dilbar. That waist, slender as a cypress, those long eyes like almonds; and the lightest milker of goats in all the Falqani." He held up a queen. "Her face should be here, Sanjar, instead of this cross-eyed hag." He played the card and lost it to an ace.

"She's a pretty woman. Say that and have done."

Ahmad looked at him scornfully. "Pretty! You call Dilbar only pretty! If a brown bear were pounding me to death with its paws, I suppose you'd call it rough. And the black scorpion's sting—annoying. Pretty! What a beggarly word."

"There are words for stories round the fire, and words for the tent. Now we are in the tent."

"Even so, 'pretty' is muddling, to say the least. As well call the shah the warrior."

Sanjar sighed. "How you go on! The foreigner talking to Dilbar—is that what's turned your head?"

"The foreigner?" Ahmad echoed suspiciously. "I've heard nothing of that."

"Didn't Dilbar tell you? I'm surprised."

"I've been milking all afternoon, then with Ghazan Khan, until the naming feast. What happened?"

"Play, will you," Sanjar said.

Ahmad tossed a card on the rug. "Tell me," he urged.

"The foreigner with two pairs of glasses went directly up to Dilbar. He spoke to her by way of the interpreter—and to no one else."

As Ahmad considered this, his face slowly relaxed. "I'm not surprised. Dilbar stands out. He doubtless knew she was the lightest milker of all the Falqani."

"How should he know?"

"Such news gets about. Even in Shiraz they speak of Dilbar's milking." Ahmad played his last card, lost the game, and dealt the second hand. "What did the foreigner say?"

"I don't know exactly. I had it from Mahin. She was at the loom with Dilbar. It seems he asked to see her clothes."

"Her clothes!"

"She went and fetched them from your tent."

Again Ahmad's face softened from a frown to a smile. "Ah, yes, he wanted to admire them. Everyone knows she weaves the warmest clothes in the Madaleh."

"He took them up, one by one, in his own hands."

Ahmad's smile faded. "That was impudent. I don't like that. I should have told him so to his face."

"Then he sprayed them with perfume."

"Perfume. That was strange! What happened next?"

"Then he went away. But he took one of Dilbar's skirts with him."

"Stole it?" cried Ahmad.

"Dilbar didn't seem to mind."

"She who loves her skirts! I don't understand this, Sanjar." He passed a hand over his brow. "Did he take a skirt from Mahin?"

"He didn't look at anyone else's clothes."

"Did he put perfume on the other women?"

"Not as far as I know."

Ahmad folded his arms and dropped his chin. "There's something dark here, Sanjar." Laying his cards on the rug, he gave himself up to thought. Presently he raised gleaming eyes, and asked in a tense voice: "Do you happen to remember the story of Khosrov the Tabrizi?"

"Where he's carried away in an eagle's claws and dropped in the sea?"

"No, no—not that one. Khosrov loves a princess of Samarcand. But Qutalmish also has an eye on her. He is ugly and hunchbacked, so the princess will not look at him. What does Qutalmish do? He disguises himself as a perfume-vendor. He takes all the little bottles with his poisons and philtres and goes to the palace, pretending they're attars and scents. There he sells a perfume that is really a love potion. When she puts a drop on her silk dress, she falls under his spell. Then he carries her off to his castle. Later, of course, Khosrov rescues her."

"I remember. By cutting off two tigers' heads with a single sabre-stroke. I don't believe that's possible."

"Have you ever swung a sabre at two tigers?"

"No, but I've . . ."

"Then," retorted Ahmad severely, "you have no right to say it's impossible."

"I didn't say impossible. I only said . . ."

Ahmad lifted his hand. "Let me finish. When he's driven from his castle, Qutalmish disguises himself as a beggar. He comes to the palace and cadges alms. The princess takes pity and gives him a diamond from her neck. Because it is hers and has touched her body, the diamond gives Qutalmish power over the princess. He holds the diamond in his hands and recites incantations that spirits her to him. There is an excellent battle with rivers of blood, and finally Khosrov kills Qutalmish. But for a time the princess seems utterly lost." He looked expectantly at Sanjar. "Doesn't something strike you?"

"About the story?"

"About Dilbar—and the foreigner."

Sanjar looked puzzled. Ahmad leant forward, very stirred. "Supposing this foreigner has cast a spell on Dilbar?"

"Why should he?"

Ahmad lowered his voice to an impressive whisper. "Because he's in love with her."

Sanjar laughed. "You're worse than your father! With your head full of stories, you believe the wildest things."

"Laugh if you like, but it may be true. Why should he perfume her clothes if he's not in love?"

"He saw her only—how long?—the time it takes to say the morning prayer."

"He saw her almond eyes. One glance of those eyes was enough for Ahmad."

Sanjar remained sceptical, and after a moment raised a new objection. "Why did he leave, then? If he loves Dilbar, he would have stayed, or tried to take her with him."

"There's truth in that," Ahmad conceded. "After he left with the skirt, did he see Dilbar again?"

"He went later to your tent—Mahin saw him go."

"To our tent!" cried Ahmad. "What did he do there?"

Sanjar shrugged. "I've told you all I know. Now, it's you to play."

Ahmad played a few tricks abstractedly, then, suddenly tossing his cards on the rug, rose to his feet.

"Where are you going?"

"To Dilbar. I must hear what happened after."

"Finish our game."

Ahmad looked scornful. "Cards—at a time like this!"

He hurried back to his tent, where Dilbar, after the last feed, was laying Hussein in his cradle. "This foreigner!" he cried.

"Quietly," she murmured, rocking Hussein. "He's almost asleep."

"This foreigner," he repeated in a bellowing whisper, "with two pairs of glasses."

Dilbar smiled. "Yes, I have lots to tell you."

"I know about the skirts and perfume," he said. "Sanjar had it from Mahin." He looked at her cautiously, as though even now a spell might be on her. "What do you think of him?"

"He was cross that we wore seven skirts."

"I mean—did he strike you as handsome?"

She gave him a teasing smile. "Handsomer than some who think themselves handsome."

"Handsome—he hadn't a hair on his head!" Ahmad's suspicions were strengthened. He remembered that the princess after the spell had found the hunchback Qutalmish irresistible. He looked anxiously at Dilbar. "How do you feel? Strange?"

She seemed puzzled. "Strange—no. Only a little tired." She glanced down at her son. "He's asleep now. Come to bed."

"Wait," said Ahmad. "Those skirts he perfumed—you must wash them first thing tomorrow."

She laughed. "Like a clump of pink oleanders, those clothes were. I washed them this afternoon."

Already washed—Ahmad felt a little relieved. More calmly, he continued, "Sanjar told me the foreigner came to this tent. Why was that?"

"To spray it. Against lice and fleas, he said."

"Lice and fleas in our tent! What an idea." Ahmad sniffed at the air, still redolent of insecticide. A sweet smell, something between basil and reseda, certainly a perfume, perhaps a love potion to be breathed sleeping at night. "What else did he do?"

"He gave me presents," said Dilbar with a touch of pride. She took from her skirts a packet of darning-needles. Removing one she held it up to the light. "See how fine and sharp it is."

Ahmad felt the point with his thumb. "Yes, a strong needle," he conceded. "All the same, gifts from strangers: I don't like that. Ahmad can give you all the needles you want." He looked at her reprovingly. "Did he give you anything else?"

Shyly Dilbar fumbled in her skirts and produced a round flat object the size of her open hand. Ahmad looked at it with wide eyes.

"A mirror!" he cried.

For chieftains of the Falqani and for families living in the plains the mirror played an essential part in the marriage ceremony. When the couple were led to the nuptial chamber, the bridegroom was allowed to see his bride's unveiled face in a round mirror. Very often it was his first glimpse of her. The mirror was the very symbol of married love. And Ahmad, the Ilkhan's servant, knew this.

"A mirror," he repeated, horrified. This was indubitable proof that the foreigner loved Dilbar, that his perfumes were love potions. In a grave voice he told Dilbar. A year with Ahmad had partly initiated Dilbar into a world where extraordinary things happened as readily as in ballads. But she received the idea cautiously.

"Don't forget, he sprayed other tents."

Ahmad thought a moment. "Pretended to. These magicians are wily. He didn't want his plans known."

Dilbar looked sadly at the mirror in Ahmad's hand. "Give me it back," she pleaded.

"To that foreign magician—yes!"

"Please, Ahmad, I love my little mirror. He meant no harm. It was because he'd taken my marigold skirt."

The skirt! It had slipped Ahmad's mind. He looked at Dilbar in alarm. "With that in his hands he can spirit you away. I shall wake one morning and find you gone. Dilbar gone for ever!" He drew back in horror from his own prediction. After a moment's silence he took a deep breath. Hands on his hips, he announced gravely, "There's only one thing to be done: ride after this knave, make him confess his dark plans, and seize the marigold skirt."

"But, Ahmad, he speaks a strange tongue."

With a wave of his hand, he dismissed the objection. "No need to make him confess. Enough to drag him from his donkey and beat him. I'll throw in his face the needles and mirror. 'Take these magic gifts,' I shall say, 'Dilbar has a man who can give her needles of gold.'"

"Give back the mirror?"

"Certainly—it's charmed."

She looked at him doubtfully. "You'll get into trouble."

"Trouble! Don't worry for me! Ahmad can win his battles." He considered a moment. "I shall leave at dawn. Ghazan Khan told me they've taken the Isfahan trail. I shall gallop into the rising sun, rifle slung, dagger in my belt, to rescue you from this foreign prince with two pairs of glasses." He encircled her waist with a protective arm. "Ahmad will show the Falqani Dilbar's worth."

"A prince? Is he a prince?"

"Who said he's a prince?"

"You did."

Ahmad's eyelids flickered, but only for a moment. "Yes, of course he's a prince—from a land beyond Hindustan."

"How do you know he's a prince?"

"How do I know?" With a frown he pondered, then whispered tenderly, "Why, it's clear as sunlight. Who but a Falqani or a foreign prince would dare to look on those brown eyes?"

Dilbar was softened and a little intrigued. "Are you absolutely sure he's put a spell on me?"

He looked at her anxiously. "Don't think too much about the spell. The whole affair is in Ahmad's hands." He swept up the mutton-fat lamp which lighted the tent and with a majestic puff blew out the flame. "Come now," he said gently, "seeing I must ride away at dawn."

Next morning, packing his saddle-bags for the journey, Ahmad caught sight of his friend, leading a troop of goats to water.

"I'm going after him, Sanjar," he called, and explained that a spell was on Dilbar.

Sanjar looked at him coldly. "You are the one in a spell."

"He sprayed a love potion and gave her a mirror."

"Perhaps in his country it is the custom to give mirrors."

"To a girl—at the first meeting! A likely notion!"

Ahmad untethered his horse and began to curry its coat.

"You're not really going!" said Sanjar anxiously.

"Yes, my mind's made up. At last I have a chance to perform heroic deeds for Dilbar."

"Ahmad!" his friend upbraided. "You still think you're telling stories round the fire!"

"Stories! This is a good deal more serious than stories—as that foreigner will find to his cost."

"You'll never catch him up."

In a lordly voice Ahmad retorted, "A horse can overtake a donkey, I suppose, when it's ridden by a rider avenging his wife's honour."

"And what will you do if you find him?"

Ahmad laid a hand on his horn-handled knife. "Why, what Khosrov did. I shall tear him from his donkey, this foreign prince magician, and cut his scrawny throat."

"And the gendarmes?"

Ahmad paused, adjusting the girth. "Gendarmes?"

"They'll strike like lightning. And since it's a foreigner, perhaps the army too."

Ahmad looked at him doubtfully. "You don't mean it?"

86

"About foreigners they're very particular. And since you say he's a prince, there might be trouble, even war."

"War?" boomed Ahmad incredulously.

"Supposing the army killed Ghazan Khan, would we leave a single soldier alive in the province of Fars?"

Ahmad lowered his eyes. "Perhaps I shall not kill him. Perhaps I shall only use my whip: frighten him to the verge of madness. That will teach strangers to come meddling with Ahmad's wife."

"Even so, the gendarmes will arrest you. When that consul was shot and wounded in Shiraz, they seized everyone they could find, even turned part of the governor's house into an extra prison. There were a good few locked up, I can tell you."

Ahmad recalled the incident. He remembered even more vividly what had happened to his daughter.

"Perhaps I shall not whip him. But I must get back the skirt."

"No harm in that. Ask him for it—don't use force." Sanjar turned to his goats, which had begun to bleat loudly. "Be patient! Be patient! Your master and humble servant is coming." With a gesture of farewell he led his troop down to the stream.

Ahmad continued to harness his horse, but with less gusto. Presently he saw Dilbar's mother, Bibi, approach. She was a tall, forceful woman with a jutting chin, and she carried a six-weeks lamb on one shoulder as though it were a kitten.

In a sharp voice she asked, "What's all this nonsense I hear? Going to the plains to kill a magician!"

"Not kill," said Ahmad quickly. "Just to return the mirror and needles, and get back the marigold skirt."

"Dilbar doesn't want the marigold skirt. It's old and worn. Ghazan Khan has promised her a new one, much better."

"He can put spells on that marigold skirt."

Bibi tossed her head. "Spells! You think too much about spells. Think of Dilbar and Hussein. The busiest season, and you go off on a jaunt to the plains. Who will tend the lambs? And Dilbar busy all day with a new rug for the Ilkhan."

"Lambs, rugs! There are more important things. Deeds a woman wants—deeds for a man to prove his love."

"The best deed you can do is stay where you are—help Dilbar with the milking."

87

"Milking ewes!" Ahmad retorted scornfully. "Anyone can do that. It takes a brave man to confront a magician!"

He spoke with fire, and continued bridling his horse. Bibi, having eyed him warily, changed her tactics.

"We all know you are brave," she said in a friendlier tone. "But even the bravest are cautious. They don't rush blindly into great danger."

"Danger from the gendarmes?" said Ahmad coolly.

"From the man himself. If he's a magician, and a foreigner too, be sure he'll guard himself with jinns and invisible armour."

Ahmad stared at her, disconcerted. He had not considered this side of the affair.

"You say that to keep me from going."

"No, I say it for Dilbar's sake. He'll be up to a thousand tricks. Offer you poisoned sweets that twist your body in knots. He'll make short work of you, for all your courage."

Meanwhile news of the wild plan had spread. His acquaintances and those who listened to his stories liked Ahmad. Impulsive perhaps, but warm-hearted, a willing lender and as Ghazan's shepherd enjoying a certain prestige. If they found fault with him, it was because he idealized himself and Dilbar. They did not believe for one moment that the foreigner had cast spells, but a group of them now approached, to urge Ahmad on. They hoped for a little excitement, and that Ahmad would come back from the plains, tail between his legs.

"All ready to go!" one of them cried in a hearty voice. "At last the great Ahmad has a chance to prove himself."

Ahmad eyed Bibi. Down to earth, but a sensible woman. And then there were the gendarmes and army. Trying to look casual, he said:

"They left last night. I doubt if I'd catch them up."

"They were on donkeys. You have a horse."

"There's work to be done here," said Ahmad in a dutiful tone. "I'd like to go, but I can't leave Dilbar—not with Hussein. And a new rug begun."

They nodded knowingly. "And how often have you claimed you would saw in half anyone who so much as looked twice at Dilbar. Now you say a foreigner has cast a spell, and you do nothing about it. Is this the way to prove that Dilbar is the lightest milker among the Madaleh?"

"Among all the Falqani," Ahmad corrected.

"More shame on you, then. An empty boaster—we thought Ahmad was more than that."

He looked round unhappily. His own honour and Dilbar's honour were at stake. And yet, it was true, one did not lightly attack foreign magicians, of unknown power. After a moment he tethered his horse and turned to leave.

"You're going on foot?" they cried.

"I'm going to consult my father," said Ahmad with dignity.

Ahmad's father, Ismail, was also a storyteller. Ahmad had learned all his stories from him and had the highest regard for the "old one". He consulted him often: for instance, about how to describe the magic rose in the tale of the cadi's unfaithful wife, give it a red colour, a fragrant scent, thorns which pricked, while still making it a little different from any other rose. He also consulted Ismail about the no less intricate problems of real life. Like his son, Ismail was strong, but very wiry. His face was unusually lean and his eyes sunken. He did not know his own age: Ahmad thought he was about seventy. Like Ahmad, he was impulsive and easily open to suggestion.

Ahmad entered the tent and saw with surprise his father lying on the ground in one corner, covered with blankets. He rushed up, puzzled and very concerned. "What is it, old one?"

"I am ill," moaned Ismail.

"Ill?" That was a word the Falqani seldom used. When a man was ill, it meant there was little hope left. Ahmad looked at the thin face. It did look tired and drawn. He felt his father's brow: it was burning hot.

"When did this happen?"

"Very suddenly."

"Two days ago you were well enough. Remember how we shot quail?"

"Two days ago," he murmured, "I did not know how ill I was." He began to groan.

Ahmad had never seen his father like this. He did not know what to do. He looked pityingly at the thin face and searched for some way to give him pleasure.

"I know," he suddenly said. "We roasted a lamb last night. We hoped you were coming and kept back the kidneys—grilled the way you like them. I'll fetch them now."

A few minutes later he returned with the kidneys on a skewer. He knelt down and showed them, but the old man moaned again.

"Look how well Dilbar has cooked them."

"Can a sick man eat kidneys, Ahmad?" He turned away, facing the tent-skirt.

Ahmad was more anxious than ever. He had never seen his father refuse kidneys. "I'll leave them here, just in case."

He went outside, to the other side of the tent, where his mother sat, rocking milk into butter in the shade of the tent-awning. He asked her what was wrong with his father.

"Nothing at all," she answered placidly.

Ahmad stared at her. "How can you say that? Anyone can see he doesn't look well."

"Of course not—he hasn't closed his eyes all night, worrying about his so-called illness."

"I tell you, his brow is burning with fever."

She showed no concern. "Did you count the blankets on his bed? He's piled up all his and all mine. Is it surprising his brow is hot?"

Ahmad considered this. After a moment he asked, "When did his illness begin?"

"Yesterday. When one of the foreigners came."

"Which one?" asked Ahmad.

"It doesn't matter which."

"It matters very much." Ahmad sighed. His mother was a good woman, full of sound practical sense, but she was not a storyteller. "Think now. Did he have two pairs of glasses—a white and a black?"

His mother lowered the goatskin of milk, and put a hand to her chin. "Yes, that's right. How did you know? He took off the black pair when he entered the tent: I remember now. An Isfahani came with him. First the foreign man put a cord round my head, then wrote in a little black book. Next he put a cord round Ismail's head. He drew it away and looked at him strangely. Then he put the cord round his head again, and wrote more words in his little black book. He said something in his language, and the Isfahani told Ismail what he had said. 'You look pale and thin,' that's what he said to Ismail. 'Are you sure you're not ill?'"

"Ill!" cried Ahmad. "Did he dare ask that?"

"'Ill,' he said. Then he went on, 'If I had my way, you'd be in bed.'

Well, you know how your father is. A foreigner who can write, with a new clean shirt and a tie. As soon as we were alone, he began to mutter: 'Ill! Ought to be in bed! Face pale and thin!' I laughed at him. 'There's nothing wrong with you.' 'Thin and pale,' he repeated. 'Even strangers notice it. I'm going to lie down.' I took him by the hand. 'You are going to milk the goats and after that see your grandson named.'

"Just then Dilbar came in. 'Look at my presents,' she cried. We both looked. The only mirror in this tent is the one I brought with my dowry; you dropped it as a baby, and now its face is cracked like mine. It's over there, in my box, with my red and white fard. You can see only your mouth, or one eye at a time. Ismail spies this fine round mirror. He takes it from Dilbar and looks at himself. He grows paler than ever. 'This can't be me,' he cries. Dilbar and I—we laugh. 'Of course it's you. Don't you recognize yourself?' 'This thin face,' he goes on, unbelieving, 'with all the lines. So old and worn.' He looks at us, terribly worried and anxious. 'The rich stranger was right. I must be ill.'

"Dilbar laughed again and left with her mirror and needles: she had to suckle Hussein. Your father went on and on about his sick face. Then all at once he seized the blankets and lay down on his bedding. There he has been ever since. But he's no more ill than you or I. It's all that stranger's doing."

Ahmad listened with growing anxiety. "There's something sinister here," he said finally. "I'm going to look again at the 'old one'."

He entered the tent and squatted down beside his father. "Tell me about this illness, father. Have you pain in your arms?" With his two hands Ahmad pressed his father's arms from wrist to shoulder.

"No pain in the arms," his father announced.

"In your legs? Move them about and feel."

Ismail shuffled. "No pain in the legs."

"Where is your pain?"

"Not in any one spot. It's everywhere, you might say. I feel ill. I know I am ill, the stranger said so, and I saw my face in the mirror."

Ahmad returned to his mother, nodding gravely. "It's just as I suspected."

"That there's nothing at all the matter?"

"Everything's the matter. This stranger is a magician. He has

91

already put love potions on Dilbar's clothes and in our tent. Now he has put a spell on my father."

His mother stamped her foot. "A spell!" she cried angrily. "Oh, Ahmad, you and your father and all your stories!"

The charge left her son unperturbed. "He's in great danger. The poor old man may die. But on no account tell him so."

"Were you born without sense? Why should anyone want to kill Ismail?"

"This foreigner's in love with Dilbar. So of course he wants to get rid of all who stand in his way—you, me and Ismail. He starts by the 'old one'."

He paused and sized up events. Dangerous to meddle, but even more dangerous to leave things as they were. Dilbar spirited away, his father dying in agony. These were the horrors which lay ahead unless he took action. Action at once.

He faced his mother, jaw set, and said solemnly, "My mind is made up. I am going after the foreigner. I'll force him to unbind these spells."

His mother looked at him open-mouthed. "Going after him! What good will that do? You'll only make your father worse, taking it all so seriously." More gently she continued, "Surely you know, Ahmad, how he gets ideas, and in a few days they pass. Laugh him out of it, that would be more to the point."

Ahmad looked at her with pity. "There are certain things women will never understand. It is for us to protect you: to act, not talk."

With that he left the tent. He was on the way back to see Dilbar, when he recalled Bibi's warning. Khosrov had worn a magic ring when he attacked Qutalmish in his castle. He too would need an amulet. For this there was only one person to consult: the widow called Fatima.

Every tribe had its expert in astrology and magic, usually a woman. They were consulted in diverse predicaments. They cast horoscopes, prescribed a mixture of mandrake to secure a husband's love (but it must not be eaten with pickles or it would drive him mad) and sold charms such as cowries: eye-splitters to ward off the evil eye.

Ahmad told Fatima of his plans and that he wanted a specific against poisoned sweets, indeed against any poison. Fatima said only one thing would give him protection. That was bezoar, a stony concretion found in the stomach of goats and related animals. Fatima had an antelope bezoar: most efficacious of all. She showed him the little grey stone. It would cost him a skinful of clarified butter. Ahmad told her he must talk over his purchase with Dilbar.

He walked to his tent and told his wife.

"But Bibi has a bezoar," Dilbar exclaimed. "She'll lend you it gladly."

"What sort of bezoar?"

"Why, a goat's."

Ahmad shook his head. "That is no good. Only an antelope's bezoar is effective against all poisons."

Dilbar looked surprised. "I've never heard that before."

"Neither had I," Ahmad admitted. "But Fatima was very definite."

Sadly Dilbar said, "A skinful of clarified butter. For a piece of stone."

"A very rare piece of stone," urged Ahmad. After a pause he said doubtfully, "Of course, I could go without it. From more danger, more merit."

"No, no," said Dilbar quickly. "Tell Fatima I'll pay tomorrow." Then, almost with regret, "They're expensive, Ahmad, your noble deeds."

So Ahmad bought the specific against poison and Dilbar sewed it into his tunic. He asked Ghazan's permission to be away a few days: Sanjar volunteered to perform Ahmad's duties in the Ilkhan's tent. Towards noon, his horse saddled, Ahmad stood ready to leave. Dilbar was now acquiescent. She liked the idea of her honour being protected, and she trusted Ahmad's strength and astuteness would keep him out of harm. She had made him milk-balls: these with a barley cake provided by his mother were packed with the needles and mirror in his saddle-bag.

Sanjar and Bibi, seeing that they could not dissuade him, stood by with advice. Already they had prevented him from taking his rifle: he carried only his horn-handled knife, used for gelding rams.

"Don't sleep on a westerly slope," said Bibi. "That's where the dew falls thickest."

"Don't draw your knife unless you're attacked," said Sanjar.

Ahmad snorted, "I'm the one who's attacking."

"Then keep clear of blue uniforms."

When Ahmad had mounted, Dilbar untied from her skirts a screwed-up piece of cloth. From it she took the only coin it contained: a five-rial piece, the price of a few cigarettes. As he kissed her and Hussein goodbye, she handed it to Ahmad.

He looked in surprise at the coin gleaming in her palm. "You keep it," he said. "I have no need of money."

"You never know," said Dilbar.

"But five rials—it's too much."

"To please me," she said.

Ahmad, very touched, took the coin.

"Don't spend it unless you have to," said Bibi.

Ahmad flicked the reins and, while his family commended him to God, rode away at full gallop, beyond the last line of tents, and out of sight.

That day passed, and the next. Sanjar performed Ahmad's duties with a heavy but scrupulous hand: other friends helped Bibi and Dilbar to milk and shear their sheep. Ismail, weary of lying in bed and very hungry, decided that a light meal of sheep's kidneys might restore his strength. His wife persuaded him to take off some of his blankets. Already he said he was feeling less ill.

The camp was speculating about the outcome of Ahmad's journey. Some hoped he would succeed, for they considered the tribe's reputation involved. Even those who had hoped Ahmad would be made to look foolish, as the third day passed revised their views. It would be a pity not to hear any more of his stories. They visited Dilbar all through the day to see if he had come back.

On the evening of the third day Ahmad returned, and rode straight to his own tent.

Dilbar threw her arms round his neck. "Oh, how I missed you," she cried, then, stepping back, drew her hands down to his. "You're not harmed? Are you sure you're not harmed?"

"Ahmad's all right," he said curtly. He unbuttoned his tunic and pulled out her marigold skirt.

"You got it back!" she exclaimed. "How well you've done!"

She wanted to hear everything, from start to finish, but he was silent and gruff. Worn out, she supposed, by the long ride. She noticed his face looked drawn, as he walked to his father's tent.

His mother, in high spirits, welcomed him back. "Your father's out with his sheep," she explained.

Ahmad's face brightened. "He's well?" After a pause he muttered, "Then the spell has gone." But his voice lacked the ring of triumph.

"The mirror has gone, you mean. The day after you left, he began to forget about his poor lined face. He only heard his sheep bleating to be milked, and his goats whining to be watered. At last he could stand it no longer. He got up, did his day's work, and at sundown said he felt strong as Rustam."

Back in his own tent, Ahmad asked for food. After eating a bowlful of pilav, made from the remains of the lamb, and *mast*, he called for another: something he seldom did. Afterwards he took from his pocket a coin and handed it to Dilbar. She gave a little cry of astonishment.

"The five rials!"

"Are you surprised," he asked eagerly. "Really surprised?"

"Yes, yes—and glad. I was saving for a comb. A pink comb." She clutched the coin to her breast. Then her eye fell on the empty bowl.

"You went hungry, Ahmad—to bring it back?"

"That food in the plains!" he said with the show of a grimace. "I'm glad I waited for your pilav."

But when she and Bibi questioned him about what had happened in the plains, he replied flatly, "We men act. We don't always talk about what we do."

That night, as he and Dilbar sat outside their tent by the fire, his friends came one by one for news, but he would not answer their questions. He said Ismail was out of harm's way and Dilbar too—that was enough. They went away disappointed and later returned in a band.

Sanjar stepped forward, looking aggrieved. "I did your work, Ahmad, while you were gone: your other friends helped. Three days you were away. We have a right to know what happened. Did you do all you planned?"

"I brought back the skirt. Show them the skirt, Dilbar."

She held up the piece of orange cotton. Sanjar looked at it, half-convinced.

"Yes, but how did you get it?"

Ahmad did not answer.

95

"You found it lying on the hills!" one of the tribesmen cried; another said, "I don't believe you even saw the foreigner."

Ahmad stirred, looking very confused. He saw Dilbar give him an expectant glance. There was a great deal at stake.

"Sit down and I'll tell you," he said gloomily, rising to his feet. They sat in a circle round the fire.

"I rode down from the hills," said Ahmad, in a voice which steadily gathered strength. "All night and day I rode, past the village of Shahr Kurd. I looked in the ruins, I looked in the tea houses. Not a sign. Where had the foreigner gone? Changed himself into a snake or a scorpion? Everything suspicious I had to examine. I saw a peasant hoeing in the fields. 'Have you seen three foreign princes pass this way?' I asked. He wrinkled his brow. 'How did they look?' 'They had brown riding boots and black glasses.' 'No,' he said, 'No one like that.'

"On I rode, taking the Isfahan trail. I came to the village of Firuz. I saw a little girl, leading her father, a blind beggar. 'I'm looking for three foreign princes, with black glasses and brown riding boots.' 'I saw them,' she said. 'They passed here in a car.' 'How long ago?' 'An hour or more. You've missed them now.' 'You don't know Ahmad,' I cried. 'He'll catch them up.'

"I spurred on my horse. About nightfall I came to the village of Abbasabad. I met a man driving an ox. 'Have you seen three foreign princes with black glasses and brown riding boots.' 'Yes,' he said. 'They're asleep in our caravanserai.' 'Be careful of your ox,' I said. 'One is a magician.' 'All are magicians,' he replied. 'They unrolled loose coverings and changed them into beds, not mattresses but high beds such as they sell in Isfahan. They unrolled more canvas, and this became chairs. They cut open a metal box and took out peaches—peaches in springtime!' I lifted a hand. 'Enough. These are the men. But one is a worse magician than the others. He gave a mirror to Dilbar, my wife—the lightest milker of all the Falqani—and he has laid my father at the door of death. Now I am going to make him pay.' 'It is you who must beware,' the man said, starting to tremble, 'a foreign magician can do you much harm.' 'Ahmad doesn't come unprotected,' I said. I showed him the bezoar bought from Fatima for a skinful of clarified butter, and the sheep's-eye my mother put on my wrist the day I was named.

96

"A crowd had collected to listen. The headman of the village came forward and whispered, 'The foreigners are asleep. Now is your moment.' 'Not at all,' I replied. 'The Falqani scorn to strike down a sleeping enemy.' 'But this is a magician!' they cried. 'Even a magician,' I said. 'I shall wait till morning and meet him face to face.'

"It was dark now. The headman said, 'Come and pass the night with me. My house is small and unworthy, but your presence will shed on it perpetual lustre.' With nowhere better, I said I'd come. It turned out a fine house, surrounded by willows. After a glass of tea he showed me the garden, with a round pool. You've never seen such a pool: big enough to drown everyone in that village and still have water left. Rose bushes too: the biggest I've ever seen; great melon-sized blooms, all scarlet as blood."

"You smelled that scarlet in the dark!" heckled one of his listeners.

Ahmad flung him a scornful look. "Two nights ago the moon was full. I could see everything in the garden. Apricots and plums and peaches—just the beginnings of unripe fruit—but I could tell they were going to be huge and juicy.

"That night I slept in a bed, with white sheets, and at dawn I went to the caravanserai. The foreigners were already astir, loading cooking-gear and blankets into their car. I crept up to their alcove, fingers round my knife. The one with two pairs of glasses was there, a tin kettle in his hand. It looked like a kettle, but it might have been some sort of pistol. 'You foreign prince magician,' I cried, 'now is the hour of settlement, for the spells you have put on Dilbar and Ismail.' He looked at me open-mouthed, gave a great cry of terror and dropped the kettle with a crash. Then he bolted out of the caravanserai."

With a brisk flourish, Ahmad paused dramatically. "So he got away," cried his listeners, disappointed.

"Got away! With Dilbar's honour threatened! He ran into the street. I ran after him. Fast as a hare, but I was a greyhound. 'Wait till I squeeze my hands round your throat,' I cried. Again he howled a wild cry of terror. At last I came close: I managed to curl my fingers round his collar. Any other man I should have held. But this was a magician: with the strength of a jinn he twisted free, then into a gateway he dived. I followed like his own shadow. Then I drew up. Blue tiles all round the courtyard. A blue dome and one thin tower with a wooden balustrade. A mosque. We were standing on holy ground."

Again Ahmad paused. "Sanctuary," whispered his listeners, awe-struck. "Go on," they cried.

Ahmad pretended uncertainty. "Is there any more?"

"Yes, yes."

He passed a hand over his brow. "I'm not sure I remember." He aroused their curiosity to the pitch he wanted, then continued.

"Sanctuary. Even a magician I couldn't touch there. He stood panting, eyeing me like a trapped weasel. After a while he edged his way back—knelt and drank from the flowing stream. Just then a figure came into the courtyard, in white turban and brown camel-hair cloak. A mullah. He peered at the figure crouched drinking, and turned to me. 'This man is strangely dressed. He looks like an infidel.' 'He is an infidel,' I cried, 'and a magician. He has put spells on my wife and father. I was going to seize him, when he ran in here.' 'An infidel drinking in the sacred mosque of Abbasabad!' The mullah's eyes blazed. He strode over to the magician. 'Eater of pig-flesh—do you dare make a sty of this holy mosque!' He waved him towards the gate. The foreigner went down on his knees. 'Let me stay,' he whined, 'or I shall surely be killed.' 'And do you deserve less, committer of sacri-lege and binder of spells?' The mullah called two of his attendants. They seized the foreigner and led him struggling out of the mosque. The mullah went first. 'This way,' he pointed, going down one of the alleys. 'Where are you taking me?' the foreigner cried. 'To the cadi.' 'What wrong have I done?' 'What wrong! Heathen that he is, he asks what wrong!'

"We reached the cadi's house. The cadi was an old man with a long grey beard, his face dark and wrinkled as a lambskin from Azer-baijan. Behind him on a shelf were piled many books. After listening to the mullah's charge, he said in a deep voice. 'This is a very serious offence.' The foreigner began to whimper and tremble. The cadi opened one of his books and turned over the pages. At last he read out, 'Any infidel who enters a sacred mosque shall be liable to an instant fine of thirty tumans.' He gave the magician a piercing look. 'You must pay the fine at once, to me.' 'Thirty tumans!' he cried. 'That will leave me a beggar.' 'Either pay the fine,' said the cadi, 'or go to prison.' 'Prison? For how long?' 'Until you or your family can scrape up the money.' The foreigner felt in his pocket and drew out some notes. 'After all, I decide to pay.' These the cadi took and counted, then waved him away. 'You are free to go.' That was Ahmad's moment. Ahmad stepped forward. 'Not altogether free, sir. I have one or two affairs to settle.' I seized him by the arms, led him out into the alley and flung him on the ground. 'Mercy!' he screamed. 'Mercy!'"

Again Ahmad gave his listeners time to speculate. When he continued, it was with even bolder gestures. "I threw down the mirror and needles. 'Take back your magic gifts, and swear to unbind the spells on Dilbar and Ismail.'

"Already he had strewed ashes of repentance on his head. 'The spell on Ismail I will lift,' he said, 'but not the spell on Dilbar.' 'So!' I cried. 'You saw her brown eyes like almonds and wanted her for yourself. Isn't it true?' He had to admit it. 'Unbind the spell on Dilbar.' He looked defiant. 'Not till the sun rises in the west.' 'Swear to unbind the spell and return her skirt, swear or I'll saw you in half with the backbone of a fish, even as King Jamshid was sawn.' (Ahmad swung his right arm backwards and forwards with gusto.) That did it. His eyes started popping, like a sheep just slaughtered. 'Let me go free and I'll swear.' 'Swear never to return to the Falqani—though you live to be Solomon's age.' 'Yes, I swear.' 'And now give me Dilbar's skirt.' He said the skirt was in the caravanserai. I half-dragged him there by the scruff of the neck. He opened a tarpaulin haversack, and looked for the skirt. I was watching him carefully all the time, his hands in case he drew a pistol, his lips lest he call on some jinn. He knew this and took no risks. At last he found the marigold skirt. With a whoop I seized it and, holding it high like a flag, I strode to the gateway. There I turned and flung him a terrible look. 'Practise your magic if you must, but on other women, not on Dilbar, wife of Ahmad the Falqani. This time I let you off lightly, but come again to perfume Dilbar's tent, and you'll make a voyage of discovery into a vulture's maw.'"

Ahmad looked round in triumph. His listeners nodded, satisfied. "You did well," some of them cried. "A Falqani knows what's what." After questioning him about his return journey, they discussed his doings among themselves. No one believed they had turned out quite like that—it was a "story round the fire": but they had no doubt that Ahmad was embroidering what was essentially true. They had to admit he had proved himself, and defended Dilbar's honour.

Dilbar was the only listener whom one of the team had actually addressed, and only she remembered that Ahmad and the foreigner spoke different tongues. That night she said nothing about it, but next morning she taxed her husband, and learned what had really happened.

Shortly afterwards Ghazan Khan summoned his shepherd. He held a letter in his hand. He had heard about last night's story and looked at Ahmad with curiosity and amusement.

"A message has just arrived from one of the team of enquirers. It's long and rather complicated. Briefly, what he says is this: That you overtook him on the Isfahan trail, very angry, and charged him with flirting, with putting love potions and spells on Dilbar. At first he didn't know what you could mean. Then you spoke of the marigold skirt. He told his interpreter to explain exactly why he had sprayed her clothes and the tent. He gave you the skirt and agreed to take back the needles and mirror. He explained why he had offered them. He asked whether you understood. You said you did and you came away. He writes hoping no harm has been done, and sending apologies." He looked at Ahmad with mild reproof. "Well, what do you say to that?"

"These foreigners . . ." Ahmad muttered gloomily.

"Is the letter true?"

"Yes, Ghazan Khan," he admitted, more gloomily still. "But don't you see . . .?" He searched Ghazan's eyes.

"I think I see."

Ahmad shifted his feet and looked appealing. "Dilbar knows what happened—but no one else."

Ghazan laughed. "Don't worry, Ahmad. I only wanted to untangle the knot. I shan't give you away."

CHAPTER SIX

ONE morning, a fortnight after arriving in the uplands, Ghazan received a letter from Khosrov Mardam. Just as when opening a book of verse by Abu'l-Atahiya he could be sure, no matter the poem, of finding a spirit of melancholy, so the mere handwriting on the envelope identified the sort of message it contained. Contrariwise to certain angels, Khosrov seldom announced anything but bad tidings: it seemed his rôle in life. But his motives were always the best motives of friendship: to warn.

Ghazan was tempted to keep the letter by his side for a time. He had a tendency to let bad things accumulate, then confront them together, rather than allow them to intrude, here and there, in his life: part of a general instinct to intensify the moment, either for good or bad. But remembering events at the Shiraz road, he sensed a latent urgency and, as soon as the messenger had left his presence, opened the letter.

It contained no precise information: Khosrov wanted to see him about an important matter which he was unwilling to entrust to writing. Ghazan could expect news, then, such that Khosrov wanted to watch his face when he heard it. Not out of malice: but Khosrov was a connoisseur of subtle moods, of reactions and the disguises which covered them.

When he told Rohim that he was going to see Khosrov, his cousin spat and said:

"That shadow of a man! What good can come of visiting him!"

It was not a particular antipathy. Rohim treated all Persians outside the tribe as potential enemies, to be respected only if they shot or rode well. And Khosrov had never mounted a horse in his life.

Two hours after leaving the encampment Ghazan, accompanied by Ahmad, entered the first of Khosrov's villages. He was a rich man, though not as rich as many, owning some sixty villages in the plains bordering Falqani summer quarters to the north. Marginal land had given rise to trifling disputes, but these could not be avoided in country unfenced, unhedged and without the landmarks of trees. Khosrov's family had for centuries been friendly with the Falqani khans, and Ghazan usually saw Khosrov every spring when he visited his estates from Isfahan, where he led the retired life of an absentee landlord.

The village appeared in the extreme of poverty: houses crumbling, children ragged, fields cracked and dry. Traditionally, produce of agricultural land was divided into five parts, one share each going to those who provided water, draught animals, manual labour and seed, while the landlord received one-fifth. As often as not the landlord also provided irrigation, oxen and seed, thus receiving four-fifths of the crops. In villages belonging to Khosrov most tenants had become virtual serfs, having had to borrow seed in a period of famine or through sickness fallen in arrears over stipulated work.

Many of his fields were planted with opium, which brought a greater revenue than grain. The white poppies had been planted a foot apart last autumn for spring harvest. Ghazan saw workers busy in some of the fields. Just as the petals were about to fall, the seed-capsules were scored with a three-bladed knife, making three small gashes the length of a finger-nail. This was done in the afternoon. From these gashes the opium exuded in white tears, to be collected at dawn next day. The process was repeated twice, and there lay the element of risk in opium-growing, for a sudden shower could wash away a year's profit. The liquid was poured into large copper pots, simmered over a very slow charcoal fire, then allowed to dry. Six times this was done, six times the crust removed. The remainder was smeared, a pound at a time, on thin planks with a wooden spatula, dried in the sun and finally scraped off for rolling into cakes.

Ghazan passed the opium fields and, an hour from Khosrov's house, came to a high grass-covered tumulus among almost total ruins. Little remained above ground: a wide threshing-stone, collapsed walls, the pattern of houses on the earth, as though traced out for building. As with camels after they had lost their teeth, the age of such dead villages was impossible to tell at a glance. It might have flourished at any time during the last three millennia, might have been burned and looted by any one of a series of foreign invaders, for Persia's past had been the destruction of such villages as this, their rebuilding elsewhere, their destruction again. Yet precisely because this dead village was impossible to date, Ghazan considered it a fitting avenue to Khosrov's house.

Khosrov's ancestors had belonged to the first known dynasty of Persia: the history of Khosrov's family and country was one. So that on this route Ghazan always saw himself riding through Persia's past.

The land of Persia was a passageway between Europe and Central Asia, its plateauland, devoid of natural frontiers on east and west, a bridge linking Turkey to both India and China: a bridge across which seven leaders or dynasties had marched, trying to unite Europe and Central Asia in a single empire.

Achaemenid kings from Fars, from these very hills—Cyrus, Darius and Xerxes—had made the first attempt, but their hopes had foundered at Marathon and Salamis. Five generations later Alexander had revenged the Persian invasions of Greece and, during his own short lifetime, linked Europe with India. After Alexander's death Persia for nearly six centuries preserved her independence under the Parthians, an invading people from the north. They and their successors, the Sassanids, successfully opposed the third attempt to unify East and West: that of the Roman Empire. Weakened by so prolonged a struggle, Persia fell almost without resistance, in the seventh century, to Arab invaders and became one of the eastern limits in an empire of which Spain formed the western bulwark. In place of Zoroastrianism Persia received the new Muslim religion and a new script for her spoken language, but an already advanced civilization enabled her to retain her identity and exert influence on her nominal rulers at Baghdad. In those days Shiraz had been a great city and her people still boasted 'When Shiraz was Shiraz, Cairo was one of her suburbs.'

It was as though Persia had learned the resignation of Islam to sustain her, in the thirteenth century, during the catastrophe of her history: a devastating invasion of Mongols, who finally succeeded in realizing what their predecessors had attempted in part: unification of the landmass from China to Hungary. This vast empire soon broke into mutually hostile states, of which Persia was one; many of them, in the fourteenth century, were conquered by the next great unifier, Tamerlane. In Isfahan Tamerlane built a pyramid of seventy thousand human skulls, as though to overawe all future Persians; an empty boast: the pyramid tottered and with it, before the fourth generation, the Timurid empire. Nonetheless her neighbours continued to dream, and their dreams became Persia's nightmare, their ambitions her despair. In the sixteenth and seventeenth centuries, the Ottoman Emperors, seeking expansion eastward, challenged Persia in a series of unsuccessful wars. That had been the last great attempt at unifying, but by no means the last invasion of Persia.

Although his tribe had no written records, Ghazan, by collating oral traditions, family names, rug-designs and the tribal dialect, had built up its probable history. Three clans of the Falqani claimed descent from the Turkish tribe of Khalaj, one of the twenty-two branches of the Ghuz Turks who migrated out of Central Asia from the eleventh century onwards. Had the gradually encroaching desert swept them forward like a sandstorm? Had the Great Wall of China baulked a more rewarding journey eastwards to the Pacific? The Falqani traditions gave no clue.

The Falqani, as opposed to the purely Khalaj sections, believed that Hulagu Khan led them from Yarkand in Central Asia in the thirteenth century, their name being derived from a village near Yarkand. Under Kerim Khan Zend, who ruled Persia in the second half of the eighteenth century, Jani Agha, a Falqani chieftain with Khalaj blood, became a close associate of Zend and was rewarded by being appointed first Ilkhan of what was to become the present-day Falqani Il or tribe. When the Qajars ousted the short-lived Zend dynasty, the sons of Jani Agha were mutilated or blinded. From Ismail, the elder, subsequent Ilkhans—including Ghazan himself—were descended. During the last century the tribe had been joined by foreign elements—the Shalguli, his mother's tribe, possessing Lur and Kurdish blood; the Pardalun and Adashuri from Bakhtiari country—but these had now become merged with the older stock.

So the people from Turkestan entered the land of Persia and became part of her story. For two thousand five hundred years its pattern had been traced in blood. Persia's villages had been sacked from east and west, had exchanged hands again and again, but the image on the Persian coin, instead of being effaced, had grown brighter and more precise. Great suffering had brought out her character in marked degree. Despite the invasions, everything, nearly, had remained as it always had been. Saadi had written under the Mongols, Hafiz under Tamerlane, yet the language of their poems was spoken at the present day. Tribes had migrated in the days of Darius's glory, and still they migrated. Villages and towns were overturned, yet the underlying desert remained unchanged. Houses were built now as Sassanians had built them; fields were tilled and irrigated in a way familiar to the Arab invaders. And so, as his horse's hooves rang on the fallen rubble, in the ruined village which he could not date, Ghazan rode through Persia's past thinking of his friend.

Khosrov traced his ancestry back to Mardonius, nephew of King Darius and the great general of Xerxes' army. His family was generally admitted to be one of the oldest in Persia. (Ghazan prided himself on a long ancestry, but on his visits to Khosrov, whose blood was traceable for twenty-four hundred years, he felt himself a parvenu.) But the line was in danger of dying out. Though he had taken four wives, Khosrov was still childless, and he believed he would never have an heir.

Nothing in the exterior of Khosrov's house suggested wealth or luxury. It was surrounded by the usual mud walls, such as protected the occasional willow and thin stream of a village, but within lay orchards thick with leaves and pools surrounded by rose bushes. After months in the bare hills, Ghazan found himself quite out of place, as though he had stumbled into women's quarters. While Ahmad led their horses to the stables, he approached the square, two-storeyed mud-brick house. Slipping off his sheepskin riding boots, in woollen socks, he was shown by a servant into a large room, without chairs, a variety of sweets set in silver trays on a long, low table in the centre. Khosrov seldom left his bed until late afternoon, and for some time Ghazan was left alone with Timurid miniatures, silks, brocaded cushions, Tabriz carpets: all luxurious, and blended like the plumage of a pheasant's tail, and all old.

When his host at last appeared his heavy-lidded eyes showed that he had just risen. His body was small and slight: dressed in a perfectly cut grey flannel suit. If most faces were cheap goods hammered out in the bazaar, Khosrov's was a metal dish in which a craftsman had drawn on centuries of tradition to find the perfect grouping for his pattern. The bones were small and fine, the cheeks full, the nose slender and hooked, the brow high and wide; only the chin slipped away a little short. His soft step and the careful way he sat down suggested that such fine workmanship was fragile. If so, he had preserved it well, for Ghazan's face by comparison appeared lined and worn, though the Khan was ten years the younger.

They exchanged lengthy greetings and compliments to cover the merging of memories and new impressions, a reassessment of each other. Ghazan offered his host two brace of partridge and in return received a gift of fruit from Isfahan. Water pipes were called for and lit. When each was puffing from a gurgling porcelain bowl, Khosrov spoke. His voice was high-pitched but melodious.

"One meeting a year, Ghazan! Yet every year we promise better."

"You're invited whenever you choose to come."

Khosrov made a little pained grimace. "The stench of goats—you know how it turns my stomach."

"We'd pitch you a tent apart."

Khosrov considered. "I'd have to bring these," he objected, indicating his bibelots. "Without certain books and objects of beauty—well, I shouldn't be myself."

"A pack of my mules will carry them up."

"They'd be spoiled or broken. Besides, it's not my world, Ghazan. It's you who must come to us." Very earnestly he continued, "Last month, in Shiraz, I was talking to some of your friends. We agreed it's time you came down to the plains for good."

"To do what?" asked Ghazan, rather amused.

"To live as your gifts demand. Dream your dreams, read the poets, let your friends visit you, talk with you and hear you talk. Savour life for a change. Why not? I enjoy my wealth, make it serve my demands. While you—on what did you dine last night?"

After a moment's surprise, Ghazan replied: "Barley we had, cooked in mutton fat."

"I ask you! And the fat was probably rank. You spiced it, doubtless, with talk of some loathsome internal diseases of sheep. You have to admit, Ghazan, your life's getting thoroughly brutish."

"Yet it can't be changed."

"The shepherd of your people!" Khosrov slightly mocked. "How virtuous you are!"

"Why make a virtue of it? I've told you before I love the life."

"A certain pride of possession, can that be it?"

"No, quite different." He tried to explain to Khosrov his joy in that rare harmony between man, his work, his beasts and the earth: not as a finished product but still being created. In that creation he and his people were heart and soul involved. It depended partly on them: they were almost the sap rising. Because it was continuous, it had a timeless quality: each moment seemed touched with infinity. Ghazan believed it would never end, for within the hills lay God and, returning to God, man became part of the earth.

Through his people his joy was multiplied. Thousands he knew by face or name: his own personal following were almost an extension of himself, and his relations with them, whether adjudicating their disputes or setting his seal on their marriages, were more important than anything he did alone. In spring, sails crowded, he felt himself running bows under before a persistently favourable wind.

Always the same course. The past showed one simple pattern, like the successive diamond-shapes in their rugs, each year resembling the one before and differing only by its position within the series. He did not count the "lost years" of settlement. Those he would never willingly recall. Yet he was aware that, paradoxically, the separation they had entailed was the very condition of his joy.

Khosrov listened with interest, not in the least discomposed, and replied, with an air of triumph, "All you say bears out my argument. With so much capacity for enjoyment, you direct it to—tribesmen and their sheep."

"After all, why not?"

"Because, my dear Ghazan, there are finer pleasures. It's so long since you tasted them, you've doubtless forgotten. Stay here a few weeks, then come to Isfahan. Drink wine instead of milk; shift your gaze from the desert to a garden."

"You make that garden sound inviting, Khosrov. But in spring . . . Impossible."

His host looked hurt and disappointed. "If your friends cannot persuade you," he continued in a harder tone, "perhaps your enemies can." He met Ghazan's questioning look coolly.

"I have just arrived, Ghazan, from our great metropolis. It may interest you to know that government policy has recently changed."

"Is it not always changing?" said Ghazan. "Like the Governments themselves."

"Ah, but the Government remains unchanged. Rahimi is still Prime Minister. Your dear friend Rahimi!" He blew a precise smoke-ring and watched it uncoil. "It seems he has not forgotten Shiraz!"

Ghazan stirred uneasily. He had not forgotten either, though it was

107

nine years since he had faced General Rahimi as the result of the most important decision of his life.

In 1946 Russia was about to effect a *coup*. She had promoted a movement for self-government in Azerbaijan and refused to withdraw her troops from Persia's northern provinces. For over a century Britain had guaranteed the independence of Persia as a bastion protecting India, but war had reduced Britain's power and, anyway, her eastern empire was then being whittled down. Persia had had to face her northern neighbour alone.

In the autumn of 1946 the Prime Minister, Qavam, reshuffled his Government to include three members of the Communist Tudeh party. Persia's fate seemed sealed. And the Falqani stood in particular danger. The Tudeh party had persistently clamoured for settlement of the tribes. It had several reasons to hate them. Proud of their traditional ways, they proved impervious to propaganda; as the most virile part of the population, they were the mainstay of independence; and rule by hereditary lords was to the Communists anathema.

To protect Persia and to protect his people, Ghazan had acted quickly and energetically.

"No, Rahimi is not the man to forget," Khosrov continued. "Your ultimatum: dismiss the Communist ministers; Qavam's refusal—and then your attack that autumn. Bushire, Kazerun—one by one Rahimi's garrisons fell. He drew back on Shiraz. And down from the hills swept your shepherds—thousands on thousands. What could the poor man do?"

"It wasn't as easy as that," objected Ghazan. "Rahimi was German-trained, with three thousand troops, automatic weapons and stores of ammunition. They were ordered to resist to the death. But we stormed and took the concrete outposts. Only then did they throw up their hands. I myself disarmed fifteen of Rahimi's officers."

"I forget the unpleasant details. Anyway, Shiraz was yours for the plucking. Then the second ultimatum: dismiss your ministers or I seize Shiraz. This time Qavam yielded. Winter forced you to scatter—but the three Communists were dismissed."

Quietly, but with feeling, Ghazan concluded: "Persia remained Persia."

"That was your great day, Ghazan. But now Rahimi holds the whip hand."

In August 1953 General Rahimi had seized control of Teheran after nine hours' fighting in which three hundred people were killed. Since then Ghazan had been anxiously speculating whether he would try to exact revenge.

"It seems Rahimi has drawn up a new plan for the tribes. It is still secret. But a cousin on my father's side, Colonel Malik Mardam—do you know him—rather fat, with grey hair and a passion for Russian drinking songs?"

"I met him once, in this room, two years ago."

"Malik has a post in Intelligence at the War Ministry, and I went to see him on your account. This much I learned. A division is to be withdrawn from the Russian frontier and moved to Fars."

Ghazan hardened his jaw. "And its purpose?"

"My cousin wouldn't tell. But with Rahimi in power it can bode you no good."

Ghazan had listened with growing anxiety. Even another brigade in Shiraz would have swung the balance of power in the army's favour: but a whole division! Captain Morteza and the Major must have known—hence their confident manner. General Bahrami's 'forbearance' was an attempt to lull him into a false sense of security. What was their plan? To try and disarm his people? Or simply to "maintain order", that is, prevent further protests should the Government decide to collaborate with the Tudeh party?

Khosrov leaned back on his cushions, studying his guest. "Now listen to my advice, Ghazan. Leave your people to the trouble which clearly lies ahead. Retire to Garden of the Pines. While there is still time, make your own little perfect world."

Ghazan became aware of the gulf between them: too deep to ford with all his values and beliefs. An inherited "family" friendship: but it had to be kept in repair and handed on. He contented himself with tossing an answer which Khosrov could grasp.

"I don't believe in private worlds."

"Because they can be shattered? But your own way of life is even more vulnerable. It involves thousands, for and against. It belongs— and you with it—to the old Persia."

By "old" he meant traditional in attitude and values. He had discussed this more than once with Ghazan. They agreed that not a single atom of form or idea perceptible to the intelligence must be omitted from any vision of the truth, and that such omissions were precisely the prevalent failing. They agreed that the jewel of experience was tinged with many colours. The wonder it excited, the Hand that made it: these mattered, not its weight in carats.

"An exquisite brocaded shawl," Khosrov continued. "And as it wears thinner and thinner, I wrap myself ever more tightly in its folds." Again he glanced appreciatively at his treasures. "While you . . ." He made a gesture of exasperation.

"I praise the past, Khosrov, but not above the present—velvet or sack-cloth. I was born under the sign of Capricorn, and under that sign I shall always live."

Khosrov met his unwavering dark-brown eyes with a final, not very hopeful appeal. "You were made for better things than petty political feuds. Come now, withdraw into pleasures which cannot be blasted." Then, yielding to Ghazan's silence, "Well, if not for a lifetime—at least for tonight. You will do me the honour of staying? We shall eat and drink and talk about life."

Ghazan accepted. He detested no news more than vague news, which made it possible to believe not only the worst, but every variety of worst, and he felt the need of entertainment. Glasses were brought in and filled with red wine from Khullar, a village thirty miles from Shiraz, where Khosrov claimed the best vintages were pressed. He chose to ignore the Muslim prohibition of wine; as for Ghazan, it did not conflict with his religious views. They drank, speaking little until they should catch and mingle in the mood of the wine.

"Hoist the purple flag," said Khosrov, "and the army of troubles retreats."

"Have you, too, an army of troubles?" With a smile Ghazan waved to vases of cherry and pear blossom. "Is their scent less fine this spring than last?"

Khosrov replied gravely, "You strike closer than you think. Don't you see, Ghazan, the stock is played out, the zest, the joy in sensation is dimmed. We are debtors to the energy our fathers so riotously expended. For us there remain the grape and the poppy . . . But I was forgetting: you are not of the faithful." And in the cup of his smile he instilled a drop of contempt.

Perhaps he is right, thought Ghazan. This man's veins are fed from the mainstream of Persian history—surely he, if anyone, has a right to speak for our country. And his voice rings truer now than if he chose to be oracular.

"All we can do is listen to the memory of sharper joys pulsing in our blood. The sun has sunk—had already sunk before we were born."

He raised and let fall in a despairing gesture a small, perfectly manicured hand. Like a girl's hand, thought Ghazan, and felt himself suddenly hostile.

"And the great Mardonius, could he not count back twenty generations without glimpsing Adam? No, Khosrov, we are all old and we are all young."

He saw the futility of argument. Khosrov simply looked out across the twilit garden, where the green leaves had already surrendered, where roses hung like white flags.

"For twenty years I tried to grow a variety of rose without thorns. After grafting and regrafting I obtained those white blooms. Their thorns are fewer, but they are much more sharp." He smiled wryly. "The dregs of the bottle are left, but we can find pleasure in the dregs; no, Ghazan?"

The servant refilled his glass for the sixth time, but Khosrov was far from drunk. He disliked that form of dreamless intoxication.

"Tell me, Ghazan, is it not good to talk when the sun has gone down, to feel night closing round, and to match that feeling in words? To welcome the darkness, which sharpens touch and taste, and by shutting out the world unites two friends?"

A cloth was spread on the velvety green Tabriz carpet and dinner served: rice flavoured with cinnamon, over which they poured the yolk of raw eggs and a sauce of butter and chicken; young lamb roasted on skewers; a variety of sweets: *gaz* and fig-paste which they called *rahat lokoum*, a corruption of its Arabic name meaning "ease of the throat", molasses and *peshmak*—buttered sugar crystallized like snowflakes or thistledown, in cones and pyramids.

When the remains had been taken away, Khosrov called for opium pipes and a brazier.

"Can I tempt you, Ghazan? My news has shown you life in its true colours. Come, join the faithful."

He spoke cajolingly, watching his friend's reactions. Every year Khosrov invited him to share his dreams, every year Ghazan had declined. He would have liked to explore this path out of the world,

III

perhaps to discover new selves, but the habit challenged everything he prized most. Tonight, however, he hesitated. Khosrov's threnody seemed in tune with the dismal news which he wanted to put out of his mind but could not.

"Sooner or later you will see things my way. Throw off those childish illusions that you can master events: you wear yourself out against the tide. Choose the poppy, Ghazan, nature's own antidote to the pain in human nature."

Slowly he allowed himself to believe Khosrov's words. He picked up the grey, long-stemmed pipe and fingered the small blue and white porcelain bowl pierced with holes. Opposite, Khosrov picked up a knife and cut off several flat pieces from the fawn-coloured stick of opium, then with a small bellows blew the charcoal brazier until it glowed. Holding a disc of opium with a pair of tongs against the porcelain bowl, he lowered the bowl to the glowing coals, spread the melted opium like wax over the porcelain and through the stem began to inhale its fumes. After drawing half a dozen times he replaced the blackened cake with a new disc of opium.

Still undecided, Ghazan looked beyond his host, at the hanging Herat silks, at the illuminated Timurid miniatures and pottery glazed in imitation of Sung ware. A life of enjoying other men's beauty—ending in this cloud of smoke. But, he argued, the poppy need not become a denial of action. Momentary oblivion, repose for his taut muscles, release from an endless series of decisions: these could be his. Later he would come fresh to his tasks.

With the tongs he lifted a piece of opium and began to melt it, savouring the consequences of his act, a little anxious at the thought that soon he himself would be melted, scattered.

As he inhaled, Khosrov said, "At last you draw the first breath of true life!"

"Let me be the judge of that."

The smoke was tart and unpleasant to his taste. He felt himself tense, determined to combat drowsiness. When he inhaled for the fourth time, past and future became lost in a present whose rhythm grew steadily slower, until Ghazan could differentiate even the most fleeting half-thoughts and impulses. This gave an impression of power. Then his hand and the pipe it held seemed to assume an added dimension, to impinge. He saw Khosrov arrange a cushion, then recline. These movements loomed strangely large; Ghazan felt almost that they were his own.

"Were our pipes filled from the same poppy, Khosrov?"

Ghazan distinguished every phase of his host's smile, saw it blossom in his teeth, ripen as his lips swelled, then fade in the lines about his mouth.

"You know nothing yet. You are a novice in these rites. And they are rites, my friend."

At first Ghazan thought he meant a cult of the self, smoke being the incense, then he found his sense of kinship growing and extending to the carpet, the cushions, a marquetry box on the table. All were gradually fused, until they became so many parts of a whole, like the tiny inlaid polygons of pistachio wood, of pear and walnut which constituted the box's mosaic sides. He had had the same experience after reading the Sufi mystics, with their exhortations to lose identity in the greater Being pervading the world, and he wondered whether Khosrov had meant the word "rites" in this sense. But so close did he feel to Khosrov that to put the question seemed an absurd denial of their relationship, as though the right hand were to convey a message to the left.

He inhaled for the sixth time and laid down his pipe. He felt a stillness as though fountains had suddenly ceased to play, and in the pools lay silent waters of contentment. The tart smoke obscured everything but itself, giving an illusory sense of peace. The drug laced his mind with an equivalent peace, which became the condition of his vision.

The sun rose cloudless, and he too rose from a dreamless sleep and the bare earth of the hills. The sun, striking the film on his eyes, arched all he saw with a rainbow. He felt like Adam setting out to explore and taste a world newly created. The sleeping tents, the bare brown earth increased his sense of vitality, of privilege. Scent of cranberry, the smallest leaf, distant insects droning: everything invited his praise, but he would not identify himself with any one earthly object, lest he lose the sense of being so alive and alert. How long he had sought the true in the half-true, like the taste of butter in the taste of butter-milk! That day, with the light so bright in earth and sky, seemed destined for discovery, for the revelation of truth.

He mounted Milk of the Moon and rode east to the highest peaks of the Zagros. The jagged crests of snow were the silver bezel for one flawless turquoise. As he climbed, the air grew cool as water drawn from a deep well. The wind made music in the hollowed rocks. Pattern and harmony ripened to such a pitch, he grew more and more certain with each instant that some hidden secret would be disclosed. But what secret, and how? He looked ahead, perplexed, and saw a fissure in the mountainside. Suddenly, with a stir of excitement, he was aware. No one told him, he did not reason it out, but he was aware. The snow leopard: he would find it on the heights that day.

The snow leopard. A beast, but also very much more: because he had sought it so long in vain, everything elusive, rare, beyond his grasp. The earth's hieroglyphics, the supreme, divinely written text he had for a lifetime been trying to decipher—the snow leopard would be the key to that. Everything would be revealed. He would find himself face to face with truth, with his own self, with . . . the words would exist only when he saw.

Still he climbed, as though climbing to heaven, and with no less awe. The snow, reflecting the azure light, seemed to dovetail with the sky, grown paler. He felt his thighs gripping the moving horse, and felt himself astride the whole earth. Grey storm-clouds were blowing up. Though the rising wind almost swept him from the saddle, he reached the cloud-swept summit. Long he waited there for the snow leopard, the revelation. But still the clouds rolled in, thick and massive, veiling all, sweeping him into their foam. He struggled against them, hoping that lightning would flash from the black clouds and reveal the still, unseen goal towards which he and all creation had been travelling. This desire was like the last pin-point of light at the mast-head, as he sank beneath the engulfing clouds in sleep.

Sunlight woke him. For a moment he did not know where he was. Instinctively searching for his rifle, he felt the slender pipe, and remembered. He sat up and found himself alone. His dream he passed in review. After all, he had not entered a new world. And he was a little disappointed. An all too familiar day-dream, less enjoyable for being out of control.

Suddenly he remembered Khosrov's information and rose to his feet, tense and self-critical. He called for a servant but to his surprise no one answered. Khosrov was never to be disturbed before afternoon. He could not wait till then, even at the risk of bad manners; could not extend what now he considered desertion. He wrote a brief note of excuse, then walked to the stables, where Ahmad was currying the horses.

They retraced yesterday's route. Khosrov's news was only for Falqani chieftains' ears, but Ghazan did not hide his first experience of opium.

Ahmad turned and stared. "You're making fun of me!" Then, as Ghazan denied it, he blurted out in dismay, "Never do it again, Ghazan Khan. Once you can escape, but the second time! Forgive me for speaking out."

Ghazan reassured his servant. He thought, no need for the pipe and poppy: all the time I have had opium in my own heart.

"Opium: for sheep excellent, for men pestilent," Ahmad moralized. He gave his herds the drug when they had dysentery. "By the way, you didn't pocket a little?"

Ahmad, too, had been indulging in dreams. After stabling their horses the previous afternoon he had joined the three menservants in the back part of the house.

"They were far from friendly," he told Ghazan. "They said we drove our flocks through the villagers' green wheat. 'Have you ever seen that with your own eyes?' I asked. No, they admitted, but everyone knew the tribesmen's ways. Then they began to eat. They claimed their master gave them meagre rations and they had none to share with a Falqani. Think of that, Ghazan Khan, not even a flap of bread, under the same roof. I watched them eating and thought, next they'll pretend there's no room for a Falqani near the fire—and I'll end sleeping in the stables. I said to myself, it is time the Falqani uses his wits. I asked, very casually, whether they had heard about the sickness among us. No, they answered, and they didn't want to. What did Falqani troubles matter to them? More than five hundred have died, I said, and thousands are vomiting day and night. They stopped eating and asked, Could it be cholera? Like cholera, I said, but worse: it marks the skin. Then I rolled up my trouser leg and showed my birthmark. You know, Ghazan Khan, the violet patch on my right calf. They stared at it and grew pale. One asked, Have you had this sickness? It started a month ago, I said. It should be cured soon. That did the trick

—you can imagine. All three bolted for the door like hares. I had rice and chicken for dinner and slept by the fire."

"So that's why no servant came when I called!"

"I didn't think they would fall so easily," Ahmad admitted.

"No Falqani would have believed quite so tall a tale—but then," he laughed, "we know each other's ways."

CHAPTER SEVEN

On his return Ghazan became judge of his people. He needed no mask, no formal clothes. The rôle was a simple regulation of simple lives. The Falqani had no written code, but exact traditions learned in the school of life. Justice still resided in the soul. They had no letter, only a spirit of the law, Muslim in principle but with notable variations. For instance, women had equal rights with men, keeping title to their own dowries, inheriting property and disposing of their own flocks—relic perhaps of a matriarchy; whereas elsewhere in Persia only in living memory had women been accorded a far smaller measure of equality. Yet the fangs of justice were still undrawn. If a man were killed in a quarrel, his family must hunt out the murderer and kill him. Retribution exacted, Ghazan would intervene, riding to the home of the murderer and asking his family to forgive. That request was never disobeyed. If a couple were found in the act of adultery, they were buried in liquid plaster, from the feet upwards, in full view of the tribe. He had never had to enforce this death sentence, but now and again he would stumble on ruins of these white graves, dating from his father's khanship. Such penalties were expressly deterrent, for the Falqani believed that no humanly devised punishment could better a man.

That day the cases before Ghazan were not capital offences. Disputes about ownership of beasts, grazing rights, inheritances, which the head-man or chieftain had justly settled, but which had nevertheless been brought to Ghazan himself. Every tribesman had this right.

One of the cases was an appeal from Tughril's decision. Tughril entered the court tent and gave Ghazan his usual bluff, slightly mocking salute. With him were a Shalguli headman and one of his section, both about forty. They stood there awkwardly, while Tughril handed Ghazan a fine Mauser rifle with walnut stock and silver mountings.

"This gun is in dispute, Ghazan. The headman says it has always been his: this man, Nasir, claims it was stolen a month back, and replaced by another—this." He handed Ghazan a cheap, old-fashioned

Turkish matchlock. "Nasir brought his wife to witness that the better rifle was his. But when I questioned her, I found she could scarcely tell a gun from a pistol.

"I had six eggs set up at three hundred paces. Both men are good shots, with nothing to choose between them. I made each fire three rounds with the Mauser. The headman broke three eggs. Nasir didn't even crack one. It was clear the Mauser belonged to the headman. No one can fire a rifle so well as its owner: only he knows the feel and kick and sighting."

Ghazan listened with only one part of his mind. The army division, its automatic weapons, guns and mortars: these trooped before his eyes. What did the ownership of one rifle matter when a whole way of life was threatened? Why thrash out this petty dispute while the greater lay still undecided? Since injustice throve, let it thrive here too. Let each grasp what he could from a grasping world.

But when he looked closely at the antagonists, all gawky limbs and anxious glances, the mood passed. With a sigh he turned his full attention to the case. Perhaps Nasir had a just cause: an aggrieved man might well miss three shots in a row. He questioned the men not so much for their answers as to gain time while he thought of a means of trial. Private judgment was useless: he had to show them the truth. Finally he ordered the two men outside, and taking the Mauser on his knees studied it in detail. Then he ordered the headman's eyes to be bound with a scarf. He was called in, and Ghazan told him to describe the distinguishing marks on the walnut stock.

He seemed prepared and spoke confidently. "On the left side a deep gash half a finger long, on the right a madder dye stain; at the end a chip out of the stock."

"No more?"

"No, Ghazan Khan."

Nasir, also blindfolded, was called in and set the same task.

"All the marks, Ghazan Khan?"

Ghazan looked at the stock while the man enumerated them.

"Run your palm along the top—it meets five indentations: three slight ones, then a deep one, then one divided down the centre like a barley grain."

Unscientific, liable to abuse, too "human": he imagined the experts' comments. All the same, he valued this straightforward statement of

118

causes and claims, man to man, in hard words that rang with a single meaning. He would not have it changed.

"The top screw has a broken head," Nasir continued. "On the left side the grain is very rough, but regular like the lines on a celery stalk. I kept it that way, without polish, so that it grips the shoulder and face. There are also smaller nicks and flaws. Starting near the stock there is a circle and line like the number nine, and further along a deep gash, where a spark flew and burned the wood."

He continued to describe the stock minutely: some of the marks were so small Ghazan had to peer to find them.

Ghazan believed the rifle belonged to Nasir, but Tughril had upheld the headman's claim. He felt his uncle's eyes on him, the squat body menacing as a storm-cloud. To flaunt Tughril's judgment publicly would still further antagonize him. The rifle was insignificant beside tribal unity. And there was no absolute proof it belonged to Nasir. It would be easy to fly in face of the facts, say that Nasir had secretly studied the headman's Mauser, and find common cause with Tughril. But he rejected this lie. If they came together, it must be cleanly.

He had the men's scarves removed and handed the Mauser to Nasir.

Turning to the headman, he said, "You have to live with a rifle many years to know it as well as Nasir knows his."

There was no need to have the headman bastinadoed: he would suffer enough from his disgrace. The men salaamed and withdrew. Tughril flung him an angry look.

"Again you blacken my face, Ghazan. How long do you think I'll stand it?"

Ghazan called after him, but he stormed out of the tent.

Leaving soon afterwards, Ghazan met Rohim and told him Khosrov's news, adding that he was anxious and intended to dispatch an agent to Shiraz. In ten days they would have more precise information.

"I'll believe this division when I see it," said Rohim coolly. When Ghazan pointed out that Khosrov had no motive for inventing, he said, "Let the army play draughts with its troops. What is one division more or less? The Falqani will always sweep the board."

"On the Guyum plain?"

"Even there." He scrutinized Ghazan. "Khosrov has been putting ideas in your head. What you need is a day's hunting."

He proposed a partridge shoot. One of his men had sighted a wild boar. Later they could try for that. Ghazan welcomed the invitation, and an hour later, shortly after noon, rejoined his cousin, who had been ordering provisions and preparing bandoleers of ammunition. Ghazan was disconcerted to find that, in addition to Rohim's fifteen-year-old brother, Karim, Tughril had also been invited. As soon as he came in sight, his uncle heaved himself into the saddle, to remove his disadvantage of stature, and turned away. He seemed in one of his sulking moods, crashing a huge fist against the neck of his horse, so that it neighed. Tughril, Rohim and Karim were riding Gulf Arabs, the distinctive Falqani mount, the result of cross-breeding from big mares by the smaller and better-bred Arab horse. The Gulf Arab had a small head with a convex brow, ears small and carried well. Grey was the usual colour. The barrel and chest were large, the body short and compact. They were very sure-footed but inclined to be delicate. Most had died off during the years of settlement, and even now first-rate horses were rare.

They opened the hunt by riding down red-legged partridge. This method saved ammunition. Most cartridges had to be smuggled across the Gulf in two-masted tall-pooped dhows by Arab adventurers, who demanded a very high price. The riders pursued the buff, dumpy-winged game across the wide plain, which offered no cover at all. At first the covey flew well ahead, alighting after two or three hundred paces to rest their wings. When the riders were once more almost upon them, they rose and after a shorter flight again alighted. This was repeated half a dozen times, the stages growing shorter, until the birds' wings were exhausted and they tripped forward through the dust. Then the huntsmen dismounted and ran after them. A grasp of the outstretched hand, the soft, warm feathers cringing, the bird's peep of alarm, the final knife-slash across the neck with an invocation to God. Only thus was the flesh rendered undefiled for eating. So the Falqani asserted their mastery over the birds of the air.

When each rider had at least three brace hanging from his saddle, Ghazan unslung his shotgun and the others copied him. The party now divided: while Ghazan and Tughril trotted across the plain, Rohim and his brother, with their servants, beat the foothills. Soon partridge were rising from nearby boulders and the huntsmen, galloping abreast, rode across the line of birds, their reins dropped, guns at the ready. At about a hundred paces both fired and brought down birds. The second time only Ghazan was successful. Now that his eye was in, Ghazan, when the bird were up, galloped with gun, half-way to the vertical, held in his right hand only, and bagged his bird a third time. This tested the horse's skill also, for each time it encountered a boulder it had to swerve so lightly as not to disturb the rider's aim. A violent lurch would have swung Ghazan out of his saddle, which had only a low cantle and a padded front.

When the two groups had exchanged rôles and Tughril had brought down a chance hawk, the party took rifles from their servants, then set off for other game, discussing their shots and the prospects of antelope. Ghazan loved hunting. He felt a pride in his own and his friends' achievements mingled with a sense of freedom and delight in the horses' speed, their necks straining in damascened harness, their feathery tails, rubbed lustrous with mallow petals, streaming behind like banners.

He had special reason for being pleased with his own marksmanship. He had a slight tremor in his left hand. His father and later Tughril had despaired of making him even a tolerable shot, far less the best of the Falqani, as his future rôle of khan would demand. He remembered his shame when he had first learned this, and how he had spent whole days for weeks on end handling his rifle, sighting it first in his right, then in his left shoulder, setting up thorn targets until he had corrected that slight fatal deviation. Now he shot among the best, though Tughril was surer with a smooth-bore gun. But the marksmanship which came readily to others was still to him the result of constant training and effort.

The hunters crossed a pass and as they rode down a stream-bed to more fertile country, two hares darted from their forms beside a traga-canth bush and raced in different directions across the plain. At a signal from Ghazan his followers unleashed their tazi, a short-haired Arabian greyhound, sometimes used in rough country against gazelle. The tazi swept forward like the shadow of a stooping falcon. In two hundred paces its long legs overtook one of the hares. Twice the dog snatched before seizing its prey, then tossed up the fat rodent and let it fall heavily, breaking its back. Ghazan rode forward and took the hare from the tazi's jaws. He turned it over, his fingers probing the fur, and was pleased to find no deep wounds. He handed it to one of the beaters. Its skin, dried and stretched, would serve to cover the wooden frame of a drum.

Presently they sighted a cluster of dark-fawn patches. No breeze blew, but the earth transmitted the beat of hooves. Narrow, straight-antlered heads cocked in alarm; long, thin legs bounded and tripped across the plain. All abreast, the riders followed, the upstanding flaps of their hats rising and falling like birds' wings. The honourable moment to shoot was just before their prey ran out of range, at about two hundred paces. But the gazelle found safety behind a spur of rock. This the riders rounded to find part of the herd dispersed far up the hills, where horses could mount only at a trot. Some twenty head were still visible at the limit of their range: the Falqani had a split second to get in a shot; Tughril and Karim dropped their gazelles. So the Falqani asserted their mastery over the fastest beasts of the plain.

They cut the animals' throats and helped load them on the servants' horses. Rohim said the boar had been sighted near a shallow marshy pond skirted by reeds. They could reach it before dusk. As they started to remount, suddenly Karim sneezed. Everyone looked at him in dismay. With a deep flush the boy apologized.

"A cold?" asked his father sourly.

"I don't think so." Very embarrassed, he blew his nose.

"Then what?" Sarcastically Tughril suggested, "A bawl of defiance at the boar?"

"I felt a tickle, that's all."

They fell silent and gloomy. A sneeze, especially in warm weather, was the worst of omens. It could not be disregarded. The question was, should they turn back? For a few minutes they fished for premonitions in a pool of silence. If anyone felt a foreboding, he had only to say and they would end a hunt which entailed danger.

"I feel nothing special," said Tughril with a show of swagger.

His sons said the same, and turned expectantly to Ghazan.

Ghazan felt ill at ease. The army officers' insinuations, his latest brush with Tughril, and now the sneeze: to which, as to all omens, he attached deep significance. On the other hand, if he turned back, he would be giving official recognition to Tughril's scheming; his distrust would hatch plans which otherwise might addle or be forsaken.

"Let's ride on," he said, but the words cost him an effort.

The servants returned with the spoils, while the four hunters went after the boar. Although the animal's flesh was forbidden as food, no quarry was so prized, for it had a fierce, wily nature and even when wounded would put up a fight. Its thick hide took the force out of rifle bullets, and usually it could be killed only by a close shot through eye or brain. Moreover, several were liable to charge together, a danger in themselves and because quick angled shots at close range had been known accidentally to strike one of the hunters.

They reached the marshy outskirts of the pond and began systematically to beat the thickest patches. For half an hour they shuttled between the warp of reeds, their horses sometimes up to the fetlock in mud, before a cry came from Rohim.

"Boar! Boar!"

Ghazan and Tughril came riding in. Karim stayed back. Tradition decreed that the first animal was Ghazan's. A wind rippled the thick reeds, making it difficult to spot a trail. Several times that wind deceived him: he started to track down his quarry, only to find he had imagined it.

Ghazan threw a glance over his shoulder—Tughril was watching him, rifle at the ready. The rôle of this second hunter was to ride in, should several boar attack at once. Who is the hunter, who is the hunted?—the question began to nag at Ghazan. He retorted with one of his father's maxims: Men will live up to your opinion of them. He would not doubt Tughril's loyalty until he had proof. But then it might be too late. He began to wish he had heeded Karim's sneeze.

These thoughts threw him off guard, so that when he saw an unmistakable brown-black shape hurtling through the reeds, he shot badly and grazed the boar's flank. It lurched, gave an angry grunt, and turned. Ghazan reloaded his rifle. His reins were loose; he held Milk of the Moon calm with his thighs. The boar lowered its head and prepared to charge, its thin tail swinging like a lash. Ghazan raised his rifle. Fifty, thirty, twenty paces away: he could be certain of hitting its eye, but still he waited, proving himself. At ten paces he squeezed the trigger.

He heard a click as the striker hit the base of the cartridge. It echoed dully through his body, tense for the explosion which did not occur. The dull click was repeated in his mind. After an instant's confusion he thought, Tughril tampered. Then the boar thrust up its tusks at his horse's chest. With a lunge of his whole body, he swerved Milk of the

123

Moon to the right, nearer the water. She lost balance and almost fell. The boar hurtled on. Ghazan saw its fat snout, its long bristles, the thick dark-brown undercoat of curly hair, then it merged with the reeds.

His horse whinnied in fear. She had never hunted wild boar before. He had to take up the reins to master her, before he could eject and insert a new round. The boar pulled out of its charge and turned. He had a dagger in his belt and a knife at his hip, no other weapon but his empty rifle. The boar lowered its head to renew the charge. If he could sidestep again, there might be time to reload. But Milk of the Moon was getting out of control. She shied and reared up, almost tossing him. He could not trust her to move in time.

Gripping his rifle in both hands, he turned in the pitching saddle to face the boar. It ran forward, dripping blood from the bullet wound in its flank. He waited until it was five paces off, striking up to rip open his horse's girth, then flung his rifle full in its eyes. It struck heavily near the right ear and ricochetted off into the reeds. The boar recoiled, seemed stunned, then lumbered off.

Ghazan had put all his weight in the blow, and for a moment thought he had struck a vital spot. Then he saw it turn to run in, grunting wildly, as though maddened by its wounds. Defenceless now, he tried frantically to spur his horse to safety. The mud was not deep—it did not hamper the boar—but Milk of the Moon was unused to it, and, hamstrung by fright, she did not budge. The boar ran in, more slowly, tired. Ghazan saw no escape. A last despairing thought flashed through his mind, Who will lead the Falqani now? He saw the black nostrils of its snout, the sharp white tusks. Even as he braced himself for the impact, a shot rang out. A dozen paces to the left a horse and rider flashed past. The boar, flung forward by its own momentum, fell heavily at his horse's feet. He saw blood spurting out at a corner of the right eye. The brawny brown body shuddered and lay still.

He looked up, cordite smoke in his nostrils. The rider who had fired emerged from the reeds. It was Tughril. Ghazan did not know what to think. In a daze, he watched Tughril ride to the edge of the mud, dismount and walk to the boar. Setting both arms and the weight of his shoulders squarely against its flank, he turned the beast over on its back, appraising it. Ghazan watched the bright film on both eyes begin to glaze.

Tughril looked up. Angrily he asked, "What went wrong?"

Ghazan saw that his surprise was genuine. He could not speak, the blood so pounded in his head. The unspilled life-blood. Retrieving his rifle, he took out the bad round and opened it with his knife. It contained no explosive. But the edges were smooth as only a machine could make them. He showed it to Tughril.

"A dud."

"So that was it." With a scowl he returned to the boar.

Ghazan did not thank him: among kin that would have been a virtual insult. But his ears were ringing with salvoes of relief. He believed he understood what had happened. Though his death would be welcome, Tughril would not take a hand in it himself. His uncle was angry because he had been obliged to do exactly the opposite of what would have suited his plans. The rescue had been reluctant, but now it could not be retracted. It had forged a new link between him and Tughril, who was trying to work free of links.

Ghazan helped his uncle to cut off the boar's head, and their hands were stained with the same blood. The dead boar was a little disappointing: it seemed to bear no relation to the hurtling, bare-fanged attacker. Tughril slung the head from his saddle: a trophy to be carried in triumph to camp. But for Ghazan it was a new, undeniable sign of their kinship.

Ghazan coaxed his horse out of the marsh, while Tughril walked to a nearby tumbling stream. After washing his hands, he stretched out on the narrow bordering strip of grass. Ghazan took from his saddle-bag a large pale yellow melon.

"A gift from Khosrov," he said, laying it on the grass. "So it should be good."

The gardens along the Zenda river around Isfahan were famous for their melons: honeydews, cantaloups, magenta-fleshed water-melons, brown-skinned giants weighing up to eighty pounds, which kept good for a year. They were sold as far afield as the capital, but there were no roads to bring them into the Zagros.

Rohim and Karim arrived, and Ghazan explained what had happened.

"Of course, the sneeze," said Rohim, with a shake of his head. But he did not pursue an awkward subject. They washed their hands in the stream and sat down. Karim stared at the fruit.

"It's the first he's seen," mocked Tughril.

"Of course not," Karim protested.

"What is it? An ostrich egg?"

"I forget the name."

"How does it taste?"

The boy thought a moment. "It's difficult to describe," he hedged, and Tughril laughed.

They sat watching the melon in silence. No one moved to touch it, or the other food they had brought from their saddles. And yet the hunt had made them very hungry.

It was the first day of Ramadan. For the full phase of a moon neither food nor water must pass a Muslim's lips from dawn to dusk. Religious law decreed that the evening meal should not be served until a black thread was indistinguishable from a white: in the tribe, until black goats merged with white sheep. Travellers were exempted, but later must make up the days they had missed. Most tribesmen observed the fast as a sacred duty, the rest conformed. Even had they wished, they could not afford, like some townsmen, to sleep through the day and gorge themselves at night.

As the sun sank, and the sparkling air turned to ash, the melon became a full moon, its reflection the longing in the faces of the four hunters. Gradually the edge left their features, they became shadowy. Ghazan sat watching his horse, tethered near Tughril's. When it merged with the boar's head, he stretched out his hand and took up bread.

Still the melon lay like a moon, casting its influence on every moment of their meal. Even through the strongly spiced smell of sheep's cheese and onions, which they munched with dry brown flaps of stone-baked bread, Ghazan imagined he could catch its fragrance. When they had finished, Ghazan picked up the fruit and turned it over in his hands, feeling the rough, slightly segmented rind, marked out for the knife. He held it for a time in the running water to cool, and its fragrance was lost in the night-stock and wild rhubarb along the banks. Then, drawing an open blade from his hip, he plunged it deep. The vulnerable skin, a few drops, then pale, white-green flesh. He divided each half again and laid the four segments on the grass, their seeds still tangled in the frothing juice at the core. Each took a quarter, Tughril first. He brushed away the seeds and began at once to eat; Karim picked them off, one by one, sucking the juice from each before broaching the pulp. Rohim lifted his piece with a quick gesture—he disdained food, disdained his dependence on it—and bit large mouthfuls, spitting out the seeds beyond his feet.

Slowly, in admiration, Ghazan raised his segment. A new moon: his own life, renewed that very day. His teeth bit into the amalgam of juice and pulp: sweet but not so sweet as to veil its flavours: each in a colour; apricot-yellow sunshine, tamarisk-green of shaded gardens, sparkling white where the river foamed under the bridge of Ali Verdi Khan. Eating, he watched the others eat, united in their enjoyment and to the earth which bore the fruit. It yielded its flesh to theirs, and they in turn yielded to it. The bond of blood was restored. Three other lives seemed to leap in him.

"Excellent. I could eat another, whole," drawled Tughril, easing himself over on to his belly. "I must find a pretext for visiting Isfahan."

Ghazan turned to Karim, "Did the taste bring back the name?"

"This must be my first," he admitted.

Ghazan savoured the last melting mouthful. "Yes, you couldn't have forgotten."

They rose and broke the circle. Ghazan felt a wrenching, as though a second time the melon had been segmented apart. He wanted to preserve the moment of unity in a world of contending wills, of fragments, of this and that. Before remounting they gathered the seeds, to be dried and used for chewing, and the rind, for one of the camp donkeys. Nothing was wasted or lost: like birds they crossed the steppes without trace. Only their prey remained.

CHAPTER EIGHT

NIGHTS passed: constellations straggled across the slopes of darkness; days passed: herds of sheep ranged fresh slopes of the green and brown hills. As tent-skirts were shifted according to wind and sun, so the black tents themselves, like the shadows of clouds, followed the pattern where clouds had broken in rain. A flotilla of goat-skin coracles fishing the green grass—Ghazan piloted them back and forth, sheering off from the shallows, seeking hidden streams.

Sometimes, in these voyages, they touched at ports. Twelve days after the boar-hunt Ghazan and Rohim were riding far ahead of the Madaleh group towards a village in the plains. There the Madaleh hoped to barter sheep's cheese and wool. Fleeces were thickening; of very fine texture because the winter had been severe; already becoming detached from the pelt; and all stained fawn with particles of soil—as though the Zagros had thrust out and branded as its own even the beasts. These fleeces would be worth half their weight in sugar and salt.

The two riders spied far-off brown mud walls. The land around lay void of figures and crops. As they approached, they saw that branches above the walls were bare, grey as the smoke of a pyre; and they exchanged a glance of surprise. Later they came to a line of mounds, some eighty paces apart, which marked the qanat, an underground channel which carried mountain water, guarded from sun and human raider, to almost every village lying in a plain. The circles of excavated earth were tumbling in: the edges rounded like a child's sand castle after the tide has flowed and ebbed. The riders stopped to look down one of the circles. The qanat was blocked, the umbilical cord severed. They knew then that the village was dead.

They cantered up to the walls. The gate hung gaping. Rohim rode in with a whoop; Ghazan followed in silence. A hush was distilled by the cracked walls, edges sucked round by frost and wind. From the dead trees bark was peeling. Lintels hung from their sockets. Padlock fixtures had been unscrewed from the outer gates of the hovels; within the courtyard pools were deep in dust; in the single room not a nail or a lamp-hook remained in place. Everything removed in a deliberate abandonment. The village then had not been attacked either by brigands or epidemic. Far away in the mountains a water-course had changed its flow, transferred its love elsewhere.

Rohim drew up at the empty jube and surveyed the village as though he had captured it himself. "See how they retreated—always they retreat," he cried in scorn. "Not even a try at a new qanat."

"For that," said Ghazan, "their landlord's to blame."

As fields depended on water from the mountains, so peasants on their landlord's silver. Building the underground rivers was a long, highly skilled operation. Only a rich man could afford the capital outlay.

But Rohim stuck to his point. "No courage, these people of the plains."

Though he did not argue, Ghazan believed it was less simple. New ideas such as land reform and peasants' co-operatives were sapping landowners' confidence; many found a better return for their money in foreign-sponsored factories in the capital.

Setting his weight against a gate-post, Rohim tumbled it with a rending crash. His chestnut Gulf Arab reared up in fright. Less for show-off than in sheer exuberance, Rohim dropped his reins and shouted to make it buck. Then, flung this way and that in the saddle, he gradually mastered and calmed it with his thighs alone.

"That's the way," he laughed to Ghazan. "The land must be tamed like a horse. But it takes men to do it."

He rode swaggering back and forth through the ruins, as though stamping down a dung heap. Then he began to lose interest. The Madaleh would have to trade in the nearest village east, Shahr Kurd. Rohim offered to return and divert them. Ghazan had to stay. He had called an assembly of chieftains there for that evening; a routine meeting to discuss pasture and flocks.

As the hoofbeats died away, Ghazan dismounted and delved into this new wreck on the coast of the Zagros. At the end of one of the alleys a dome—of the mosque, he supposed—crumbled like a snail-eaten toad-stool. The empty doorways held no secret. So silent, with the negative silence of decay. Houses now, not homes which had rung with laughter. Pieces of broken tea glasses, quills of hen feathers: these lay littered in the dry soil. Near the wall of one house a rat had scraped its hole, and turned up something red which caught his eye. He lifted it and brushed off the dust. A rag doll, no larger than his hand. The most loved object, perhaps, and so buried with the village.

He continued down the alley. Five autumns ago the tribe had traded here. Even then the jube water was running low. It had counted a hundred fires. Ahabad or some such name, he recalled. Now, as it reverted to dust, one by one the letters would drop out, like teeth from a skull.

It was afternoon when he heard, in surprise, the tramp of hooves. He looked towards the sound, wondering what could have brought Rohim back. Then he saw the horse was not chestnut but grey, and evidently tired, for it dragged slowly across the plain. A few minutes later Ghazan recognized the agent he had sent to Shiraz for news.

Ghazan had dispatched the agent with misgivings, but his mood had changed since. People and flocks were thriving. The gadfly which in late spring usually drove the sheep half-mad with frenzy had this year been absent. Day after day in the bare almost treeless uplands had dwarfed the apprehensions roused by Khosrov. Most of all, Ghazan was elated by Tughril's action at the boar-hunt.

He welcomed the agent and watched him dismount: a stolid figure of about fifty with neither the wide-set eyes nor high cheekbones of most Falqani. Indeed, his nondescript face and easy, flavourless manner were the assets with which he traded. He explained he had reached the Madaleh about noon, and from there been directed to the village. Ghazan noticed his face was lined and drawn: to be expected after five days' ride up from Shiraz.

"Well," said Ghazan, in high spirits. "What have you got to tell me?"

"Shiraz is crowded with troops . . ." the agent began uncertainly.

"Cross-eyed idiots, shooting each other's ears off." The rag doll in one hand, he sat on the gate-post Rohim had toppled. The agent stood before him. "How many?"

"Sir, it was hard to find out. And very expensive. Yes, sir, I had to spend five thousand tumans."

"What's the current price? A soldier a tuman?"

The agent looked puzzled; then, to the reworded question, replied, "One brigade has arrived. The second follows next month."

Ghazan nodded. "Which division?"

"The third."

He heard this with relief. The crack divisions were the first and second. The third had no battle experience.

"And their plans?"

"Garrison duty, they say. But I couldn't find out for certain."

"Never mind. You've done well. Very well. The third division on garrison duty. It's quite probable." Troops were moved frequently. Stationed long in one place, they formed attachments and deserted. Noticing the agent's expression, Ghazan continued, "They depress you, these ruins? If you like, you can rejoin the Madaleh."

The agent did not move. "There's more, sir."

"Nothing important?"

The agent darted an uncertain, trapped look, then fell to his knees. Ghazan frowned.

"I wish you'd never sent me, sir. The fact is I bribed General Bahrami's batman. He told me."

"What?" Ghazan's voice was no longer jaunty.

The agent squirmed like one with poison in his blood. He hid his face in Ghazan's blue tunic. His words, when they came, were muffled. "A curse on that batman for bringing such news. I couldn't believe it at first. But he swore he'd seen the paper."

"What paper?"

"A memorandum I paid the batman to read."

"Show me."

"I had to give it back."

"What did it say?" Ghazan barked out the question.

"It came from the Minister of the Interior, relating to troop movements. One passage mentioned a previous letter, a secret one." He broke off and looked up at Ghazan, frightened.

"Go on."

"I swear I would rather be blind than have read that paper." He began to repeat the text, which he had memorized verbatim. He found it difficult to get his tongue round the formal, circumlocutory phrases. Ghazan listened carefully. After a halt, the agent, clenching his fists, stammered his way into the operative sentence: "'The Government's decree whereby Ghazan Falqani is to be ordered to leave the country.'"

The agent broke off. Ghazan caught his breath. "You made a mistake."

131

"No, Ghazan Khan. I saw the seal on the paper."

"You misread the name," he suggested. "It was someone else."

"The paper was written by machine. Over and over I read it."

Ghazan knew the agent was reliable and not easily hoodwinked. There could be no doubting his news. "Exile," he whispered. One word, shouted, could precipitate an avalanche. A whisper, too. For a time Ghazan saw and felt nothing: after a sort of death he came to himself in a different world, where everything converged on the agent's message.

The first thing he saw was the rag doll. It lay in his hands as his enemies thought he lay in theirs. A plaything to be tossed here or there. His cheeks reddened, and his eyes flashed. With sudden violence he wrenched the doll apart in his hands. The arms, then the legs he ripped off, then tore furiously with his nails at the dismembered body. With a growl he hurled away the pieces.

A thought struck him. Forgetting that the agent had already spoken of this, he asked, "Was the paper stamped with a seal?"

"Yes, sir. I touched the seal myself." Huddled on the ground, he raised appealing eyes. "You won't leave us, sir? Say you won't leave us."

Exile. This man had touched the certainty of exile. Ghazan's distracted, half-seeing eyes moved vaguely over the houses, mere tents of mud. In some the joists had given way, the mud roofs collapsed. Not the agent, but the abandoned houses had spoken the message. He felt a growing revulsion against this village that served as its own graveyard. Slowly he rose to his feet.

"Bring me my horse."

Until long after he had passed the village outskirts the word Exile was pounded out by his horse's hooves, and when he found himself again able to think, he did not want to analyse it. Like a deep wound that he felt might be mortal, he preferred to prolong the shock, the suspense. Climbing into the Zagros, he immersed his pain in the hills and sky, melted with them. So for a time he rested, crushed, until the shock receded.

Why exile? For twenty centuries political rivals had been blinded or maimed or poisoned. Sensibilities had not become gentler: only three years ago a prime minister, grown too powerful, had been assassinated; by whose order no one doubted. Perhaps they feared to enter the mountains and kill him. Perhaps they were beginning to learn that some men could be more dangerous dead than alive.

And his people—what of them? He had always been more vulnerable in the things he loved than in himself. He saw the Falqani without a leader, drifting uncertainly across the hills, without order, without a certain destination. Factions arising, weakness and internecine strife. And then, profiting from disunity, the army gaining its way, collecting arms the first year, then perhaps settling his people.

That, at all costs, he must prevent. Somehow or other he would prevent it. Putting heels to his horse, he galloped as fast as he could across the skyline, in a mood of wild and bitter fury, deafening himself with the hoofbeats, keeping from his ears the question he refused to consider: Could he prevent it?

About mid-afternoon he reached the Madaleh, now encamped near Shahr Kurd. He sent for Rohim at once and told him the news. Rohim tightened his jaw-muscles hard.

"They can't do that," he half-stated, half-asked.

"They can exile anyone."

Rohim stared bleakly out of the tent-opening. "Not without reason."

"The national interest—that gives them power."

Rohim considered a moment. With a thrust of his jaw he retorted, "It can't be true. Kazem would have heard—and let us know."

Kazem Falqani, a paternal cousin of Ghazan, sat in the Majlis as representative of the Falqani.

"Under martial law they can keep decrees secret. In this case they can claim secrecy is essential."

"Would they dare!" Rohim cried. He stormed round the tent, flicking at the skirts with his riding crop, cursing Government and army. "Next, gazelle will be driving boar from their marsh!" He gave a derisive snort, then stopped in front of Ghazan and made his eyes gleam. "First they must catch you."

Ghazan curled his lips. "I agree. No pilav without the chicken."

"We shan't let them. We'd all rather die."

"Gloriously?" he scoffed, and shook his head. He walked the length of the tent, then stopped to ask in a deliberate tone.

"Tell me, Rohim, do you think the exile is aimed at me only?"

With feeling his cousin replied, "It touches every tribesman—you know very well."

"I mean, is it merely the prelude to settlement?"

As though avoiding a straight answer, Rohim issued a challenge: "Let them try a second time to settle the Falqani!"

With a frown Ghazan walked to a leather chest in a corner of his tent. He took out a blue shirt and tie. Removing his tunic, he began to put on the shirt.

"What are you doing?" asked Rohim curtly.

Ghazan's tone was hard. "Going to Shiraz."

His cousin walked over to face him. "Are you out of your mind?"

"I leave at once." The words rang with authority.

Rohim whispered, "Not to give yourself up?"

"You don't understand. Nothing has been openly announced. They don't know I know. Besides, they will not lightly anger men with rifles."

Doubtfully Rohim asked, "What will you do?"

"See General Bahrami."

"Bahrami!"

"I'll reason him out of this plan."

"Has the army ever listened to reason?" With disapproval he watched his cousin pull on a pair of fawn riding-breeches, then his riding boots. In a solemn voice he said, "Have you forgotten, Ghazan, how they seized your father?"

Ghazan met his appealing eyes, then looked beyond. "By my mother's milk," he cried angrily, "though I outlived these hills, how should I forget?"

"Had your father known his danger, would he have left these hills?"

No less gravely Ghazan replied, "Would he have stayed—knowing his people's danger?"

Rohim saw the Ilkhan's mind was made up and knew better than to argue. Ghazan gave him instructions for his father, encamped nearby with the Shalguli. Tughril would deputize in his absence, and preside over the assembly at Ahabad. Then, followed by Ahmad, who had hastily packed provisions for himself and his master, Ghazan rode with his cousin to the edge of the encampment.

As they kissed each other on both cheeks, Rohim whispered a last word of advice: "Take care, Ghazan. Don't cut your neck with your own tongue."

Five days later at Garden of the Pines Ghazan was woken early by rifle-fire: he supposed units of the Shiraz garrison were holding manoeuvres. Later that morning he was driven down to army head-quarters, speculating about Bahrami, whom he had never met.

His car drew up outside a deserted building, where a sentry told his driver that headquarters had now moved to a site opposite. It proved to be much larger though still unfinished: many windows and doors had not yet been installed and Ghazan glimpsed partitioning between rooms still unplastered. A wooden board was nailed above the main doorway. On a black background the national coat of arms was painted in yellow: a lion, right forepaw raised and gripping a scimitar, in front of the rising sun. Once it had risen alone: it was a Seljuq leader from Turkestan who had seized the crown and added his own symbol, the lion. Above fluttered the national red, white and green flag.

Ghazan, who had already sent a note announcing his visit, gave his name to an orderly and said he wished to see General Bahrami. He stood waiting, hat in hand. A king with a brown felt crown, without sceptre, orb or throne: almost a changeling king. In the hills this pleased him. No gold creased his brow, no etiquette hobbled his steps. What was the peacock throne but a tyrant's booty stolen from India: each one of its emeralds a green village uprooted, each ruby a mother slain, each sapphire a mosque desecrated? He was as well squatting on the Zagros crags, the turquoise sky his baldachin. But now he felt the need of outward signs, not to impress or overawe, but as a diagram to prove the theorem of his kingship. The abstract logic, the unseen descent—these sufficed for his people. Here in the city he would have valued clothes of purple damask, brocade stiff with pearls and a circlet of diamonds lending immediate authority.

"If Your Highness will kindly follow."

He crumpled the hat in his fist and walked up cement stairs. The orderly was carrying a medicine bottle in one hand, a rag in the other. Sniffing, he complained, "Bronchitis—there's a lot about." He looked bleakly at the yawning window-frames, then showed Ghazan into a large, almost empty room.

Behind a plain wooden desk sat a squat officer, grey hair close-cropped in German fashion, small dark eyes without a cast, cheeks fat and loose, giving his face a square appearance. His uniform was neatly pressed, a crown and three stars on each shoulder: insignia of a full

135

general. He was good-looking but Ghazan had expected someone with more presence.

"Please do sit down." Ghazan was surprised by his polite and deferential tone. He complimented the general on his new headquarters, while the orderly served tea, to the accompaniment of sneezes. They stirred the thick sugar until the glass held a syrup, sipped it, and were ready to probe each other's defences.

"I believe," said Ghazan, "that the army is adopting a new attitude towards me and my people."

The General's mouth and jaw tightened, as though, in the absence of a spontaneous mood, he were withholding signs of any at all. After thought he answered, "Which, Your Highness, we hope will lead to better understanding."

"Let's take my personal affairs first. I think I know your intentions."

Again a cautious pause. "We have the highest regard for you, Ghazan Khan, and for the appointed leaders of all the tribes. We wish only to co-operate."

"By 'intentions' I meant your plans to separate me from my people."

The General drew back his head and contracted his brows. "What plans are these?"

Ghazan had prepared himself for the army's habit not merely of hiding the truth but of making even a search for it impossible.

"The plans for my exile."

Again the General affected surprise. "Exile? What can Your Highness be thinking of?"

"I want to show you the folly of such a move."

"But, Your Highness, I should be the last person to need convincing. These last few months have we not proved our friendship? Surely *we* should not wish such a misfortune."

Ghazan recognized the jargon and felt himself in an impersonal world. This general was not behaving as Falqani men behaved, and he felt his own manhood denied. No spark flickered between them, that spark he felt with his own people, even when they opposed his will. The khaki uniform insulated, earthed.

"You have almost a free hand in Fars," he said, going back to fundamentals. "The civil authorities obey you. Even Teheran would act on your advice. I come here to you to argue out my future."

136

The General twisted uneasily. "I am willing to discuss Your Highness's future, on the understanding that the discussion is theoretical. I know nothing of Teheran's plans, which are certainly not dictated by us."

"If it is your policy—or Teheran's—to separate me from my people, the Falqani will certainly not stand meekly by. There is nothing theoretical about that."

"If we are to bandy threats!" said the General with a shrug.

"I am stating, not threatening. I want to protect my people from the blood even victors must shed."

The General would not move out to meet him.

"Why do you think we have designs against your people, Ghazan Khan? We are here for the enforcement of law and order. We shall not start shedding blood."

"Then help to prevent a disastrous move. If fighting breaks out between my people and your troops, only Persia's enemies will benefit."

The General paused and cleared his throat before answering. "Surely, Your Highness, we can trust Teheran to know what is best for Persia."

Ghazan was angry that the General, no less than the room he sat in, should be so undetermined, so unready; still dependent on others' plans; patched up with makeshift phrases.

"But you yourself, surely you see the danger. Will you stand aside and do nothing?"

"Your Highness wishes us to use our influence with Teheran. That is much to ask, but what do you offer in exchange?"

Ghazan wondered what he meant. "In exchange? Why, the 'goodwill' you prize so highly."

"I was thinking of something more tangible."

Ghazan looked at him in surprise. But there was no doubting the emphasis, the keen glance. Twenty or thirty thousand tumans would buy his help. But to pay once would be to admit dependence. And pointless too. The General would use the money to advance to a more profitable post. Ghazan rejected the idea.

"You mean, soldiers' lives? Those too."

The General's eye became dull, his voice flat. "I will do anything that makes for better relations, Ghazan Khan."

Leaning forward, elbows on the desk, Ghazan asked, with all the persuasion at his command, "Will you forward a memorandum to the Government? At once?"

The General's eyes wavered and fell. "My colleagues must be consulted."

"Consult them today. Will you?"

"Soon, Your Highness, very soon."

Ghazan tightened his lips. Soon was another word for never.

A knock at the door, and a white-haired civilian was shown in: Aga Hami, a rich tea-dealer of the town. He stretched out a hand to the officer.

"Peace be with you, General Shandaki."

He spoke the name too clearly for mistake.

"Ah, Ghazan Khan. A pleasant surprise."

They shook hands. Ghazan guessed he had been tricked. General Shandaki was second in command, an administrator without power. He was furious, but made himself join in a polite, three-sided conversation for a few minutes.

When he left his eye was caught by a photograph of the Shah over the door. The picture struck Ghazan because it was recent: most showed the youth of twenty-one at his accession. He thought, there is a man with all the medals, the one man, presumably, with absolute power. No wonder this bureaucrat twisted and turned under his eye.

On the way out, he asked the orderly, "Where is General Bahrami?"

"Gone to Teheran."

"When will he be back?"

"Not for several days." He spoke the words parrot-fashion, ending with a sneeze.

Ghazan noticed the tattered uniform, half the buttons missing; boots with uppers gaping, the way he slouched along. An officer passed and he raised the medicine bottle slightly above his shoulder, then lowered it. A conscript, and one of the poorer: those with money or wit bought themselves out. He would receive only his food and uniform: these being partly paid for by Falqani taxes. No pride, no independence, battening on others: the enemy. And yet, the medicine bottle, the sneeze. Ghazan could not hate him.

Seating himself beside his driver, Ghazan told him to return to Garden of the Pines. Just as the car began to move, Ghazan noticed an officer, surrounded by aides, strut down the steps of the still uncreated building.

"Who is that?" he asked.

His driver, a Shirazi, looked at the officer, then eyed Ghazan curiously. "Why, that's General Bahrami, sir."

Ghazan turned quickly, but the general was already hidden in his car. He had certainly been made to look a fool. It was so long since he'd lived among these quick-witted men of the plains. Gloomily he thought on the drive back, General Bahrami didn't want the unenviable task of declining requests, so he foisted me on to a subordinate. But he saw now that the persons scarcely mattered, the uniform was the same. Rohim had been right. He had hoped for too much. There could be no patriotic appeal to officers paid a pittance and forced to live by rapacity. They had to keep him at a distance, as the enemy. Cordial relations—they could not make a living out of that.

But Ghazan understood too well, and so extinguished his own anger. The evil lay in the nature of things: in a country too poor to pay its officials properly, and intelligent beyond its means. Even those who, perhaps from fear, wished to be honest, dared not challenge the system. There was no underlying security on which they could take their stand; and this insecurity was both cause and effect of corruption.

All that day he reconsidered the interview, and to his own surprise found himself returning to the photograph of the Shah. He dismissed the image, but it recurred, insisting on something. Then he saw. Somehow he must get behind the row of desks, the men too insecure to take a decision. He must talk as one man of power to another with power. Whatever the danger, the difficulties, he would go to Teheran and confront the Shah. In terms of human lives he would put his case to the final authority.

CHAPTER NINE

PERSIA had been ruled from six capitals, including Shiraz, in the last four hundred years. Teheran's status dated only from 1785, when the Qajar chieftain Agha Mohammed Khan chose the small town for his court because it lay near his tribal pastures. What it lacked in the authority of age, it now made up for in size. It was eight years since Ghazan's last visit. What he remembered as bare plots had become streets of modern, flat-roofed houses. Some had elaborate façades hiding unfinished hindquarters: he supposed the money had run out. Smooth asphalt avenues had been laid. The old small taxis, distinctive white mudguards bruised black and grey, had been joined by modern cream-and-blue buses and luxurious long cars. The pavements were black with people. The smallest shop was bigger than any in Shiraz.

Ghazan had given his driver the address of his one trustworthy friend in Teheran, with whom he always stayed. Kazem Falqani was some ten years older than he, the son of his father's sister. Under Reza Shah he had fled to Paris. He completed his education at the Sorbonne and after the abdication returned not to his tribe but to Teheran. He had become a director of one of the large banks, whose tiled façades were, with the foreign embassy buildings, considered by Teheranis the architectural glory of their city. He was moderately rich, knew everyone of importance, and had political ambitions. But with the name Falqani he found these difficult to realize.

Ghazan found Kazem's house off the Avenue Reza Shah closed and shuttered. He must already have moved to Shemran. Though Teheran was cool in comparison with Shiraz, as summer approached everyone of consequence would be moving north, two or three thousand feet higher up the slopes of the extinct volcanic peak, Mount Demavend, which dominated the capital.

Shemran, too, had grown. What used to be isolated country houses now formed part of a Teheran suburb. Towards dusk Ghazan's car drew up at a two-storeyed brick house standing in a terraced garden overlooking fountains. Kazem came round from the terrace. He had

Ghazan's long nose and open face, but he was stockier and running to fat. After his first surprise, he kissed his cousin and arranged for his cases to be carried upstairs.

Showing the way into a large room furnished in Western style, he told Ghazan that he had discovered about the decree of exile a week before and had sent a special messenger to summer quarters.

"He must have arrived after you left. But even so his news is out of date. A few days ago General Rahimi resigned. He was ill and is now in Germany receiving treatment. I thought this would prove your salvation, but I was wrong. The new prime minister is elderly and also unwell. He will not challenge the army or Rahimi. Meanwhile the decree is with the General Staff. The date is fixed for this autumn. If no one acts, events will take their course."

Unflustered, Ghazan replied, "That is why I have come. I will state my case to the Shah. When he sees its justice he is bound to reverse the decree."

Man to man. That had been his father's way. Autocratic Shahs, relying on force of will and arms, had survived by playing off religious leaders, landlords and tribal khans against one another; they in turn had survived only by a show of personal strength.

"A meeting with the Shah?" said Kazem dubiously. "Your enemies will try to stop that. And even if you succeed you'll have a hard task convincing His Majesty. He is well meaning, yes, and works for his country's welfare—as he sees it. But Rahimi served him by overthrowing Mosadegh—the detested Mosadegh who made him run for his life. Why should he take issue with an old friend on behalf of you—the son of an old enemy? Above all he wants to fulfil his father's policy. And even if you do convince him, is he strong enough to act?" He shrugged as though the answer was no.

Ghazan frowned. "Who can prevent him?"

The question, for a Teherani, was elementary. "Why, the army of course." Kazem specified the present Minister of War: main force of the new Government, one of Reza Shah's men and the most feared politician in Teheran. "If anyone is powerful enough to reverse the edict," said Kazem, "it's the Minister of War. But he hates the tribes and tribal system. I doubt if he'd even see you." After a pause, he continued more hopefully. "Whoever you approach, you need allies. Why not turn to the Assembly?"

The National Assembly of a hundred and thirty-six elected members —an innovation resulting from the impact of the West—had been established in 1907, when Persia became, in theory, a constitutional monarchy. All legislation was initiated by government departments, submitted to the Assembly and then to the Shah for his signature. In practice deputies did little more than confirm decisions of the Shah promulgated through his ministers. Since the accession of the present Shah, the Assembly had succeeded in extending its influence at his expense, but its functions were still largely advisory.

Ghazan looked sceptical. "The Assembly! With its hundred and thirty-six political parties."

With a smile Kazem protested, "Deputies have been known to act together. They could do so again." His expression became serious. "Section 30 of the Constitutional Law of 1906 runs something like this: 'The Assembly has the right to present a petition to his Majesty, through the medium of a commission composed of the President and six members chosen by the deputies. His Majesty should be requested through the Minister of Court to notify the day when he consents to see the commission.' My advice is, win over one of the influential deputies. A man like Akemi."

Kazem told his cousin something about Akemi. He was a Tabriz landowner. He liked to boast of his ancestral estates. Because of the law of inheritance, whereby large estates were soon broken up into relatively small holdings, Persia had no stable landed aristocracy. Each second or third generation had to struggle afresh to acquire land, and the respect it entailed. (The Mardam estates, for instance, had been re-augmented by Khosrov's grandfather who, during his term of office as prime minister, had embezzled one hundred and fifty villages.) Akemi had bought his land ten years ago from the profits of smuggling Caspian caviare across the Turkish border. He sat as a deputy for Azerbaijan. One village had responded too zealously to Akemi's incentives by returning him with eight hundred votes out of an electorate of five hundred. The matter had been hushed up, but Akemi's "overwhelming majority" was by way of becoming a Teheran proverb.

"He has more ambition than intelligence," Kazem explained. "But he knows which foreign countries to attack—and when. So he has acquired a high reputation in the Assembly." He added a last word of

142

warning. "Akemi is full of wild ideas—which change from week to week. I suggest you hide your intentions until you see where he stands."

Kazem was going to Kazvin next day to negotiate a municipal loan. Before leaving he arranged for his cousin to be invited to dinner by the Akemis.

Ghazan had difficulty in finding their home. The small street, off the Avenue Firdowsi, was being numbered for the first time, but by the householders themselves. Some houses were not marked at all, while several bore the favourite number 7, including the Akemis', although it stood first in the street.

Ghazan was received by a fat little man of sixty, tousled grey hair swept back from a receding brow and curling to hide prominent ears, excited hazel eyes rather bloodshot. He gave the impression of tussling into a wind.

"This is indeed an honour," he said, leading Ghazan into the drawing-room and introducing him to his wife. Had Reza Shah's opera house ever been completed, Madame Akemi would have made an ample prima donna. Brow, nose and body swelled. She wore a dark green evening dress embroidered with grey flowers and, in place of a chador, a mauve shawl. She welcomed Ghazan in a harsh contralto, continuing without pause:

"How fortunate you are to be going abroad. Have you decided where you will live? Doubtless in Holland. Ah, there is a country. The tulips! The canals!"

"Where else but in Holland?" said her husband. Before Ghazan had time to ask why, he continued, "You flew up from Shiraz?"

"No, I drove."

"What car, may I ask?"

"A Mercedes saloon."

Akemi nodded approval. "One of the new models—with flashing indicator lights?"

"Mine is four—no, five years old."

His host and hostess exchanged a slightly disparaging look. Ghazan began the question he sensed was expected. "You have a . . .?"

"New Buick. In two shades of orange. It has flashing indicator lights."

"And the windscreen washes itself," added Madame Akemi. "But

143

we can use it very seldom. My husband has so many responsibilities. Every week he speaks in the Majlis. His latest speech caused quite a stir."

Ghazan asked what its subject had been.

"Water," said the politician, and fixed Ghazan with a visionary's gaze. "A foreign company has contracted to lay pipes in Tabriz. It intends to exploit us—everyone realizes that—but only I had the sense to see how. It is charging us twice too much by doubling the amount of pipes."

Ghazan showed interest. "You mean, they're siting the works at a distance?"

Akemi looked at his wife in triumph. "Not at all. Something much more subtle: they propose to lay two sets of pipes, one containing drinking water, the other sewage and waste. I pointed out that one set was ample: water could be pumped through them by day, and the waste by night. No one wants water when they're asleep."

"What did the Assembly say to that?"

"I received a good deal of support. Now work has been suspended and the matter referred to a special committee, of which I am chairman. Two sets of pipes indeed: what fools do they take us for!"

They went into dinner. The dining-room was furnished with chromium tube chairs and, on one wall many photographs of men with Akemi's cast of face, arranged pyramidically, as though in a family tree. Ghazan was prepared for the large refrigerator below: gleaming white, but the enamel a little chipped. Kazem had told him that, just now, this was the distinctive mark of the *nouveaux riches*; when they had first bought it, the Akemis had displayed the refrigerator in their drawing-room like a Chinese lacquered cabinet.

Caviare was served first. Ghazan remarked on its excellence.

Akemi gave a knowing smile. "Not everyone is a connoisseur."

"How do you live in the south without caviare?" asked his wife.

"The new Seven Year Plan will put that right," said Akemi. He turned to Ghazan. "I have made a proposal for the distribution of caviare to store-houses throughout the country. The Caspian is ours. Every Persian province has a right to caviare."

Ghazan was struck by Akemi's tone of absolute conviction, which made the plan sound both important and feasible.

Pilav was served next: rice heaped with breast of chicken.

After her first mouthful, Madame Akemi cried, "Don't touch it, Ghazan. It's unbearably oversalted. What will you think of us?"

The manservant was summoned, he and the cook roundly abused and the dish removed. But the servant seemed to take the scolding lightly, as though such outbursts were routine. Roast lamb followed, and for dessert noodles cooked in sugar. This, said Madame Akemi, was a Dutch dish.

Coffee was served in the drawing-room, while from Radio Teheran a Persian singer chanted a highly modulated love song. Madame Akemi talked of the latest arrests and assassinations, of crimes by the Fadayan-i-Islam, the extremely fanatical nationalist group bent on regenerating Islam, of thieving servants and the high cost of living.

"You are so lucky to be escaping," sighed Madame Akemi. She affected a sudden idea. "Would you, I wonder, share your good fortune?" She gave Ghazan her most amiable smile. "I think you have your cousin's kind heart." Rising to a crescendo, she decided, "I know you have."

From the locked drawer of a table beside her Madame Akemi took a velvet-covered box. She opened it, revealing a mass of jewellery, heaped pell-mell: pendants, pearl necklaces, small sapphires and cornelians.

"Priceless. My heirlooms." She held them up, one by one, against her green dress, for her husband and Ghazan to admire. Ghazan noticed that the mountings were not heavy, like those on his mother's old jewellery, but narrow and discreet, as on Anahita's ring. "I took them from the National Bank this morning. They lie in the vaults with the Crown Jewels. Not in the same vault, but very close."

With the air of one above such trifles, Akemi said to Ghazan. "You may have heard of this rule against valuables leaving the country. Preposterous—but very strictly enforced."

Madame Akemi faced him squarely. "I want you to take them abroad, Ghazan. Keep them there in case—anything should happen."

Ghazan looked from one to the other: the husband deeply involved, but no longer so young, so quick; the wife longing for Europe's luxuries, planning their escape for the day when some enemy found it expedient to reveal Akemi's frauds. Despite Kazem's advice, he had to show his hand.

"You honour me with your trust," he said. "But am I really leaving Persia?" Then he explained why he had come to Teheran.

Madame Akemi stared at him. "You actually want to stay—down there in the wilds?" After a moment she nodded with a knowing smile. "Oh, now I see. Just long enough to sell your estates. I've heard that when the Government sells, exiles are cheated of at least two thirds. But before you do leave, come and see me again. Now don't forget."

She began to polish her jewellery, breathing on each piece and shining it with a velvet cloth, while her husband paced the room in excitement.

"You should have told me at once, Ghazan. This opens up new vistas."

"If you would be so good as to approach your friends in the Majlis," Ghazan suggested. "Your prestige would give a petition added weight."

"Nothing easier. I shall stop this scandalous exile."

"Very good of you, Akemi. If you could also raise the matter in one of your speeches."

"It is perfectly true," said Akemi, with a flourish, "that I could reverse the decree by a single speech. But that remedy might not be permanent. No, I plan something much more effective."

He paused and a hectic light came into his eyes. Radio Teheran withdrew the Persian singer and offered an imported record. Saxophones and trumpets blared.

"The destiny of our country lies in our hands, Ghazan—and with one other great power. You know the power I mean?"

Akemi turned dramatically and in a very soft voice said, "Holland." Then, sweeping away any uncertainty in his guest's face, he cried, "Yes, Holland. A land of immense wealth and—what few know— because of her resources and her allies, the nation of the future."

Ghazan was very surprised. The Dutch two hundred years ago had monopolized Persian trade, but he knew of no instance since in which their orbit had touched Persia's.

"Holland lies remote," he objected.

"What is distance today? Pardon me, Ghazan, but you are thinking in the old categories. Up in the Zagros you are out of touch. Believe me, our future lies with Holland."

He painted her power in bold, sweeping lines with verve and conviction. When Ghazan said, "Surely her population is very small,"

146

Akemi retorted, "*Was* small. The birthrate has risen by leaps and bounds."

"The Dutch Minister's wife has eight children," interposed Madame Akemi, as though that settled it.

"Holland can draw on untold millions in Indonesia. Her real wealth lies there. Whole islands of almost solid uranium." These he conjured out of the air and offered Ghazan, with a warm invitation. "Come to a little dinner. Just you and the Dutch Minister and one or two chosen friends of the utmost discretion. You will see that Holland is in earnest, and can forward your hopes."

Akemi forestalled further questions by raising his hands.

"Enough said. We understand each other."

Ghazan did not know what to think. The scheme appeared, to say the least, fantastic. He had spent only ten months of his life in Teheran, long enough, however, to know that the fantastic often succeeded. It would be unreasonable, he argued, to dismiss the scheme merely because he failed to see the reasons behind it. Moreover, the Tabrizi was a successful politician. Ghazan was in no position to disdain political support. He decided to see what Akemi was planning, and accepted the invitation.

Three evenings later Ghazan was back in the same house. The dinner was for men only. A dozen friends were assembled: politicians, Azerbaijan landowners, a former Chief of Police. Ghazan knew only two; generalizing from them and the conversation, he saw that the group were united in opposition to the army, the Government and the existing régime. Their voices were hushed, their eyes alert and glancing. Clearly it was an occasion. Their foreign guest, it appeared, had been delayed and would arrive only after dinner.

Ghazan sat on Akemi's right and was treated with marked respect. Much of the talk, vague but convinced, related to the powerful Dutch army and navy, Dutch treaties and Dutch secret weapons. The electric light failed during the last course, and candles added to the air of conspiracy. While the guests sipped arack brandy, Akemi left the room and returned with a swarthy, frog-faced man of middle age, to whom he offered his own chair. Then he rose to address the company.

"His Excellency the Dutch Minister is unfortunately unable to be present tonight. He asked to be excused on the grounds of urgent business. He could not confide what it was. I think we can guess the nature of that secret business." Much whispering. "In his place Mr. Hoocht, first secretary at the Ministry, and as most of you will know, the real planning power, has kindly consented to address us."

The swarthy figure rose and began to speak slowly in heavily accented Persian:

"It is an honour to be here tonight, to represent one great power before the leaders of another. Holland loves Persia above all countries. Not for her oil, nor her strategic bases, not for any mercenary reason—but because Persia is the mother of civilizations." Smiles and loud applause. "Egypt, Iraq, China—they too make that claim, but falsely. Your archæologists tell me Persian flint tools are older by a thousand years than any to be found in Asia or Africa." Renewed applause. "In the pages of the Zend-Avesta," he continued, alluding to the Zoroastrian scripture, "at least six hundred years old, are winged chariots of advanced design. That design others stole, perfected and claimed as their own. We know the truth—that aeroplanes are a Persian invention." Much self-congratulation among the guests. "It is no exaggeration to say that my country owes her heritage, her position as a world leader, to Persia. In the name of Holland I salute you." Mr. Hoocht paused to wipe his brow. "I turn east to honour the debt and what do I find? A great country, yes, but oppressed by a tyrannical régime. A handful of men who do not represent her real interests lay Persia open to foreign exploitation. At this very moment, as my Government well knows, a Communist coup is being engineered. Only the men gathered here tonight can form a suitable Government, with Akemi as their Prime Minister. Only men of character like yourselves, devoted to an ideal, can restore Persia to her rightful place. Action is the order of the day. Ghazan Khan, so disgracefully treated by the present régime, has already proved himself an enemy of the Communists." Applause and warm glances to the Ilkhan. "He commands a force of half a million men with the latest weapons. While my Government raises the question of Persia's future in the United Nations, Ghazan Khan will march on the capital. Together with our allies,"—here he enumerated nine important nations—"we shall send speedy and effective help. Aeroplanes, tanks, munitions—all await the hoisting of the flag of reform."

The speaker, after two awkward bows, sat down amid applause. Ghazan was so astounded that for a moment the room swam before his eyes. Guests leaned over to congratulate him. Hastily he rose. In a voice of cold fury he said:

"I have no intention whatever of marching on the capital or anywhere else. As for half a million men—I do not have a tenth of that number."

Akemi looked concerned, then smiled to his guests. "A modest man, Ghazan Falqani, very modest. And naturally at this stage he has to be cautious. He cannot divulge his plans."

In the confused argument which followed the former Chief of Police made rather too forceful a point and overturned a candle with his elbow. It looked as if the tablecloth would catch fire. Akemi shouted for his manservant. Guests backed towards the wall. The Dutch diplomat picked up the nearest glass and threw its contents on the cloth. It must have held brandy, for the flame crackled and blazed halfway to the ceiling. Guests cowered, napkins in front of their faces. Akemi fumbled with the ice drawer of the refrigerator. Finally the manservant dowsed the flames with a pail of water.

By the time the mess was cleared and a new cloth laid the argument was forgotten, only the important foreigner remembered. In turn the guests rose to show off their oratorical powers: one spoke of a silver mine on his estate, another of a scheme for turning pistachio nuts into soap—requiring Dutch capital. They talked for two hours, but Ghazan was so angry he scarcely listened.

As soon as the last guest had left, Ghazan confronted his host.

"What made you say such things?" he demanded.

Akemi seemed pained by his tone. "You're displeased? I don't understand."

"Marching on the capital—what made you dream I'd do that?"

The older man was all candour. "After dinner the other night—you told me in so many words."

"I spoke of fighting my exile, not of revolution."

Akemi laid a hand on his arm. "My dear friend, you can avoid exile only by overthrowing the régime. Holland will help. Believe me, Ghazan, this is your best hope."

Only in dreams had Ghazan seen such things occur. A certain sublime simplicity, a lunatic logic took his breath away.

"Once and for all," he said at last. "I want nothing to do with this scheme."

149

"We have money behind us. You will have your share."

"I don't want money. I want a practical plan for achieving my aims."

"Your aims?" Akemi seemed puzzled, then turned admiring eyes on his guest. "The crown!" he whispered. "I had planned a republic, but this is better. Brilliant it is! Seljuqs, Safavis, Qajars—all the great dynasties were tribal in origin. A king from the earth, to renew our vigour; from the heart of Asia, to reclaim our inheritance. Oh, Ghazan, you and I will make our country great again."

Ghazan listened, incredulous. Akemi must be mad, he thought. I can't argue with a madman.

As he strode angrily out, Akemi touched his arm and whispered, "Not a word to anyone. I will keep you informed."

Kazem returned from Kazvin the day after the party and when he heard about it, burst out laughing.

"I should have warned you. There are so many things you do not know—indeed how could you? Only when you live here do you discover which particular lies people tell, and why. Akemi is determined to be prime minister. He's not rich enough to buy the post and his family aren't powerful enough to gain it by influence. Hence the idea of foreign support."

"But why Holland?"

"It happened like this. The Akemis live two houses away from the Dutch Minister, and they have a new tennis court, one of the few in Teheran. The Dutch Minister is a former tennis champion and loves the game, so he invited the Akemis to his receptions. He treated them well and his wife spoke of the beauties of her country. Never before had the Akemis moved in diplomatic circles. Both as a result of his vanity and to feed it further, Akemi exaggerated the importance of Holland. The Minister got his tennis—and something more. Akemi felt his destiny linked to Holland's. He began to pester the Minister to support his movement, even offered him money. The Minister of course refused. Then he tried all the secretaries—but they had been warned by the Minister."

"Except Hoocht?"

Kazem smiled cannily. "Last night, unless I am very mistaken, Akemi pulled a trick not unknown in Teheran—he's too old to have invented it himself. Your swarthy Hoocht was no more a Dutchman than you or I. He was probably an Armenian, chosen because of his accent and paid to deliver a speech written by Akemi. The guests were doubtless too full of their dreams of power to notice his incongruous appearance."

Ghazan murmured a gruff phrase of annoyance, then began to ponder the implications. Behind the masquerade lay something very sinister. How could he attain his purpose amid such scheming and counter-scheming: he who had nothing to bargain with but the lives of his tribesmen?

"I'm sorry he wasn't much help," Kazem continued. "But at least no harm is done. By next week Akemi will be deep in something new. Meanwhile I'll invite one or two friends in a position to arrange that audience you want."

CHAPTER TEN

THE first of Kazem's friends to be invited was a certain Hussein Mehdi, a low-ranking Minister. He was a pompous little man of good family with blue eyes, a smooth white skin and frizzled grey hair. His career had been managed by a remarkably intelligent aunt. He himself cared less for government than the gossip of government. His tastes were Western, and he had little sympathy with the tribes. However, Kazem had lately proved helpful in financing an irrigation scheme on his Kerman estates, and the Falqani counted on his gratitude.

As soon as they were seated in the drawing-room, Ghazan put his request.

Mehdi looked irritably at the carpet. "An audience? At any other moment I should have been delighted. But now . . ." he spread his hands in a hopeless gesture. "It would be, to say the least, tactless."

"Tactless? Why?" asked Kazem.

"A month ago Fars was in favour."

"And now?"

"A byword of reproach. All because of the hospital." He turned to Ghazan. "Surely you've heard the terrible news?"

Ghazan shook his head.

"Well, it happened like this. The new hospital was completed four weeks ago. A rich Shirazi had given it to the town. A gift to the people—unheard of, and also slightly suspect. The trouble he took! Each country giving its best, just as the satrapies did for Persepolis. But instead of cedars from Lebanon for Xerxes's palace, it was radiological units from Sweden, sterilizing equipment from Switzerland. Surely you've seen it, Ghazan?"

"Only the outside. They say it's earthquake-proof, though I've never heard of earthquakes in Shiraz."

"It had to have everything," Mehdi explained. "Including—you'd never guess—two acres of lawn! Teheran hoped it would become a Medical Centre for the Middle East: she was proud of her backward south. The Prime Minister agreed to open the hospital. Plans were made. He was far from pleased with the Saadi Park on his last visit to the town of poets. You may remember—to open the sugar factory. So the Governor ordered a modern bathroom for the municipal palace, where he planned to lodge prominent ministers. The contract was sold to a cousin of the municipal procurator. He knew as much about bathrooms as anyone in Shiraz: absolutely nothing. The bath and fittings he ordered from Teheran. Ten days before the Prime Minister's arrival only the tiles had been laid. The contractor was living in a glorious world where he alone was capable of installing ministerial bathrooms. When the procurator shook him to his senses, he saw the scheme was completely beyond him. First he turned to his friends. Copious tears they could manage, but not water through pipes. At last he went to a Belgian engineer employed at the small local waterworks. 'If the bathroom isn't finished in time,' he cried in despair, 'rather than shame my family by going to prison I shall cut my throat.'

"The engineer believed him and, out of pity, installed the bath. He also added a shower. Proudly the contractor showed these off. But the procurator had never seen a shower before. He looked suspiciously at the bulb. It had been installed by a foreigner. The pipes were connected to the waterworks, run by the same man. Clearly a foreign agent planning to kill the Prime Minister by pumping poison through the noxious-looking bulb of the shower. He ordered the engineer's immediate arrest. The poor man protested and finally offered to take a shower himself. This he did amid several witnesses, emerged unscathed, and was later released."

Kazem laughed politely. "So the Prime Minister had his shower bath?"

Mehdi frowned at the interruption. "I am coming to that. The great day arrived. Naturally I travelled down with the Prime Minister. An escort of thirty, but," he added suspiciously, "you can't trust the police. I took two of my own men just in case. Everything had to be inspected; iron lungs, lawns, flower-beds, special electricity plant. Dozens of speeches in blazing sunshine. The Governor promised that cool luxury awaited his Excellency that evening. We returned to the municipal palace. In the tiled bathroom the bath taps were turned on. Not a trickle obeyed the Prime Minister's command. Then the shower. Nothing happened. Commotion. Inquiries. Arrests. At last the reason emerged. The two acres of lawn had been watered day and night for a week to keep them green. The reservoirs were empty. Not a drop of water in all Shiraz."

The Minister laughed, a high-pitched, spiteful laugh. Ghazan waited impatiently for him to come to the point.

"That was bad enough. Worse followed. The hospital has sound-proof floors, operating rooms, X-ray apparatus—everything except the one essential."

"Doctors?" suggested Kazem.

"No, there are five foreign doctors." He paused tantalizingly and lit a cigarette. "An even more disastrous defect. The hospital does not have a single patient. Not one."

"Is it possible?" Kazem exclaimed.

"Three weeks open and all the two hundred beds are empty. Too perfect! Conjured out of a bottle and nailed down by chance in Shiraz. If you wallow in a mud hovel when you're well, how can you afford air-conditioning and spring mattresses when you're ill? As for the few rich—they know the misadventures possible in a provincial hospital. They still fly to Europe for treatment. All the wonderful machines stand idle in the hospital which was to be Persia's glory and which the Prime Minister went down specially to open." Hussein Mehdi sighed affectedly. "You see now why Fars is in such disfavour?"

Ghazan frowned, puzzled and dissatisfied.

"These are trivial matters," he said.

"Trivial!" cried the Minister, shocked. "You call this blow to national pride trivial?"

"Yes, I do."

"Clearly you are out of touch with influential opinion."

"That may be," admitted Ghazan. "But granted the hospital's importance, how can it affect my request for an audience?"

"Fars in disgrace, and you the most powerful figure in Fars. Don't you see—if I put your request, I should never live it down. Never!"

He explained that by seeming to favour and forward the interests of a backward province, he would be labelled by his enemies unprogressive and reactionary. "It's more than a personal affair," he concluded with a touch of self-importance. "It would do the Government a great deal of harm."

"I assure you," said Ghazan with vigour, "that what I have to tell

154

His Majesty is in the country's best interests. It is also very urgent. My cousin and I were counting on your help."

The Minister gave Ghazan an appealing look, as though to suggest the impropriety of forcing the issue.

"Don't think I'm unsympathetic. Just the contrary. The Government opposes the growing power of the army. Eighty thousand men: a hundred thousand tons of arms and material from abroad since the war. And the foreign embassies insist on our satisfying every whim of the General Staff. Several ministers feel as I do: if we met for a talk one day, we could surely strike a bargain."

Ghazan made yet another attempt to gain the audience. Mehdi shifted his ground.

"Even if I succeeded, nothing would come of it. The Shah leaves these matters to his Ministers. He would refer it to me or one of my colleagues."

Ghazan saw from Kazem's expression that this was wishful thinking. But Mehdi would not promise either the audience or a meeting with the Minister of War. "I will see about it" was as far as he would go. The conversation drifted to generalities. Finally he rose to leave. Turning up his collar and putting on a wide-brimmed black hat, he peered cautiously out of the window before going to the door.

"Keep this meeting secret," he whispered. "You understand, my life is in danger." Stealthily he withdrew to his car, hidden in shadow at the end of the road.

"From Communists?" Ghazan asked, as they returned to the drawing-room.

Kazem smiled. "Not as far as I know. His father always had that phrase on his lips, and died peacefully in bed. It's inherited—a sign of vanity, not fear—and bears little relation to the facts."

Restlessly he paced the room.

"This audience is going to prove even more difficult than I thought. It's a bad moment: Government, Court, Assembly and Army—none well in the lead, all jockeying for position." He paused as though marking the odds on each. "Well, the Government has failed us. Tomorrow we shall try the Court."

"Mohammed is immensely rich," said Kazem. "I should say he is a year or two younger than you—and still unmarried. His grandfather

made a fortune manufacturing antiques. He specialized in Achaemenian silver bowls and counterfeit coins. He used to boast that gold
coins from his workshop were displayed as Darics by twenty-three
museums throughout the world. He married an Egyptian princess but
always remained suspect at court. His son, however, was accepted as
authentic, and Mohammed himself is highly esteemed."

The courtier presently arrived in a perfectly cut blue suit, brown
suède shoes, and a purple foulard tie, trailing the scent of eau-de-
cologne. He was handsome, with smiling black eyes and a delicately
arched nose. Compliments exchanged, he began to tell of the foreign
tour from which he had recently returned with the Shah.

"We skied and danced to the best bands and drove fast cars. The
roads! Like velvet. The whole world laid down a red carpet. I'll show
you my films one day. Just now the projector is broken and no one here
can repair it."

From a pocket he slipped out a pigskin box containing a batch of
colour photographs. In turn he held them up to the light: snow and
beach scenes, groups on shipboard, special shows of costumed dances;
explaining their technical merits.

"The food! Pâté de foie gras, pressed duckling. I brought back
menus and recipes. My chocolate mousse has had quite a success. The
wines too! At the first few dinners I made rather a fool of myself."
He laughed easily. "It was really an education. I felt I was living for
the first time. Next year I hope to go back."

A silence followed—only a short one—but it seemed to put Mohammed on the defensive. "The mullahs snarl—but whatever one does
they snarl. Patriotism is excellent—but they carry it too far. In Europe
it is already becoming out of fashion. To my mind, each country has
something to give the world, each is a voice in a chorus. One has a
duty now to be cosmopolitan. And as a people we have a wonderful
capacity for assimilating the new."

He took out a platinum case and offered Ghazan and Kazem gold-
tipped Turkish cigarettes.

"And now it is your turn, Ghazan. We didn't go to Switzerland, but
I hear it is lovely. *Vous vivrez comme un coq en pâte.*" His manner
was still breezy, without a hint of malice.

"Why do you speak of Switzerland?" asked Ghazan.

"Hadn't you heard? You are exiled to Switzerland." He explained that tribal property would be sold and the rent of a villa with sufficient income paid to Ghazan monthly by the Persian Minister in Berne.

Ghazan tried to hide his concern. He had unpleasant memories of his two years in Lausanne. He felt little sympathy for the Swiss. His teachers, for instance, who thought they knew all the answers. And their country, parcelled up and priced: the mountains, like affected children, aware they were being admired. So it seemed to Ghazan, who knew well the give and take between man and earth. He thought angrily to himself, This is an added reason for stamping out the whole outrageous scheme.

"Why Switzerland?" asked Kazem.

The courtier flushed a little. "To ensure your cousin gets up to no tricks. We don't want him enlisting foreign support, returning secretly with cloak and dagger to effect a coup! No, that would never do." He laughed lightly, still without malice. A schoolboy's laugh, thought Ghazan. He felt his anger billow like a spinnaker. Slowly he hauled it in, tried to trim his sails to Mohammed's wind.

"Pocket-money from the Persian Minister!" he smiled. "Just like old times."

Mohammed seemed puzzled, then laughed. "Of course, I'd forgotten you'd been to a Swiss school. You'll feel quite at home."

He added that, as Ghazan's passport would be made out only for Switzerland, truancy would be impossible.

For a few minutes they smoked in silence.

Mohammed's long, dark eyelashes flickered as he asked:

"By the way, what brings you to Teheran?"

Behind the casual tone, Ghazan detected anxiety.

"I have come to see His Majesty."

"Doubtless you wish to present your thanks."

In spite of himself, Ghazan echoed the last word questioningly.

"It would be only courteous. After all, his Majesty has been very kind. Anyone else would have left this business to the army or the Government. You would have had a hard time of it. But His Majesty prefers to control everything himself."

"Then I'll trust you to arrange an audience. A few minutes is all I need."

"Ah, Ghazan, the rules of the game forbid two kings to meet! There must always be one square at least between." He laughed impishly.

157

"Surely a king is a piece that cannot be taken. Yet you yourself have sketched the plans to lift me off the board."

"A rival then!"

"A prince becomes a rival by striking coins in his own name. Have I done that?"

Mohammed frowned and did not answer. Puzzled for a moment, too late Ghazan saw his blunder.

"Then you will arrange the audience?"

"I myself shall gladly deliver your thanks," said Mohammed stiffly.

"Perhaps I did not make myself clear," said Ghazan firmly, emphasizing his words. "I intend to meet His Majesty personally."

Mohammed contracted like mimosa in sudden frost. First the insult to his grandfather, now this forceful tone.

"That would never do," he muttered.

"Why not?"

Mohammed looked round uneasily. To be personal was a deadly sin, and yet . . . "You'll pardon my saying it, Ghazan, but you are—well—you live in a different world. Camels and mules; dirty, disease-ridden louts: to deal with them you have to be—as you are. At the palace I try to foster something different—above all, pleasantness and a carefree atmosphere. Atmosphere is so important. *Vous, Ghazan, vous avez un peu trop de caractère.*" He raised appealing eyes to Ghazan. "Don't you see, a meeting would be quite unharmonious."

"The lives of a hundred thousand people are at stake—and you talk to me of 'harmony'."

"Happy court, happy country," Mohammed replied, as though his words were a proverb.

The Falqani continued to argue, until at last they saw that to arrange the audience would be opposed to everything in Mohammed's nature. They allowed the conversation to wander off the point. A few minutes later Mohammed remembered pressing business: champagne had to be ordered for tomorrow's reception at the palace. With a smile that was evidently a sign of relief, he took his departure.

"These courtiers and ministers who think only of their miserable skins!" cried Ghazan in exasperation. "They stand between the Shah and his people."

Kazem laid a calming hand on his shoulder. "Between him and his enemies, too, Ghazan. Half the politicians are intriguing for a change of dynasty. Every officer believes he will follow in Reza Shah's footsteps. And still we have no heir."

Mohammed Reza Shah had no son and his five half-brothers, sons of a Qajar mother, had no legal title to the throne.

"But there's still hope," Kazem continued. "This afternoon a deputy Chief of Police is coming. He is as honest as Mohammed, and much more intelligent. Also, he has Persia's welfare at heart. I know he will like you and sympathize with your views. I believe he may arrange the audience."

Ghazan had expected someone in uniform, but Ali Ainapur, the deputy Chief of Police, arrived in a loose-fitting grey jacket and black trousers. "I like to be myself when I can," he explained. He was a tall, good-looking man with alert, effervescent eyes, a strong jaw, and a high, bulging forehead. In rather stubby fingers he twirled a rose.

After introducing his cousin, Kazem excused himself: he had business that afternoon. Ghazan offered his guest a cigarette, but he said he preferred a water pipe. Soon he was puffing at the ivory stem, while Ghazan explained what he wanted.

"You did well to turn to me," said Ainapur. "Army officers are posted here, there and everywhere; governments rise and fall: it's the police who hold the real power. Every line is tapped, every deputy watched."

A shade too much emphasis, thought Ghazan; as though he were trying to convince himself as well as me. With a word of excuse, Ainapur unbuckled under his jacket a leather holster containing a revolver, and laid it beside his chair. The white rose he placed on top.

"So, you intend to speak to the Shah and want my help. First, may I put one question?"

Ghazan inclined his head.

Watching him closely, Ainapur asked, "Who or what do you think lies behind this decree?"

Ghazan decided on frankness. "The Army and the late Government."

"True answers as far as they go. But why this particular form of revenge, of removing a threat?"

"I suppose, the most convenient."

"Yes, but why?" When Ghazan did not answer, Ainapur continued,

"I think I know. Here in Teheran we've lost faith in ourselves and our way of life. Foreign money pours in to help an 'underdeveloped' country." Ainapur spoke the phrase with disgust. "Such impertinence! In fact, our civilization is being moulded on theirs as part of a scheme for saving their necks. Theoretically the money comes as a gift, but it will stop unless we apply western ideas. Less Koran, more typewriting in the school curriculum. Censuses and plans and surveys. And, of course, tribal settlement. All in the hope of living better." As Ghazan protested, Ainapur held up his hand. "I know settlement will do just the opposite. I'm one of the very few you don't need to convince. I was born near Bakhtiari country. Their Khans are among my best friends. I was reared on tribal goat milk. It gave me these muscles." He glanced with approval at his flexed biceps, then, clasping his hands, tightened his breast muscles. Ghazan tried to guide him back to the audience, but Ainapur, fixing Ghazan with a serious look, continued for the moment in general terms.

"To my way of thinking, you are a victim of this lack of self-confidence, and the borrowed culture. But the irony is this. We adopt the treatment when Western thinkers are rejecting it. In countries whose poor have as much as our rich, the wail grows louder"—he mimicked a grabbing gesture—"'Increase our standard of living.' This sort of folly has happened before. When I was your age, education and nationalism were the great Western panaceas. Reza Shah applied them years after they had been proved useless."

Ghazan was only half-convinced "Is this money quite useless?" he asked. "It came with arms and military experts. Surely the idea was to give us self-defence."

Ainapur thought a moment. His eye fell on a large globe of the world standing in a wooden frame within reach. He sent the globe spinning, then stopped it with a firm hand and slowly turned to Western Asia. "A dream, Ghazan Khan. This globe proves it. Persia is not a giant and cannot resist giants. Despite the arms, our frontiers are guaranteed by Western interests. That is another cause of self-mistrust. And this help has made us more, rather than less, vulnerable. Money has stuck to the wrong hands. In the old days wealth came from the land in small amounts and was kept at home within mud walls. Now the rich are urged to send their embezzled funds and quick profits back where they came from. Their women dance sambas at the Darband Hotel and swim in marble pools." He screwed up his face in distaste.

"The ripples extend to us," said Ghazan. "With inflation, many of my poorer families cannot afford even tea and sugar."

On this point they found themselves in full agreement. "The poor here are even worse off," Ainapur continued. "Since the war Teheran has tripled in size. It teems with malcontents. The Tudeh party whispers in their ears: 'You chew melon-seeds to disguise your hunger, while these fat idlers circulate in their gaudy cars like worms at the core of apricots and peaches.' And the Tudeh party, itself a product of the West, offers to solve a problem caused by Western interests. But," he added with a knowing gleam, "you understand that at least as well as I."

Ghazan listened attentively. He began now to see that just as at the equinoctial tide a rise of a few feet in the ocean level was linked with a many million times greater displacement of sun and moon, so his own life swung to external pulls: the meeting of civilizations, a nation's fear of being ridiculed as backward, and the age-old motives—vanity, greed. How strong were they, he wondered?

He asked whether the Tudeh party was gaining ground in Teheran.

Ainapur smiled. "You don't expect *me* to admit that! But it is very strong, here and in the factories of Isfahan. Last autumn we discovered a plot to establish a Communist government. I myself raided the underground hide-out. Short-wave wireless, dossiers with names of the people's enemies. Pictures of Stalin and Lenin. I have some of them here." From his pocket-book he took out two samples which he handed to Ghazan. "No less than five hundred army officers were implicated. I have their files in my office—four colonels among them. They were getting instructions direct from Moscow. And I'm still trying to run down members."

He uncrossed his legs and, running a hand through iron-grey hair, met Ghazan's eyes squarely. "Teheran is full of exiles in spirit. They refuse to tolerate a true patriot. They do not hate you, Ghazan Khan, for what you are, but because you show them up, as mourners paying lip-service hate the one mourner who sheds tears."

After a pause, he continued, even more gravely:

"Corruption in the army—that we could deal with. Unfortunately it's nothing compared to the radical danger."

He looked disapprovingly at the imported bagatelles crowding the room: chairs with unstable chromium legs; telephone; electric clock; glossy magazines.

"New appetites are being artificially aroused: appetites never known here and which Persia will always be too poor to satisfy."

"Dreams of a paradisal democracy?"

Ainapur smiled wryly and shook his head. "Worse still. The desire for the latest material goods which we only think we need. Synthetic fabrics, processed foods, electric gadgets—all the frivolities of a growing urban population: our thin dry soil cannot pay for these. We hold out our begging-cups to the West. In one more respect we become enslaved."

"If we want these things," Ghazan exclaimed, "let us make them ourselves."

Ainapur spread his hands. "We can't—not at a reasonable price. To purify drinking-water we need soda. Last year we built a soda factory. But the factory stands idle. Far cheaper to import soda five thousand miles than make it ourselves. For the moment we can afford that and other necessities. But while our oil reserves fall, our appetites grow. The Tudeh party knows this. They watch in glee as foreign money nurtures our discontent. I see it all clearly enough—but what's to be done?"

Ghazan answered without hesitation. "The remedy is obvious. End this state of being helped, since it saps our will. We should buy as my tribesmen buy, for their needs, not for others', and according to our means."

Ainapur shook his head sceptically. "That remedy only a strong man could apply. We don't have a strong man. And if we did, he would turn into another Reza Shah. So you see, Ghazan Khan, Persia's fate springs from a divided nature—and your own exile springs from that." As though reading Ghazan's expression, he protested, "Don't think I'm pessimistic. I'm not. These ideas like tribal settlement and land reform make me think of my immediate superior. He has a house not far from here, with fifteen gardeners and as many greenhouses. Roses, double carnations—these he disdains because indigenous. His greenhouses are devoted to growing simple geraniums. The soil has to be specially prepared, the temperature regulated. But the geraniums will not flourish outside. It's the same with those ideas. They are sports which can never thrive in our country. So," he concluded in a tone of hope, "your people, if they are settled, will not be settled for long. And you, if you are banished, will one day be recalled."

This prospect had not occurred to Ghazan. It complicated the issue and made him slightly uneasy.

"Possibly," he said. "But if you think I'm going to kick my heels waiting for a change of Government!"

"For a change in the climate of opinion," Ainapur corrected. "At the moment certain ideas, certain people cannot survive in Persia. They must be transplanted. You are one."

"That remains to be seen," said Ghazan curtly, and began to make his request.

Ainapur held up a hand and laughed. "I know what you're going to say. 'Will you get me that audience.' But, if I'm right, the issues involve so many people, so many intangibles, that your future has passed beyond the level of personal relations. The Shah could do nothing for you. An audience is useless."

Ghazan retorted with fire, "I'm sure you're mistaken."

"Eight years since you were last here. With all respect, Ghazan Khan, how can you know? Whereas I see these politicians every day." He fixed Ghazan with a glance. "My advice is this. Make the best of your banishment. That and settlement of the Falqani will doubtless harm Persia. But only by shock, by seeing the lamentable results, will our country be brought to her senses."

Until dinner time, and then again till almost midnight, Ghazan argued his point. Finally he said:

"I shall come to your office every day until you arrange that meeting."

"You're joking, of course?" Ainapur said.

"Not at all."

Ainapur's muscles tautened. With an edge to his voice he said, "I must ask you not to do that."

Ghazan frowned. "Why not?"

"I came to see you as a personal favour to Kazem. When I leave tonight, you must consider our relationship at an end."

An affront, but why? Checking his surprise and anger, Ghazan said, "Of course, I'll respect your wishes. But you have shown such understanding. I thought you wanted to help."

"Want to—yes. But I cannot. I know you and your motives. But half Teheran believes the army's myth—Ghazan Falqani, a war-lord of alien stock bent on the throne, financed now by Britain, now by Russia, whichever is scapegoat of the moment."

Ghazan looked at him in contempt. "Surely you don't believe . . ."

"*I* know it's absurd, but my immediate superior, for instance, is brother-in-law of the Chief of Staff—he chooses to believe it. Even to seem to be helping . . ." Ainapur's voice tailed off. He buckled on his revolver, and, in a tone of apology, explained, "I have no money of my own and four daughters to marry. I'm sorry, Ghazan Khan, but I cannot receive you in my office."

With a firm gesture he stuck the rose in his button-hole and said goodbye.

Ghazan returned to the drawing-room and flung himself on the couch, bitter and discouraged. Disappointed, too, at his own discouragement. With his parent earth he felt strong; its rhythm was his strength. Here in the devious city the least official could throw him down. Yet as he saw his chances of an audience sink in a welter of rivalry and intrigue, the need to appeal to that single authority became all the more evident.

He began to pace the room. Kazem, who had been out to dinner, returned. When he heard the news, he counselled his cousin to stay several weeks or months if necessary, to intrigue with the best of them, make empty promises, play their game. But Ghazan viewed the plan with disfavour. Not strength but finesse would be required. Disguises, masks, the thrust and play of words—he saw that he could not compete with Teheranis.

"Tomorrow evening," said Kazem, "I'm going to a reception at the palace. Everyone will be there. I'll speak to the Minister of War and see whether he will help."

"Is it likely? He refuses even to grant me an interview."

Kazem shrugged. "These old men sometimes hide a streak of pity."

With a bitter smile Ghazan said, "Even assassination is too common to excite much sympathy. And it's justice I want, not pity."

He walked to the mantelpiece, opposite Kazem, and strummed angrily. His eye fell on a large white card embossed with lion and sun. Idly he picked it up and read it. The Green Marble Palace. At eight o'clock. Kazem Falqani. The name written in ink. He laid it back

164

in its place. Next to it stood a small silver samovar. He lifted the lid and balanced it on the back of his hand. He began to examine it. Isfahan work, rather pretty. A moment later he dropped the lid and seized the invitation card.

He looked at Kazem. "I've got an idea. Can I borrow this? Go in your place?" His tone was excited.

"You feel like a party?"

"This party. I will seek out the Shah and speak my mind."

"Impossible," said Kazem stiffly. Leaving aside the breach of etiquette, a reception was the last place to discuss such a serious matter. His face was too well known. Even if he entered the palace, courtiers would prevent his attaining his goal. Worse still, such a bold and unexpected step would lay him open to immediate arrest.

"I admit your arguments," Ghazan said. "But an extreme case calls for extreme action. Do you absolutely refuse to lend me the card?"

"If you put it like that . . ."

"Then it's settled. I go."

"As you like." Then, after a moment, he counselled Ghazan, "If I were you, I should speak to the Minister of War, not the Shah. The Minister is quick to act—once he's convinced."

"I'll try to see both," Ghazan resolved.

CHAPTER ELEVEN

NEXT evening Ghazan was driven down to Teheran in Kazem's car. It was not yet dark. The major domo at the guarded gate verified the royal crest on his card, then signalled the car up the gravel drive, through gardens, to the courtyard. Ghazan got out. The evening dress he disliked having to wear proved a good disguise. He joined the huddle of black and white suits and coloured dresses in front of the central doorway, keeping to the shadow. Armed sentries with steel helmets paced the paths. Two courtiers, one white-haired, one younger than Ghazan, were admitting the double line of guests. Ghazan noticed that the young courtier gathered invitations with only a timid glance at their bearers. He crossed to this line and, head high, held out his card. The courtier took it without question.

The small palace, whose outer walls were of green and yellow marble, had been built by Reza Shah. Its shape was oblong, surmounted over the stairway by a cupola. Entering, Ghazan was dazzled for a moment by blazing chandeliers. He walked forward to mount the carpeted marble stairway. He had taken hardly three steps when his eye was drawn from the guests and flunkeys to a Western-style mural directly under the cupola. It showed a steel viaduct spanning a mountain gorge. The Veresk bridge on the Trans-Iranian Railway. A train was crossing. It looked like a toy train. Yes, it was just that, in Ghazan's estimation, Reza Shah's toy railway, which had cost a generation its bread, scarcely used and run at a loss, lying from north to south like a chain across the heart of Persia. Built for what? As he turned on the landing of the stairway, he saw the answer in the opposite mural under the cupola: the ruins of Persepolis. The railway had been designed to outdo the Achæmenian building schemes. To glorify the ruler. The people's function, too: no longer to worship God, but to glorify Reza Shah. That, or the trail of blood. His own father's blood. And still the railway ran. None of the schemes were dead. The precedents had been set, the will continued to drive. And in this palace of all places he was staking the whole sum of his hopes!

He crossed to the great mirror room where official receptions were held. He felt he was cleaving a diamond. Apart from red velvet curtained windows along one wall and a far-reaching short-pile carpet which made a meadow of the floor, the room was lined with tiny fragments of mirror, fitted in a luminous mosaic along walls and ceiling, each concentrating and sending back light from the central chandeliers.

In the crowded room he recognized ministers, influential officials, courtiers, diplomats—faces only, bodies neutralized in evening dress. Ghazan had purposely arrived late, but the Shah had not yet appeared. Glasses were being handed round: cocktails and sherbets, with plates of hors d'œuvres, and cups of coffee. Ghazan took a glass of vodka and moved among the crowd. He must remain inconspicuous till the last moment. Snatches of conversation flashed, as though from the glass mosaic: "use my influence", "the ambassador told me himself", "building a much larger house", and then an elderly man took his elbow. His eyes were bloodshot, his breath smelled of vodka. Beside him stood a dark-haired girl in a gold-spangled dress.

"Honoured sir," he said shakily. "May I present my daughter."

Ghazan did not recognize the faces. Was it a mistake? The stranger drifted away, the girl was talking.

"Malik's in agonies, poor dear. You'd never guess why! Photos of His Majesty water-skiing, stripped to the waist! Communists smuggled them through. They're in all the Tudeh papers. The mullahs shriek, the Government totters." With a giggle she sipped her cocktail, then looked wearily round the room. "I do get tired of these parties. The same old faces, the same conversation, the same smoked salmon. Next week I fly to Beirut. All my friends are coming. Don't you feel you'll scream if you don't see blue waves? Oh, hello, Saiyadah." With a smile she slipped away to join her girl friend.

Ghazan walked to another part of the room, wondering vaguely who Malik might be, his eye on the uniformed guards who lined the far wall. Suddenly, without warning, the lights flickered and went off. No one seemed to pay much attention. The talk continued. A voice said: "The chief engineer must have come to the party." In a minute the lights were on again, brilliant as before, but the diamond seemed to have turned to paste. A face smiled at Ghazan: the last he wanted to see: the military attaché at one of the larger embassies.

"Ghazan Falqani," the attaché cried delightedly, and guests nearby turned in surprise to stare. "What an unexpected pleasure," he continued in French. "By the way, I know all about your little secret. Next year, migration in the Alps—up on the lift, down on skis." He laughed easily: smooth, pink-faced, with glossy, well-brushed blond hair. Like a healthy pointer. "Before the war I used to go to Gstaad. Never missed a spring. Great sport. It's a pity though—I was counting on another hunting trip."

Two years before, the attaché, on a visit to Shiraz, had spoken pointedly at a dinner of his wish to go hunting, and Ghazan had invited him up to his summer quarters for a few days' shooting. A stir had been caused in Teheran, for no one doubted that the attaché had been fomenting tribal rebellion.

With a roguish smile the soldier continued, "Or shall you retire to your room like his Excellency your former prime minister—the scourge of foreigners? Ride round and round your room all day on a tricycle." Again he laughed. "I have it on the best authority. The Government dreads a come-back, but all he does is ride his little tricycle—and oil it!"

He finished his champagne, and, spinning the glass in his fingers, eyed Ghazan with sudden curiosity. "Why on earth did they invite you here?"

In his rough Swiss French Ghazan explained his tactics. This set the attaché laughing again. Meanwhile Ghazan kept wondering why the Shah did not come. He heard guests asking the same question. His Majesty had been due back that afternoon from a tour of the oilfields. What could have happened? Wherever he looked in the room, Ghazan saw aides and courtiers watching him closely.

"You remember that big ibex?" continued the attaché. "I had it stuffed and mounted over my fireplace. It's been much admired. I had it photographed. I may have the photo here." He searched a crocodile pocket-book, keeping up the conversation. "Must be at home. I went to the Caspian last autumn. Bagged a plump tiger—the Hyrcanian tiger—it gives one a sense of history. Fair goose-shooting, too, but I prefer the big game."

Though the attaché treated Persia as a potential cemetery for its wild life, Ghazan liked him and his sense of humour. It amused him, also, to watch rich Westerners trying to return to a state of nature, while rich Teheranis made a fetish of civic life. At any other moment he would have enjoyed a talk. Now he himself had a quarry to hunt down.

Amiably he suggested, "Perhaps we could meet one evening. I should like to hear about that tiger."

"No, Ghazan," said the attaché firmly, taking his arm. "I haven't seen you for two years, and may not see you for twenty-two. You don't escape so easily." He laughed and seized another glass of champagne from a passing tray. "But where is the Centre of the Universe, the Shadow of God on Earth? I have to see him about this new personal plane he's ordered." The attaché glanced at his watch. "He really is very late." Sipping his champagne, his eyes met and began to stare at Ghazan's. "Of course," he exclaimed. "I thought it was me, but it's you they're watching."

Ghazan frowned and gave him a questioning look.

"Don't you see—palace officials tremble at the thought of another attempted assassination. They probably think we're all your henchmen disguised!" He flung back his head and roared with laughter.

Ghazan looked incredulous. "Surely they wouldn't dream . . ."

"Why not? Last summer they arrested our first secretary at a party in these very grounds. They thought his shooting-stick was a stick for shooting people."

Ghazan ran his arms down his close-fitting evening dress. "How could I be carrying a pistol?"

"They're too nervous to think of that."

Ghazan looked bleakly round the room. He was still being watched. Perhaps the attaché was right. They would not risk putting him out, with foreigners present. A progressive nation had to handle things progressively.

"And the décor's in keeping," continued the attaché. "You know the secret history of these lovely mirror rooms?"

Ghazan forced himself to attend. "The ainekar? Does it have even an open history?"

The attaché wrinkled his brow in mock censure. "Shame on you, Ghazan! Some say the mirrors were smashed by the bullets of would-be assassins. That is apocryphal. The true story is this. Nasr al-Din Shah was visiting Paris. He took a fancy to the large mirrors at Versailles and ordered copies for the Gulistan palace. After a journey of

169

four thousand miles the mirrors arrived in as many pieces. The royal treasury was empty, so the Shah had the broken pieces installed as mosaic. And here we are, still admiring the fashion."

He broke off as an official walked on to the raised part of the room reserved for the Shah, and held up his hands for silence.

"I have an announcement to make. As you know, His Majesty is returning from the oilfields by rail. We have just received a telegram to say the train will be delayed twenty-four hours. A landslide has blocked the line."

"A landslide!" gibed the attaché to Ghazan. "They always say that when a wheel tumbles off the engine."

A polite murmur ran through the room, but Ghazan's disappointment and surprise found little echo. Almost at once guests continued talking normally. Then Ghazan saw a squat man enter, flanked by aides, some in uniform. A hush fell on that part of the room; guests made way; their eyes fell before the proud, even insolent expression with which the newcomer surveyed the party, as though summing it up and dismissing it as unworthy of his attention. Hands and fingers hung absolutely still by his side. He had a presence lacking in all the other guests: among Turkish delight and marzipan he seemed hard nougat. "The Minister of War," the attaché whispered.

Ghazan felt a surge of hope. If he could speak to the Minister, the Shah's absence need not be fatal. With a word of excuse to the attaché, he hurried through the crowd. As he came near the Minister's entourage, two aides slipped forward and barred his way.

"Ah, Ghazan Khan, an unexpected guest," one of them sneered.

They stood shoulder to narrow shoulder. Ghazan had grown used to the barrier of word and will, but this physical confrontation angered him. Only with an effort did he keep his hands from the scruff of their necks.

"Kindly let me pass," he ordered.

"One or two people are most anxious to meet you," said the second aide, "over in the far corner."

"Delighted—after I have spoken to the Minister of War."

"That can easily be arranged. Not tonight, though. His Excellency is tired and only a limited number of guests can be presented."

Ghazan looked angrily at the two aides, wondering what to do. As though enacting his dilemma, the lights, as had happened earlier, suddenly flickered. They did not go out, but the aides looked up to the chandeliers. Ghazan seized his chance to walk past.

A moment later he stood facing the Minister. His small, extremely alert brown eyes came level with Ghazan's tie; he had full lips, a strong, hooked nose and closely cropped grey hair. On his left breast, like a section of pomegranate, gleamed the high Order of the Lion and Sun. Despite his age—he looked about sixty-five—Ghazan had the impression of compact power, of a man cast in bronze.

The hush had grown. Someone dropped a glass. A woman giggled. Another aide smoothed over the difficult position by presenting Ghazan like a welcome guest.

"His Highness Ghazan Falqani."

The Minister looked him up and down. "What do you want?" His voice impressed Ghazan like a sleek, grooved rifle, after the rattle of pop-guns.

"To talk to you," he answered firmly. "State affairs at a reception— not quite the thing. But since you decline to admit me to your office . . ."

Again the Minister asked point-blank, "What do you want?"

"An answer first. Can you reverse this decree of exile?"

The Minister's eyes flickered. Deliberately he raised his vodka glass to his lips. Ghazan watched, trying to sum him up. His policy no less than his power the Minister owed to Reza Shah. The son of a Teheran shopkeeper, he had been trained as an engineer in Germany. Reza Shah had employed him in the construction of his railway and later put him in charge of all public works. Both were strong-willed and outspoken; they quarrelled repeatedly; for ten years he was in and out of favour. The war years he had spent interned. Lately he had come again to the fore as one of the most outspoken advocates of oil nationalization.

In an even voice the Minister said, "Yes, I have power to reverse the decree."

A statement of fact? Ghazan could not be sure. Holding the Minister's eye, he urged.

"I want you to use that power."

"So!" It was almost a sneer. "Ghazan Falqani comes whining for mercy!"

"Demanding justice!" Ghazan retorted with warmth.

171

"You storm like a provincial lawyer," the Minister scoffed. "Yet, why not? It must be distinctly unpleasant to lose at a single throw absolute power and many millions of tumans."

Ghazan drew himself up. "I have come to plead my people's case, not my own."

The Minister gave him a cutting look. "One thing I cannot stand: that is cant. Let us strip the cant. Why not admit you speak for yourself? What shame in that? You are not the first to blubber. Even Reza Shah groaned through those four years of exile. His letters to me from Johannesburg were the tortured cries of a strong man in a strait-jacket: roaring for the lost throne, the lost hoard. Useless cries of regret!" he concluded, without pity.

"Since you speak of Reza Shah, at least His Majesty knew why he went. But I have been given no explanation."

Mocking eyes met his over the vodka glass. "Let us say—you leave in the country's best interests."

The words roused Ghazan to fury. "Spewed out like an emetic, to calm a fever? If I believed that, would I be here, protesting? The opposite is true. This is the first stage of dissolution." He hung on the word, then continued with rising intensity. "The Ilkhan binds the Falqani to each other and to their land. The Ilkhan you remove, in order to remove his people from the hills. But remove his people, and you remove the flocks; remove the flocks and you remove the grass, for only their browsing mats the turf, promotes new shoots. Remove the grass, and you remove the soil. The hills themselves are exiled, blown or washed away. Southern Persia goes to the sea and wind: dissolves in dust."

The Minister sniffed in contempt. "What if the hills go? I care very little for your grass or all the grass of Persia."

"Grass has always been our life."

"Not any more. It is merely the green baize door leading to the deep vault, the safe-deposit where our bullion is stored: dark viscous oil, festering in the shadow of the hills. Under the hills—there are the foundations of the new Persia."

Incredulous, almost horrified, Ghazan looked at the Minister as though he were guilty of outrage. "Shift Persia's foundations—from living to dead matter!"

"Gold too is dead. Is it any the less powerful for that?" He eyed

Ghazan contemptuously. "Have you ever visited Abadan? I thought not. How then can you know the power of oil?" The word set his deep voice pulsing: it seemed to release hidden passion strangely at variance with his cold manner. "A black greasy inheritance amassed over a myriad millennia, for this chosen generation to spend. Oil enough to spin the whole earth like a titanic turbine. Gushing up like a wild beast in the derrick cages, led tame to the refinery—*our* refinery now—the city of massive machines, where we crack all the stored sunlight, where we crack the sun itself. There is a sight worth all your grass: the tall steel columns, a modern, greater Persepolis: the new power-house of Persia."

"Not columns," contended Ghazan, "but dead trees, doomed to fall, for once the body has been snatched, the tomb remains empty."

"There is more than one tomb, as you call it—more than enough, anyway, for our lifetime."

"But not enough for ever. Whereas the grass over the tombs—that *can* be renewed for ever."

"Grass!" he spat out the word. "Who will buy grass? Tankers from east and west sail into Abadan, begging a black cargo. Millions of tumans the pipelines pump back to Teheran. The streets light up, the shops pile high their goods, the banks swell with new, hard wealth."

Ghazan decided to meet the Minister on his own ground. With dignity he said, "My people, too, provide wealth. Though they live on bare hills, they are not beggars. Milk, clarified butter, cheese, lambs—with these they fatten Southern Persia. Spring clip-wool from Falqani sheep provided the carpet under our feet; taxes on the Falqani helped buy these velvets, this marble."

The Minister had been signalling a servant, who now approached Ghazan. The Minister's eyes, the eyes of all the aides had shifted to a point beside him. The servant was offering him a bronze tray. On it stood a silver basin of white sugar lumps, in the centre of four red and green enamelled cups, full to the brim with black coffee.

"Coffee, Ghazan Khan?" The tone was everything: invitation, challenge, threat, in one.

Ghazan felt himself closely watched. He thought of his father and hesitated. Indisposed, supported to the door, to an ante-room. In five minutes finished. His eye fell on the writing embossed round the edge of the tray: "What the Unseen sends us can have no defect." Had the tray been chosen to allay his suspicions? A refinement of cunning? Then he thought, if I refuse the coffee, the Minister will think I fear him: then he will do nothing for my people. If I am to help them, I must take this coffee. With a steady hand he dropped a lump of sugar into the nearest cup and lifted the cup from the tray. The Minister, then the aides all declined. They watched him raise the cup to his lips and deliberately drink it at a gulp. It was so hot as to disguise all taste.

"Wool, dairy produce—now we come to the point." The Minister gave him a knowing look. "Those wealthy shepherds must bring in quite a tidy profit. Especially when you can count, and they can't." Ghazan flashed angry eyes. "Admit it—why not? We have to make what we can. But those flocks you have milked quite long enough. Now it is our turn."

Ghazan was studying his own reactions to the coffee, and held himself in. "Every spring taxes are paid."

"According to Turki arithmetic. I prefer the Persian variety. It puts less emphasis on subtraction." He looked round at his aides, who smiled obediently.

"Send your own men to count," Ghazan invited.

"In the hills? The hills offer too good a hiding place. We shall count them ourselves—on our own ground."

"Their bones you'll count, if my people are settled."

Almost with admiration the Minister said, "How tightly you cling to your golden fleeces!"

All the time Ghazan was assessing his own feelings. He could detect the stimulus of caffein, nothing else. The harmless coffee seemed to make the Minister suddenly harmless. Conscious of a new upsurge of strength, he answered again with spirit:

"Not mine, but theirs, ours, Persia's. Why divide our goods, set one against another: when we all stand or fall together, on the same stretch of land? The money from wool and milk which the Falqani keep—do you, with your new wealth, begrudge it?"

"I begrudge every last tuman," said the Minister coolly. "I shall comb the coarsest hair from the thinnest goat, squeeze the last drop of milk from dry udders. It takes many drops of milk to buy a gun or a plane, yet guns and planes Persia must have. Too long she has been humiliated."

With this issue Ghazan had already come to grips. Unhesitatingly he answered, "If you seek strength, why decree weakness? How many times have the tribes rallied to drive off invaders? The tribes are Persia's strength. And their strength comes from the hills, which swell down the flanks of Persia like rippling muscles. If those muscles grow flabby and fail, what use are armaments? And so, I claim, the national interest demands you reverse the decree."

"You talk very big for a shepherd," the Minister taunted. "But your views are still those of a single individual, while this decision has been taken in consultation with experts. One man must go for the good of many."

Ghazan glowered. Though he considered it irrelevant and unfair, he met the objection. "You pit numbers against me! But I too can call on numbers. I speak for every one of the tribes: Lurs, Kurds, Baluchi. Their fate is implicit in mine. The best blood, the marrow."

The Minister drew in his lips and nodded with studied surprise. "This is most interesting. Self-appointed leader of all the hordes—yet you wonder we tell you to go!"

"The ambitious see ambition everywhere. I ask only to serve Persia. With my people on the hills I would stay as a camel-herd."

"But you prefer to lead—not one tribe but all—and to threaten. The massed ranks of billy-goat horns—I must confess I do not find myself trembling in my shoes." He looked round at the listening guests, then with a deliberate motion handed his glass, empty of vodka, to an aide. "And now, if you will excuse me, I have other important matters awaiting."

He turned to go, but Ghazan moved with him, holding his eye.

"You still have not answered me," he charged.

"Since you seem to have a weakness for cant phrases, let me answer like this. You will serve Persia best by ceasing to serve her, love her most by leaving."

Ghazan threw in his last reserves of passion. "Your Persia, perhaps: a monkey on a stick mimicking a mode. I take my stand on another Persia, which for seven centuries my fathers served: older and more enduring. A thread with seven hundred strands—that cannot be snapped with blunt words. When your guns are a heap of rust and the last drop of oil has burned itself out, your ragged children will sigh for the lost hills, the lost tribes. And your name will be cursed with Omar's."

175

"And you, I suppose," the Minister jeered, "are the new Ali. How holy you have become!"

"My people's cause is no less just than Ali's."

The Minister drew up his shoulders and again made to go.

"Will you shrug away a hundred thousand lives?" Ghazan exclaimed.

The Minister turned from the listening guests with a scowl. For a very long time he wrestled with Ghazan's eyes, but he could not throw them. Finally he asked in an irritable tone. "What is it you want?"

"I have told you. Justice. A fair hearing."

A long silence followed. Ghazan saw anger now as well as dislike in the Minister's face. But when he spoke, his voice was devoid of emotion. "I tell you what I will do. I will appoint a commission of five members to examine your case."

Surprise held Ghazan silent. Had he made his point after all?

"A commission?" at last he echoed. "With power to decide?"

"They will have no power. But they will make a report, which will be available to both of us."

Ghazan collected his thoughts. "Who will the members be?"

"Impartial, well qualified men. If their findings are favourable to you, I will reverse the decree. Surely nothing could be fairer than that?"

Ghazan thought to himself, once my case is down in black and white, put to the test of reason, an impartial commission cannot help but see its justice.

"Do you agree?" asked the Minister.

"Very well. I accept the idea of a commission."

"Then submit a memorandum tomorrow to the Minister of Court— stating your case."

He turned away to his aides, while Ghazan stepped back among the other guests. He was well pleased with the interview. He felt he had accomplished something at last. The chatter and frivolous laughter no longer jarred on him, but he had no reason for staying. On the contrary, as he made for the door, he noticed Madame Akemi in mauve satin talking to a red-headed foreigner. She saw and signalled to him. He smiled distantly, changed direction and quickly left the palace.

On the drive back he went over the Minister's arguments. Money, not for itself, but to give Persia weapons. These were already obsolete and, anyway, settlement would not yield sufficient money. How could intelligent men like the Minister fail to see that? Remembering other conversations in Teheran, Ghazan decided that blinding nationalism could believe anything it wanted to believe.

Twenty minutes later he was discussing events with Kazem. Kazem was very hopeful. Several commissions had sat that year—it was the latest fashion—and had issued surprisingly independent reports. The names of members were never announced for fear of pressure and bribery, but he might be able to learn them.

With Kazem's help Ghazan composed a memorandum. Giving seventeen reasons why his exile was against the national interest, he claimed that the Government had overstepped its powers and that the decree was invalid. Next morning he submitted the document to the Minister of Court, who would himself deliver it to the commission. On his return he said to Kazem:

"I have done everything I possibly can. My case is just. I have only to wait for the decree to be reversed."

Days passed with not a word of the commission. Eagerly Ghazan scanned the papers, hoping for news, for at least some support. He read long editorials advising the new Government to pursue the path of progress, while avoiding the precipice of precipitancy, to sweep the country clean of corruption, without changing the broom of temperate bristles, to adopt all that was best in foreign thought without disowning Islamic ideals. But not a word, editorial or otherwise, hinted at his presence in the capital. The muzzle of censorship gripped tight.

Inquiries to the Minister of Court were deftly parried. Summer moved towards its zenith. Even in Shemran the long days were stuffy and thunderous. The rooms in Kazem's house were large, but to Ghazan they seemed narrow cells. He waited restlessly, like one who having long walked barefoot now sits wearing shoes that pinch.

It proved almost impossible to inquire by telephone. Either the line was out of order, or a wrong number was given, or, when he was being put through to the right extension, the call was cut off. Almost every day he was obliged to drive down and seek news in person. On June the fourth an inquiry to the Ministry of Court elicited the reply that the appropriate person to consult was the Chief of Staff—an unexpected and sinister development. No one could explain how the matter had come into army hands. Inquiries to the Ministry of War were also averted, this time by an aide. A week's delay at the very most, he promised. But the week passed without news and Ghazan began to grow very angry.

From a friend in the Ministry Kazem learned that certain vital but unnamed documents had been mislaid. No announcement would be made for a month. But just as earlier optimistic forecasts had proved wrong, so with this pessimistic one. On June the twentieth Ghazan received a note signed by a colonel on behalf of the Chief of Staff asking him to present himself at the Ministry of War: the findings of the commission would then be announced.

At four o'clock on June the twenty-first (by Persian reckoning, the first day of Tir, the fourth solar month) Ghazan drove down to the Ministry and gave his name, which was telephoned and approved. A private soldier led him into a courtyard, where a small antiquated Skoda tank with a broken gun stood in the centre of beds of pansies; up a stairway on the wall of which hung a trophy-like mosaic of daggers and muskets, to the quarters of the Chief of Staff. Here the colonel of his letter received him and with obvious relish announced that the Chief of Staff was engaged in conference, and would he mind walking across to the building opposite where an officer was waiting to receive him.

The officer proved to be a mere captain, but Ghazan was so eager for news that he swallowed this studied insult. He was a lanky, gloomy-faced young man, with sad nervous eyes. He raised a feeble smile, which fluttered like a flag at half-mast, but when he saw Ghazan's expression quickly lowered it. He asked Ghazan to sit down on the other side of the bare wooden desk, and after the formal politenesses and a recapitulation took out a file, from which he began to read the findings:

"In view of the fact that the new Persia has taken its place proudly among the great progressive nations, the presence of armed bands represents an anachronism which cannot be tolerated. His late Majesty Reza Shah took effective action which the War obstructed and in some cases undid. It has been decided, therefore, to appoint a senior military officer to fulfil his late Majesty's plans and bring the lawless tribes to order. The first tribe to be settled will be the Falqani."

Ghazan clenched his teeth and tapped his fingers angrily on the desk. This was the first official confirmation of settlement.

"It is undesirable," the captain continued, "for the present Ilkhan to remain with his people, and since his presence elsewhere in Persia would induce his tribe to resist efforts for their betterment, it has been decided that Ghazan Falqani shall be expatriated.

"Ghazan Falqani has submitted a memorandum stating that under his leadership raiding has ceased, no provocative action has been taken against the army, and that his people pay annual taxes. He pretends that his exile would be not only unjust but unprofitable to the régime by promoting disunity and resentment. He also claims that if settlement is to follow, the Falqani will suffer sickness and famine, as they did before the War."

The captain paused and moistened his lips. He glanced anxiously at Ghazan. The paper began to tremble ever so slightly in his well-manicured fingers.

"To these points it is answered first, although the Falqani claim to have abandoned raiding, there is no guarantee that they will not resume it. The rising nine years ago is recalled, foiled in time by the Shiraz brigade. Secondly, if relations with the army have improved, this is entirely due to the army's forbearance and strength. Thirdly, tribal numbers have probably been underestimated, and taxes paid are believed to be less than those due.

"As for the exile of Ghazan Falqani, the charge of injustice is misdirected, since every care is being taken for his welfare abroad; as for tribal resentment, an army colonel will ensure that the tribe acquiesces in this scheme for their betterment. Regarding welfare, careful plans have been made to protect health and provide arable land. It is therefore unnecessary to interfere with the decree of exile, which becomes effective after the autumn migration."

Ghazan felt cold, numb with cold. The sun had fallen. Glaciers of ice crashed through his world, blasting mountains, obliterating gardens. Nothing escaped, nothing would be the same again.

"It cannot be true." His words came in a whisper.

"That is the message I have been charged to deliver."

Slowly Ghazan came to himself. One by one, he considered the implications, then turned his gaze on the sad-eyed captain, the uniform. He felt a violent desire to know more, to find and come to grips with his enemy.

In a voice cold with indignation he asked, "Who were the members of the commission?"

The captain contracted his brows. "I am naturally not free to disclose their names."

Something in his tone, a timid smugness, roused Ghazan to even wilder fury. He must discover who had concocted those lies, who were depriving him of his heritage.

"I have a right to know," he said, rising. "I demand to know." He banged his fist on the desk.

Like a squid the captain ejected a defensive screen, "All I can do is record any objections. These will be considered and if necessary answered in due course."

By the same impartial commission. Anger rushed ahead like a rabid dog. As Ghazan approached him, the captain rose and retreated to the far wall. Ghazan seized and began to shake the captain's shoulders. He was outraging every form of politeness, but he cared nothing. Let him be a Falqani again. The captain wobbled, absolutely without muscle, and the three stars on each shoulder began to clatter.

"Tell me," Ghazan said, no longer loudly, but thrusting the words in like a dagger, holding the captain's eyes, trying to pierce the hierarchy behind them. But fear stiffened the captain.

"How dare you lay hands on an army officer? I shall report this. There will be serious consequences."

Ghazan took him by the throat. "Tell me."

The uniform fell, laying bare the white skin.

"I don't know," the captain whispered. It was a plea rather than a statement.

Ghazan thought, Why does he say that, why not "I can't tell; I'm forbidden to tell"? Surely he must know, and yet he seemed to be speaking the truth.

"You do know, and you're going to tell me."

Then Ghazan caught a look in the sad eyes which was not merely fear: the furtive look of one who hides a secret. What secret? Suspicion flashed and went out: no, too outlandish. He held the man tighter, wondering what to do next. Again suspicion flashed and this time caught fire. A great new doubt rose and awed him, so that he put his next question almost solemnly.

"Did the commission ever meet?"

The sad brown eyes closed. Ghazan tightened his grip on the smooth white throat, squeezing out the truth.

180

"Was there a commission at all?"

The brown eyes opened with an appeal which Ghazan rejected. Then the whole face went to pieces. A word escaped the white throat, mangled, almost indecipherable. But Ghazan understood it: it meant "No". Something seemed to strike him in the breast, spinning him over and over; then after the moment of shock a dull ache, growing, spreading through his mind.

"Tell me more," he said flatly.

It was easy now. The dam had been breached, and the captain was prepared to pour out all he knew.

"For your ears only," he whined. Ghazan reassured him, at the same time relaxing his grip.

"The Chief of Staff opposed a commission. He went to the cabinet. Bargaining must have been done. Orders were given that the commission had met in secret. But in the original document handed to me the question of taxes was not answered. I took it to my colonel and asked whom to consult. The colonel told me the idea of a commission had been abandoned—the Chief of Staff had refused interference from civilians, even from the Minister of War. He wrote out the answer about taxes. The colonel said no one outside Headquarters must know."

Ghazan raised a hand to his eyes. A pawn between intriguers—this was the justice for which he had impatiently waited. He cursed himself for a fool, gullible even when he knew it was rash to trust. The captain, more confident now, was watching him closely. Ghazan hated the sight of him.

"Tell your Chief of Staff that the Ilkhan of the Falqani is not accustomed to treatment like this. He will couch his reply in action, not words."

He flung out the threat, turned on his heel and left the room. Why had he yielded to that last flourish? Nothing but weakness—but that was how he felt now, and tired too: the crumpled handkerchief of a conjuror.

Eyes on the ground, incapable of consecutive thought, Ghazan walked back to his car. He told his driver to hurry, but in the heavy evening traffic the car was held up several times, once in a square Ghazan had not previously traversed. Moodily he stared out of the window. His eye fell on a statue of a man in uniform, mounted on

181

horseback. It held his attention, for human effigies were foreign to the Muslim creed: no man, the saying went, was great enough to strut in triumph over his own bones. He asked the driver who it was.

"That?" he said with a touch of awe. "That's the old man—Reza Shah."

Ghazan recalled, then, that several statues in Teheran and elsewhere had been erected by Reza Shah himself. He mused on this during the drive back.

With Kazem, Ghazan analysed this final development. One thing clearly emerged. It had been found profitable at the highest level to sacrifice even the pretence of justice. Kazem guessed the army had gained its way by agreeing to let government officials share in collecting Falqani taxes. Ghazan pushed distrust still further. The commission, he thought, was an empty promise to bridge that awkward moment at the palace. But no amount of explanation offered an escape. Kazem said bluntly that, with the Shah, Army and Government united, the decision was unchallengeable.

"Unchallengeable, yes, but for a different reason." Ghazan's voice was unusually solemn. He rose and stood over his cousin with gleaming eyes. "At last, Kazem, I have discovered my hidden enemy. His name is on everyone's lips. He is taken for granted, and so at first I did not recognize him. A man of iron will, with boundless energy and ambition. I should like to grapple with him, to kill him. But I cannot." He paused and said bitterly, "My enemy is already dead."

"I don't understand."

Loud and deep Ghazan exclaimed: "Dwarfed in the shadow of a statue, every one of them. The statue of a mounted warrior. The statue of Reza Shah. Reza Shah is dead, but it is he who rules Persia from his grave."

He walked to the window and looked fiercely down on the city spread out below. Then he turned and again stood over Kazem.

"Reza Shah is the hidden king—black on a black square. No one is strong enough to reverse his decisions. No one is strong enough even to prevent their fulfilment. And the irony is this. Because he ended his life in exile, the evil he planned will never end. A tyrant martyr! Who can resist that combination of power?"

Muttering and gesticulating, he walked the length of the room, then raised his arm in sudden exasperation. "Oh for my father's age! I should have checked that will, toppled the Cossack from his horse with the battering hooves! I was born too late, and now he has ordered my exile."

With a moan he returned to the window. There he stood gazing intensely, like a man, on the eve of a lifetime's parting, memorizing the face of the girl he loves.

A long silence was broken by Kazem. He spoke with unusual tenderness. "In my heart I never believed you would reverse the decree. And only now do I see the consequences. It is not you only, Ghazan, but Persia's soul which has been sentenced to exile. If that is lost, our country as she now is will cease to exist. A colour will fade forever from the spectrum."

Ghazan listened moodily. "Yet the facts are past dispute. I have tried every possible way."

"It is true," Kazem agreed with conviction. "You have left nothing undone. Nothing."

For a long while Ghazan stood thinking, head in his hands. Another will stronger than his: that was a dilemma he had never faced before. The inevitable: one could not resist the inevitable. It was a word which recalled his boyhood days in Shiraz, long discussions with his old teacher: the order of syllogisms and prayer. He turned with sudden resolution.

"To stay here is useless. I'll return to Shiraz."

"Stay a while longer, Ghazan," he cousin urged.

"No, I must leave at once—tomorrow."

Kazem looked at him curiously. "What calls you to Shiraz?"

"I want to consult the mullah Mahdi. Direct counteraction has been tried and failed. The mullah is a saintly man. He may know other remedies."

CHAPTER TWELVE

GHAZAN found his old teacher sitting in one of the arcades off the courtyard of the Great Mosque in Shiraz. He wore a long sleeveless square-cut cloak of camel hair and a white turban. As Ghazan approached, he looked up from the manuscript he was reading. Ghazan saw dark eyes half-hooded by heavy lids, a curved nose, sharp as a prow for breaking unknown seas, a dry thin toothless mouth: a face neither beautiful nor ugly; a shade, rather, translucent of very bright light. He seemed surprised and pleased to see his old pupil—they had not met for three years—and gave him a place on the rug. For a while they spoke of general subjects: times were still very difficult, the mullahs' power everywhere infringed. He had been ill with arthritis and could now only walk with support.

"My grandson," said the mullah, "has become my mainstay."

He smiled at a lad sitting quietly beside him, heedless of his elders' conversation.

"You have taught him already to meditate!"

"Alas, no," the mullah replied gravely. "He would be playing if I let him." He looked up at the antique ceiling. "But this building is crumbling. If he runs about, he shakes down plaster and loosens the turquoise tiles. Once they fall, where shall we find money to repair them?" With a bony hand he patted the boy's pale cheek. "It does him no harm to learn to be still. And you, Ghazan Khan, do you find time to be still?"

It was a favourite question, and Ghazan found himself answering with one of the mullah's sentences. "Not very often. But the turning earth sees new constellations, and we perhaps see new facets of our Beloved."

"May be," murmured the mullah, studying his visitor closely.

Then Ghazan said that he was soon likely to be exiled; that he had come to him, as teacher and friend, to find the meaning of this threat, and perhaps a remedy.

"The Ilkhan of the Falqani—can he be exiled?" the mullah asked sharply.

"So it appears." And he went on to explain the turn of events.

Before he had half-finished, the old man flushed and dropped his eyes. Ghazan, by a change in the density of the silence, believed he was frightened, even angry that his powerful and generous protector should be threatened. More than astonished, Ghazan was disappointed. Perhaps as a boy and during long absences he had idealized his master. Then he thought, I am unfair; wisdom is like perfume: the bottle must be protected.

"How must you view this exile?" the mullah repeated Ghazan's question in a dry tone. "You know very well, so why do you ask?"

"Perhaps to hear it from your lips. From the lips of one with authority."

But he doubted his own words now. Prolonging his boyhood attitude of unquestioning trust, he had come as though to an oracle and found a poor, withered man, wise but human. Even though the mullah might be actuated only by a search for truth, Ghazan could never positively know that. So the interview shifted to quite a different plane: Ghazan faced his master as an equal.

The mullah said indifferently, "What is exile to the selfless man? A Sufi can worship as well in one country as in another."

Ghazan looked at his master in dismay. With deep feeling he said, "To me exile means living death. I have known it once. I hated my years in Lausanne."

The mullah flipped the pages of his manuscript with a disparaging gesture.

"You felt homesick. Any boy would."

"Very homesick: though that is not what I dread now. I longed for our hard bare hills, for friendship based on the same dreams, yes, for my old teacher. I lived in Persia by proxy, in the poems of Hafiz and Saadi, in my memories, longing for a miracle."

His school in Lausanne counted eighty boys from a variety of countries. French was meant to link them but served only to emphasize his different values. The subjects he liked to discuss—his people, his family, his horses and greyhounds, Islam—even the masters shunned as though indecent. The other boys liked him but were ashamed to show it, for they despised the East. They called him the Gipsy. For his part he had found himself, as it were, paddling in the shallow end of life. The only lesson to arouse his enthusiasm was biology. He could still remember his excitement when he put his eye to a microscope for the first time, and within a leaf discovered a whole new world.

Through his fingers the Mullah passed a rosary of gleaming yellow topazes, ninety-nine of them, one for each of the divine names.

"And a miracle happened," he said impassively.

In the same intense tone, Ghazan continued, "Reza Shah was forced to abdicate. I booked my passage back for the end of term. One by one I tore off the leaves from my calendar, until the last day of all, when the annual sports were held on the lake. I remember so well that last day. I won a swimming race—the hundred-metre free-style. I heaved myself, dripping, out of the water, and walked to the dais. There the headmaster handed me a silver-plated cup. I took it but I didn't really want it."

The mullah eyed him sharply. "Why not?"

"It was merely one more thing, one more fact. I had too many facts already. I wanted to understand the meaning of life. And the silver-plated cup was all I brought back from Switzerland. Gradually I came to see its significance. They had taken my single-mindedness, buried my truths with their truths, so as to be almost indistinguishable: then handed me a trophy to place on the tomb."

"I don't understand you," the mullah said, stirring uneasily.

"Don't you see, I could no longer accept unhesitatingly my own instincts and habits and traditions. For instance, I grew up with two beliefs about shooting stars which the tribe holds simultaneously: that they are human lives passing away, and that they are arrows fired by divine command at demons who mount on each others' shoulders to see what is happening in the seventh heaven. In Lausanne I was told they were insignificant pieces of stone, that their light was energy transformed by their collision with the earth's atmosphere. This I accepted, but up in the Zagros when a star falls I still pray for a departed soul."

The mullah began to show signs of sympathy.

"I think I see now. You could no longer be an unquestioned authority to yourself?"

Ghazan nodded. "Yet that was my new rôle with the tribe. You understand now why I hate those years abroad? Because they are still with me, still affecting me daily."

"You were a boy then. Impressionable. Now exile would trouble you less."

186

Ghazan's face clouded. "No, not less," he replied with conviction. "A lifetime would bring total eclipse. Sun above moon, and darkness on the earth. Total darkness." His voice sank to a whisper. "I fear to lose my own self."

The mullah caught at the words. For the first time he spoke with feeling. "Ah, but that is precisely what you must do. All pain, all evil come from the self." He fixed Ghazan with stern eyes. "I know you respond to images, so I will put what I mean in an image. A lover knocks at the door of the Beloved, and a voice from within inquires, 'Who is there?' 'It is I,' says the lover. Sharp comes the reply: 'This house will not hold me and you.' The door remains closed, and the dejected lover finds his way to the wilderness. He fasts, and weeps, and prays in solitude for a long time, then returns to knock again at the door. The Voice asks, 'Who is there?' 'It is you,' replies the lover. The door is opened. The lover and the Beloved are face to face."

Ghazan pondered this for some minutes. "In exile," he at last replied, "I shall lose all sight of the door. It won't be a clean, total loss for greater gain, but a muddle of many parts, disjointed. You remember, before I left, I seriously thought of becoming a dervish. I wanted to remain in the world, but follow a course of discipline and prayer—as the saying goes, in order to rise above myself. You taught me the rudiments. But abroad the thread was frayed. The dervish's ideals seemed slightly absurd. I returned with my intention weakened, but not quite dead. It would be easier if it were dead. But it still wags a feeble tail."

The mullah bowed his head, his lips moved as though in prayer He seemed to lower a pail into a deep well. When he looked up his expression was coldly austere.

"Have you ever made the pilgrimage. Either to Mecca or to Meshed?"

"Never."

"Why not do so now?" the mullah continued persuasively. "Go to Meshed as a simple pilgrim, in utter poverty: be alone as much as possible. Let the difficulties of the journey speak. Try and learn on the way and at the shrine the meaning of what is happening to you. For I see you are no longer a disciple to obey my words without question."

So the mullah, too, had sensed that change in their relationship, and

187

perhaps been hurt by it. Ghazan felt angry with himself, but seeing no anger in the mullah's eyes, his own passed. Then he turned to the idea of pilgrimage. It made little appeal.

"I who am forever journeying—must I embark on yet another?"

The mullah's tone was scrupulous. "If you are to be exiled, it is well that you should have performed this obligation. Later it would prove impossible. And by praying on the way you will come to see the wisdom behind this decree."

Ghazan was aware of the white turban wound, circular fashion, like a huge white cupola above the mullah's head, lending his words solemnity. It seemed right that an impasse at the human level should be raised to the spiritual. But, at this crucial moment, how was he to spend several weeks going to the far side of Persia and returning?

"I remember," continued the mullah, "my own pilgrimage to Mecca. Months I spent on the way, then the joy of kissing the black stone: focal point of so many minds, so many prayers. A kiss of betrothal. The stone was worn hollow with kisses. I met a tailor there who had set out penniless from Taourir in Morocco. He had left as a youth and spent seven years on the way. He had taken a wife and had three sons—all on the long pilgrimage, for he was poor and worked to travel—so that there were five who could claim the title of Hajji. He was delaying his journey back. He thought of it as a departure, not a return. Mecca was the centre: home. No matter how fleeting your visit to Meshed, you can experience the same reorientation."

He paused and looked closely at Ghazan. "Your old ideals, do you still value them?"

"The spirit of the dervish?"

The mullah nodded assent.

"I still believe in poverty, I suppose. We live, all of us, the simplest life. And the lessons you taught me I try to apply. Without much success," he added regretfully. After a pause he said, "One in particular I shall always remember." His eyes flashed and he spoke the words as though they were holy: "'Look at the earth that you may know yourself. It will reveal you to yourself, because you are earth and to earth you will return.'"

The mullah repeated his words.

"Yes, there is wisdom in that. But have you learned it, Ghazan?" Have you stripped away the hard layers of self?" He paused doubtfully. "I wonder. Otherwise would you be here, kicking against the pricks?" and the mullah softened his words with a smile.

"I am not simply myself," Ghazan protested. "If I were, perhaps there would be peace for me. I am also the one on whom five noughts depend: a hundred thousand people. Good people, who deserve a devoted leader. Only I can protect them from persecution."

"Alas, Ghazan," the mullah said sadly, "you still think in human terms."

When he heard this, Ghazan sensed an unbridgable gulf. How could this townsman understand, this greybeard who had breathed only the dust of books, so that he was scarcely more than a speaking book? He hid his pique, but again the mullah must have felt it.

"You think I theorize: isn't that so? But what if your tribe were wiped off the earth—your tribe and the whole of Persia too: would that detract one unit from the power and beauty of the Beloved?"

Suddenly crimson-cheeked, Ghazan exclaimed, "But I love my people—surely one love cannot conflict with another?" He searched the mullah's eyes, then asked in a defiant whisper, "Would you have me acquiesce in my people's destruction?"

The mullah frowned. "You put the question badly. Is it destruction to be released from this world, to find that unity with the Beloved for which we were made?"

Ghazan shifted his ground. "I don't mean only physical death—but degradation, spiritual and moral. They will be stripped of their treasure—the rigorous day-to-day life under God's sky which unites them. They will be settled and fall to quarrelling, idleness, confusion of loyalties."

The mullah made a circle of his topazes, and scanned them as though they were the years of Ghazan's life. "Can you be certain the future holds that? But even so you must resign yourself."

Ghazan winced like a thoroughbred colt as the steel curb crushes its velvety mouth, and the leather martingale bows its neck. He was suddenly aware of his hard muscles, and deep chest: all the possible actions which he carried like unborn children. He drew himself up.

"Was I given the power of choice only to choose to yield it?"

"Yes, Ghazan. That is what you must do. And the only real suffering lies in hesitating to yield it."

As he pondered the mullah's words, a curious image came to Ghazan. When a ewe yeaned a still-born lamb, the Falqani made an incision down the length of its hindquarters and peeled the fleece off the dead body. Then he cut off the front paws near the shoulder, and slit the rear paws. This shirt he put on a living lamb, one of twins of a ewe with insufficient milk to feed both. First the rear legs were inserted, then the head through the opening of the neck, finally the two front paws through the sleeves. Then the disguised lamb was set to the ewe which had lost its own. At first the ewe would sniff warily, then, recognizing its smell, allow the lamb to suck.

I am the second lamb, thought Ghazan, and the mullah is trying to force on me this dead fleece of resignation, to make me a creature half-living, half-dead, with two tails.

"Never," he cried, and the mullah started. He detested noise.

"You were always proud, Ghazan Khan," retorted the old man, catching some of the other's fire. "Up in the mountains, your will unchecked, you have grown prouder still."

"And should not a Khan have a certain pride!" Ghazan was stung. He liked to think of himself as stripped of temporal ties, and this old man would prove him subject to delusion as well as desire! The mullah's cheeks had become grey. Ghazan remembered how he hated "scenes", for, as he used to say, "they rippled the calm pools in which the Friend is mirrored."

"We had better speak of other matters," the mullah suggested shakily. "But think about what I have told you. I have your good at heart. Remember how we studied Rumi in this very arcade: after reading his verses together, were our hearts not linked?"

This appeal to one of his dearest memories softened Ghazan.

"Forgive me for storming. One day perhaps I shall recognize your words as true." The phrase, struck out in appeasement, resounded. "Could it be that every age has its own truth? Your grandson, for instance: he must forge a self before he can think of losing it. Others there are who must reassemble their scattered selves."

He pondered this notion. The mullah's counsel of resignation he could not wholly cast adrift. It was made fast to a mooring dug in at low tide: in childhood; perhaps earlier still, seven centuries ago when the Falqani embraced Islam. He must dive to grapple with the mooring chains. And he must dive alone.

"I shall go to Meshed," he said quietly. "Pray that my footsteps make a straight and continuous line."

The mullah gave an approving nod. "You will not regret this, Ghazan. A privileged opportunity you—the Ilkhan—have, of showing perfect resignation by resigning your rights, your title, your possessions: all that you value: in a single heroic gesture." Reading Ghazan's face, he continued more discreetly, "I shall give you a letter to a mujtahid at the shrine. He will be pleased to guide you. He and I studied theology there before you were born. And on your return don't forget to come and see me."

Ghazan said he would.

"I make a further suggestion. After the noon prayer a few men gather under my direction to chant zikrs. Today will you join them?"

Ghazan agreed. Supporting himself on his grandson's shoulder, the mullah slowly rose and tottered to one of the adjoining halls.

Presently from the wooden-fretted balcony of an adjoining minaret the muezzin called the faithful to prayer. Ghazan went out to the courtyard, from the shadowy arcades to a dazzling sun. In the brown sluggish stream which lazed through the flagged yard he washed his face, his arms, the parting in his black hair, his right leg and foot, then the left. He passed a little of the weedy water over each. With a single light thrust of his muscular thighs he rose and stood towards Mecca, his hands open on each side of his face, concentrated, intense. "Allahu akbar," he said. God is most great. Then he recited the opening chapter of the Koran. He bowed from the hips, straightened up, knelt down and prostrated his forehead to the ground. He sat back on his haunches, then prostrated himself a second time. This first "bowing" done, he rose and repeated the movements twice, ending with a final prayer.

Afterwards, he went to the bare hall of unadorned brown brick, where seven men of different ages were gathered. Some seemed bazaar porters, one a student, another a shopkeeper. They had removed their hats and jackets. On his arrival they silently divided into two ranks on either side of the mullah. At a signal from the mullah they began to exclaim, steadily and eagerly, the first lines of a hymn. Not for ten years had Ghazan participated in these Sufi rites, but he recognized the music and soon recalled the words. The exclamations slowly rose to a chant, and the tempo increased until in a burst of frenzy the stanza ended.

Regaining their breath the men knelt in a circle on the earthen floor.

"Subhana 'llah—Glory be to God."

"Alhamdu li- 'llah—Praise be to God."

"Allahu akbar—God is most great."

Thus they chanted, with a violent movement of the head over the left shoulder, then back over the right, at first slowly, then quicker. Ghazan's mind stood apart, a curious spectator, aware that the movements were designed to dizzy his gaoler senses and free the soul; aware, also, of artifice. A frond stirring on knotted pines, the silent coiling of a snake: he preferred these to turn the lock.

But soon Ghazan was caught up in the rhythm. Words: the same tattoo of teeth, throat and tongue which that morning had served to express exactly his desires, mood and character, now, repeated in unison, beat his own retreat, brought anonymity, dissolution. He and the men beside him, separate coins, were melted down in the goldsmith's cruset; the inscription, value and face on each disappeared as they merged in a single votive crown.

They chanted until their voices grew hoarse and sweat stood out on their brows. The words lost themselves in each other, their panting breaths were one breath: they were driven to the limits of endurance. At last the mullah raised his hands.

"He lives! He lives! God lives!"

The new cry they repeated at first slowly, inclining the body to the ground, then faster, until all stood up. Each placed his arms on his neighbours' shoulders and turned round the room with a tripping step, crying exultantly now, "He lives! God lives!" Soon Ghazan could no longer think at all, as his lungs strained to quicken the chant, which carried him finally to his prize: the last silence, when he hovered and glided like a hawk high, high above the small, insignificant earth, almost in heaven.

CHAPTER THIRTEEN

GHAZAN decided to make the pilgrimage an act of penance: to go on horseback, with only one servant, directly to Meshed—across the great salt desert. He had heard this was a difficult route, seldom attempted, least of all in midsummer. He wrote a letter outlining his plans, instructing a servant to present it in person to Tughril. Then he summoned Ahmad and told him to prepare for a cross-country journey of three weeks. Ahmad listened, first astonished, then indignant.

"But, Ghazan Khan," he protested, "we have no pack-animals."

"Our own two horses will carry enough."

"If we eat like sparrows," Ahmad murmured to himself. "And where's your escort?"

"We need none."

"The Ilkhan of the Falqani without an escort!" Ahmad looked as if he had seen a prodigy.

"The Ilkhan has become a pilgrim. Take two goatskins, some rice and dates, with barley for the horses."

The first few days of their journey followed an easy pattern. They rode north-east, off the road, from sunrise to noon, then halted at a teahouse for bread and eggs, remaining in the shade of willows for two or three hours, then continued riding. Tension, danger and intrigue in Teheran had tired Ghazan, and he welcomed the restful days. At nightfall they halted at a caravanserai, where Ahmad lit a fire, fed the horses and prepared a meal of rice. Sometimes he borrowed a kettle and stewed tea he had brought unbidden. His high spirits and good humour made him an excellent travelling companion. He was proud to be accompanying the Ilkhan on a long journey, from which he would return with stories (even if nothing much happened), a reputation and the title Meshedi. He had only a vague idea where Meshed was and of the difficult terrain ahead. One thing still troubled him. He could not understand why they travelled like beggars. The master's humility humiliated the servant. At the caravanserais he boasted that they were pilgrims and that his master was a wealthy lord. As evidence he showed the other travellers Ghazan's fine white mare. That did not convince them. "If your master has a lot of money," they sneered, "why isn't he fat?"

The country became poorer, vegetation dwindled, stretches of desert grew wider and less broken. On the sixth night they stopped in a village between Yezd and Kerman, tumbling into ruin, with no caravanserai. Ahmad wanted to ask for hospitality at the one large house with a garden, but Ghazan said pilgrims must choose a poor lodging. They approached the first man they met, middle-aged but very thin and stooping, hugging a few sticks to his bony arms. When he learned their destination, he invited them to his house.

He led them down an alley lined with the exterior mud walls of courtyards and crude wooden doors, each with a heavy padlock. Through one of these they entered a tiny courtyard where three thin goats and a frail ox lay chewing. Tethering their horses, they entered the mud house: a single room without furniture, a few mud-caked mats on the floor, rags of clothing hanging on nails. A kerosene lamp hung from the ceiling: below sat a woman and three young children, the smallest in her arms.

After an exchange of greetings, the man began to whisper to his wife. Only then, by the light, did Ghazan see that his stoop was a form of hunchback. Ghazan guessed they were speaking of food. The children's bellies were distended and the smallest was coughing. The whispered conversation ended: the man seemed relieved and motioned their welcome. The woman rose.

"She is going to buy bread," he explained.

But no money had changed hands and Ghazan believed she was going to borrow. With a show of unconcern he said, "Don't let her trouble. We have more food than we can easily carry. You will do us a service by sharing it."

Ahmad fetched rice from their saddle-bags. The woman was reluctant to take it, and to save her pride Ghazan made up a proverb: "The rice of pilgrims brings good fortune."

While the woman lit a fire and put water to boil his host talked to Ghazan, squatting on the floor.

"Last year pest and drought ruined the barley. That's why we're a little short."

Ghazan showed sympathy. "And your landlord, is he a just man?"

194

"He is a landlord."

As though to change the subject, he took the youngest child on his knees and rocked him to laughter.

"My son," he said proudly. The other two were girls. All had muddy complexions, as though they ate only mud. Ghazan rumpled the boy's hair playfully.

"A sturdy child: what God wills. How do you call him?"

"His name was Ali. Now we call him Manuchehr."

"You speak in riddles," said Ghazan questioningly.

The hunchback took this for a compliment and chuckled to himself. Then he became serious. "The child has been ill, you see, coughing, forever coughing. An old woman in the village knows about such things. A jinn inside him, she said. Sew up the boy in an ass's skin, she told us, change his name when you take him out: afterwards he will be well. We did this, and so the child is no more Ali, but Manuchehr."

"And it is true the child coughs less," his wife added.

The hunchback wanted to know where his guests came from. Shiraz, some two hundred miles away, was to him remoter than the constellation Jabbar, but he said he knew the place from the poems of Hafiz. He paused to recollect, then recited:

"Shiraz, city of the heart,
God preserve you . . ."

He tried to go on, but remembered only a word here and there. Ghazan waited, then completed the verse for him. Their eyes met. For the first time the hunchback smiled, accepting, welcoming. They had found a mutual friend, buried nearly six hundred years ago, yet still living; they were no longer strangers.

"We shall pay a visit to my uncle the potter. I think you would like that?" The hunchback's voice had become warm, and the tone of pride suggested the potter was a man of consequence.

Ghazan followed down nameless alleys lined with ill-fitting doors along the twisting jube, and entered a dim, small workshop. In the far corner a hole in the floor gave access to a firing-oven; opposite the door stood a bench and stool. A man of about fifty with black hair, his head bent, was turning a pot on a wheel, revolved by his right foot. Nearby stood a youth with short beard, painting flowers

195

on finished pots, while a boy turned a stone to crush minerals for colour and glaze.

"Peace be with you." The greeting was given and exchanged with no interruption of work. The potter's head remained bent. His hands were grey with liquid clay. It ran down his supple fingers to become part of the pot he seemed to be creating out of himself. After turning and modelling, he drew a piece of marked cord from the bench to measure the rim's diameter. Having enlarged it, he measured a second time. Lifting the pot he set it upright on a wooden tray at his left, next to others. He fumbled a little finding a place for the pot.

The painter led Ghazan down steps to a big stone oven, where the glazed clay was fired.

"They remain here fifteen days," he explained. "Like animals: a long gestation, a long life for the pot."

Ghazan lifted one of the smaller bowls, ornamented with green leaves and purple flowers on grey. He examined it admiringly, aware of the workers, grey with clay, in the dim room: straining without pause, like stem and roots, to produce, out of shapeless earth, these symmetrical leaves and flowers. Not fine work, but Ghazan was astonished that anything new should arise from this crumbling village. He had never heard of pottery being made in Southern Persia. Local clay was used, the painter said, and the pots sold only in that village. The flimsy white plates and cups stamped with pink roses for sale in every town came, the painter believed, from a town called Japan. Japan or Baghdad, he wasn't sure which. As he seemed very anxious to make a sale, Ghazan bought the bowl for twenty rials.

With a swirling sound the potter's agile fingers built up a new pot from the base and scooped out the centre. The hunchback explained that his guest was a pilgrim. Only then did the potter lift his head. Ghazan could not help starting. His eyes were like sockets, covered by the lids except for a scar-like seam at the bottom: empty walnut-shells.

The hunchback said, "He has been blind only since winter. He used to have eyes with power. He could make the sick sleep, and often when they woke their sickness was gone."

The potter wiped his right hand on a cloth and stretched it out to find Ghazan's arm. His face turned too, like a sunflower.

"At Meshed," he pleaded, "pray to the Imam that my eyes may see."

Ghazan looked down to the sensitive deputizing hand. Every day since Shiraz he had met blind beggars crying for alms beside little stone shelters outside the villages. Malnutrition and trachoma had deprived them of sight: hundreds of thousand there must be up and down the land.

He tried to show confidence. "I shall. And I am taking with me one of your bowls. Surely you made no finer, even when your eyes were bright."

The potter nodded and repeated his request. Again Ghazan promised.

On the way back the hunchback said with pride and regret, "You cannot imagine how fine his eyes were: almost black, and piercing. They understood more than eyes should do. They blazed too high and burned themselves out. Now they are resting, hidden, dark."

Ghazan turned the bowl over in his hands: a shape without colour in the dark alley, and for a moment knew what it was to be blind.

Back in the house the woman served rice with melon seeds and goat-cheese in a single copper dish. Here not even tea: just the produce of their goats, and perhaps a soup of split peas.

The men ate first, lobbing the food into their mouths with their right thumbs. Afterwards the children and the woman ate with the quick animal movements of the long famished. The poverty oppressed Ghazan: only slightly worse in degree than that of some of his people, but it seemed of a different kind in the mud den—permanent, without hope. He was careful to show no pity: these people lived on their shreds of pride. Instead he belched his approval of the meal and conversed with his host, who now showed no reserve. He remarked that visiting the potter they had passed many houses but few men.

"It is a marvel there are any at all," sighed the hunchback. "Every year the desert encroaches. The tunnels in two of our three qanats are falling. To save them hoops of clay will have to be inserted. But the landlord lives in Teheran and his bailiff won't spend the money. Even in a wet year our bellies are seldom full. An armful of grain to the blacksmith, one to the carpenter, another to the bath-keeper; a tenth of my harvest to the village headman. After the landlord has taken seven tenths, what is left for seed and fodder? Two years ago the bailiff made me sell my share of the crop on the threshing floor at a price he fixed. I had no choice, otherwise he would have withheld water."

"If you owned your land," asked Ghazan, "would you be better off?"

The hunchback pushed out his lips doubtfully. "In the next village the men own their land. Along troop the tax collectors. Each has a little book written on very small pieces of paper in a peculiar style even the headmen cannot read. He's inherited that, like the job. But the point is, when the book was written that village was three or four times as large. The rate is eight in the hundred, so the men still living there pay about thirty. The richer owners entertain the collectors and pay less: the poor make up the difference."

"So they drift away?"

The hunchback shrugged. "It's either that or starving. They sell their oxen for slaughter and go to the towns."

The girls came to show Ghazan their amulets: beads with a turquoise glaze and knotted cord bracelets against the evil eye. The boy had been coughing and crying all evening. First his mother rocked him, then scolded and slapped his cheeks. At last in exasperation she slipped a tiny piece of opium under her thumb nail and inserted her thumb in the child's mouth. As a boy, Ghazan had seen this habit in Gulf villages. If practised to excess, the child was blinded, sometimes killed. This mother's extreme poverty would keep her son from harm.

The hunchback turned down the lamp. They rolled up where they were in blankets. Ghazan lay awake, listening to the child's coughing tail away. Already an addict, he thought. The Ilkhans had kept the Falqani free from opium-taking, which, anyway, was incompatible with so strenuous a life. But in villages like this three-quarters of the aged ate opium three times a day. There was no stamping it out, for Reza Shah had made opium a government monopoly, and its sale brought many millions of tumans annually to Teheran.

Ghazan thought, this is one village I shall never altogether leave. It had re-enacted boyhood memories of settlement. Blindness, sickness, personal slavery—and finally abandonment of the land, a felling of the trees within, spiritual erosion: these lay ahead of the Falqani.

"Learn on the way to resign yourself," his master had said. "Who are you to know what is best? Would you usurp the rôle of Providence?" But, lying awake, listening to parents and children roll and groan in the rough seas of sleep, Ghazan felt only anger and revolt. How could he ever learn to resign his people to this?

CHAPTER FOURTEEN

THEY started again at dawn. The whole family came out to wish them well: Ghazan thanked them warmly and praised their hospitable roof.

"Pray for us at the Imam's tomb," were their host's last words, his shadow stretching crooked on the ground before him.

"And they need our prayers," said Ahmad contemptuously, as soon as they were out of earshot. "All the world is our home. Wherever we choose to pitch our tents. But these villagers are stones, not men. And such sickly children. Why deck them with trinkets? Saffron on mouldy rice!"

They passed the last stalks of barley, a last lonely willow like a colophon: from text to the bare endpapers. The ground was streaked by *kavirs*, thick crusts of salt. Winter rain and snow, descending from the hills in streams, lost themselves in the porous slopes of eroded foot-hills and emerged again at the lowest level of the plain, the water now full of salt, and oozing up to the surface in patches of glittering white, in spring deep as quagmires, but now dry. Beyond stretched a waste of black gravel and irregular expanses of grey shales and sand, red or reddish brown, covering hard rock salt. Clay bluffs reared up at inter-vals, blunted by the prevailing north-westerly wind. From these signs Ghazan calculated they were at the edge of the Dasht-i-Lut, the Naked Desert.

This was the dry heart of Persia, seldom watered by rain-bearing clouds, most of which broke north on the Elburz and west on the Zagros. The furnace-hot simoom which blew in late summer could turn the unwary traveller into a dry and withered mummy; hence the name was sometimes held to signify Desert of Lot. For many days Ghazan and Ahmad could hope to find neither wells nor villages, unless it were ruins lying like wrecks on the bed of what had once, in the cretaceous period, been a great sea. The spouting whale had yielded to one-humped camels, which occasionally crossed in trains, carrying between Meshed, Kerman and Yezd.

They kept direction by the sun. The thud of hooves broke absolute silence. Call of bird, patter of scorpion or lizard, humming insect— these were unknown here. They seemed to lie in the empty palm of an old man's hand. By noon the salt had penetrated the hot air and increased their thirst. They ate bread, travellers' bread, twice-fired, and fed their horses about a pound of barley—bought in the last village— then drank from one of their two full goatskins and gave to the horses. At dusk they could find no fuel and huddled together in the sudden cold. After their evening meal of dates, clarified butter and bread, they searched for a place to sleep—no easy matter, for beneath the sand the solid rock base was segmented into hollows divided by thick walls and covered in parts by upright salt spikes, like a fakir's bed.

On a level clearing Ghazan wrapped himself in his blanket and stretched out. Ahmad sat, not at a distance, but beside Ghazan and, hiding his feet in the blanket folds near Ghazan's shoulders, lowered his body until his head lay at his master's feet.

Ghazan sat up. "What on earth are you doing?"

From the direction of his feet came a mumbled reply. "Protection from the palis."

"The palis?" Ghazan had never heard the word.

"The desert vampire." Ahmad explained, "It attacks men asleep in the desert. It licks the soles of their feet and drinks their blood."

"It's you who seem to be licking my feet."

Ahmad would not laugh. "You don't understand. This is the way to trick it. The palis will turn round and round us and think we're a two-headed man without feet."

Ghazan let him have his way. That night they were not attacked, and next morning Ahmad boasted that Ghazan had a most resourceful servant. During the day he enumerated other terrors of the desert scarcely known to Ghazan. One was the nesnas.

"A cousin of Dilbar," said Ahmad, "was travelling between Shiraz and Bushire. He saw a lamb by the roadside. No one there, so he picked it up and slung it across his saddle. Later he looked round: the lamb had grown so huge that head and tail were dragging along the ground. He had the wit to throw it off, galloped away and escaped with his life. Otherwise . . ." shaking his head, Ahmad hinted at un- speakable horrors.

Then there were "those who are better than we", a circumlocution for "jinns"; malignant spirits who by night, as snakes, black cats or in human form, attacked from wells or ruins. Whistling attracted them: that was the devil's language. Sometimes they would possess a man, and could be driven out by offering bread and salt. Ahmad insisted they must not be harmed; if by ill chance he saw one, Ghazan was to recite the Chapter of the Jinns from the Koran. Each night Ahmad left them propiatory crumbs of food.

"Worst of all," he warned, "is the devalpa. He appears as an old man. 'Take me up on your shoulders,' he'll plead. You must never do that, otherwise long twining legs like snakes will spring from his belly and twist round your neck: and he'll cry, 'You are my slave and must work for me all your life'. There's only one way to get rid of him: make him drunk." Which, as Ghazan remarked, in the present circumstances might prove rather difficult.

As they penetrated deep into the desert, Ahmad claimed to see or hear these beings. His imagination more and more gained control. No longer did he invent droll stories to explain ruins or rock shapes. In the middle of the night the shepherd afraid neither of jackals nor any other tribesman would wake Ghazan, gibbering and pointing at some jinn or ghoul. Ghazan tried to bring him back to earth by speaking of Dilbar and Hussein, but the darkness of desert and sky shouted down his words.

On the fourth day Ahmad became worse.

"Did you hear that?" he suddenly asked.

"There was nothing to hear."

"Yes, I heard it. A voice over there." He pointed south. "It moaned, 'Ahmad, you are heading for danger. Come this way: this is your path.'"

Ghazan explained that given the sun's position, their course must be right.

A little later Ahmad said, "Our betters may be playing with the sun. To them it is an orange-coloured ball. They toss it here and there at will."

This became an obsession. He repeated his claim about the voice. At first Ghazan argued; then, noticing an occasional gleam in Ahmad's eye, an undertone of excited laughter, Ghazan's mouth hardened to a tight line. Unmistakably Ahmad was enjoying his terror, making an orgy of fear.

201

Next morning, their fifth in the desert, Ghazan woke to find Ahmad haggard, his black-bearded face drawn. All night he had been too frightened to close his eyes, and spoke only of jinns. Ghazan had to force him to mount, then spoke of things they could both see, peculiar shaped stones or a stunted tamarisk growing between white streaks of salt. Ahmad sat hunched on his grey horse, silent and white-cheeked. He seemed infected by the mildewed, leprous waste.

Towards midday, without a word, Ahmad put heels to his horse and swung round at a canter southwards. At once Ghazan followed, shouting at him to stop. In three hundred paces Ghazan's faster horse had brought them level. Dropping his reins Ghazan lunged and seized Ahmad by the waist. His servant slipped free with a twist which shook off his hat. They galloped on, manœuvring. Ghazan caught Ahmad by the tunic collar and drew both horses to a trot. Ahmad still struggled wildly. The strain drew his saddle sideways; a cord snapped and the full goatskin of water flopped to the ground. Both riders turned and drew up. The wooden plug had been forced out and water was spurting on to the sand with a gurgling sound. Ghazan leaped off his horse and ran to the fallen goatskin. By the time he had replaced the stopper, the goatskin hung loose and lifeless.

He rounded on Ahmad. "Idiot!" he shouted in fury. "Son of a burned father! Brilliant heir to a long line of asses and goats! Cross the desert without water would you, you camel!"

He called his servant every outrageous name he could think of. Ahmad seemed not to hear. He dismounted and stood staring at the pattern of darker brown, the water's own grave. Kneeling, he grovelled with his finger-tips in the wet sand, trying to save a few drops. Then he buried his face in his hands and sobbed. Beside the slowly shrinking stain a few salt tears fell.

The goatskin on Ghazan's horse was half-empty. Hardly ten mouthfuls remained in the other. With strict rationing they had five days' water for themselves and their beasts—just about enough to carry them across the desert. It would be safer to retrace their steps—Ghazan knew that—but pilgrims could not lightly turn their back on Meshed. He decided to continue.

Visible danger seemed to have shocked Ahmad back to his senses. For hours he rode quietly beside Ghazan. Under the hot sun they were like two pots in the firing-oven. No shadow, not even a fly's. They had forgone their noon drink; soon their mouths were parched. When they spoke, it was always about the lost water.

In the late afternoon Ghazan saw ahead a shimmering, silver-white expanse distinct from the dusty beige sand and the blue sky. Soon trees appeared on the far shore, reflected in its surface. Ahmad saw it too and they agreed it must be an illusion. These occurred even in bare tribal country and Ghazan had already alerted his mind against them.

But as they rode on and still the water shimmered, Ghazan began to succumb to the desire of his dry throat and the evidence of his eyes. They couldn't be distrusted for long: they accurately reflected his clothes and saddlebags, Ahmad and his grey horse. They might be mistaken about a few drops, he argued, but not about this vast expanse. He had heard of no inland lakes, but the desert was unexplored. Unknown water, and if it were fresh! It lay at least two hours away: time to dash in often, feel the cool liquid over his legs, splash it over his dusty hair, wash and drink. They rehearsed how best to enjoy it. But the lake lay further than they had imagined. Finally they marked it by a nearby bluff. Still they talked of water: grey and black as it gurgled out of a newly greased goatskin, the mud-coloured rain which fell near the Gulf, pink water in redstone hills, the bottled tasteless water of Teheran. And their eyes remained fixed on the shimmering undeniable expanse ahead.

They passed the bluff and agreed they must have mistaken their marker, for the lake still lay far. Again they marked the lake. All afternoon they rode through the dusty sand until the sun had sunk almost to the horizon. Suddenly, before their watching eyes, like mist or a rainbow, the lake vanished. Desert on all sides. They had crossed it as the Israelites crossed the Red Sea. At first they could not believe it, then in a rush of disappointment they filled their parched mouths from Ghazan's goatskin.

Ghazan puzzled over the incident. He had seen water and walked over the dry place where water had been. Surely no dew fell in this wilderness. Had he divined an underground lake? Or seen the wet film over his own eyes? And why did he come upon such lakes so un-expectedly, like a dream after many dreamless nights? Yet this had been no dream. And the lakes were never found on uneven ground or tilted: they obeyed all laws but the fundamental law of contradiction. Perhaps the sun-entranced earth could produce water for a time on its surface, just as fakirs could by force of will produce running welts on their skin. Till late he discussed the water with Ahmad. On one point they agreed: these imaginary lakes where they took imaginary baths and drinks were remembered long after draughts of real water; invented to satisfy the thirst of the mind, they endured—as though compensating for their non-existence.

In the next days Ghazan tried to exalt his mind to the object of the pilgrimage, but it showed itself earthbound, insisted on things. Sometimes he saw well-built towns of stone, with towers. No one issued from the gates: he and Ahmad were the only travellers towards them, yet so close did they lie, so threatening in their silence, he instinctively kept his rifle at the ready. They were so dense Ghazan refused to call them mirages. Either they were the ghosts of departed cities, buried under the desert: souls which hovered when no one was near, faded gently before the living intruder and returned when he had passed; or they were the idea of perfect cities, projected by the mind, almost created. Did they fade as his faith in them faltered: could sufficient strength of mind keep them in being: might he ride under the archway and touch with his hands the well-cut stone, the smooth blue faience of mosques?

But they remained illusions. Ghazan was very much confused by them. He thought, if I cannot know even these simple facts belonging to the present, how certain can I be of the still more deceptive future? Exile, even settlement, may somehow turn to good. My fears for the Falqani may be as illusory as these airy cities. And he began to think better of the mullah's counsel.

On the eighth day a sandstorm blew up out of nowhere, breaking the desert silence with a whirling sound and the skidding of grit against salt rock. Earth and sky intermingled; the flat surface became so many moving mountains and it was they who had to be still. Dismounting, they made their horses lie and crouched behind them. Puny things, kneeling for mercy before the hot wind: how different, thought Ghazan, from that saint for whom the simoom was more pleasant than a spring breeze, who stood on burning sand as though on silk or broidered cloths. For himself, he could not rise above his discomfort: howled back curses at the wind. The dust suffocated them and rasped their throats. Into their ears and under their fingernails the burning sand swept, prising their bodies apart. For several hours they lay like this: gasping, dry as cinders, half-buried by the air.

204

The whine softened to a hum, the hum to silence. Stumbling to their feet, they shook grit from hair and beards, gulped a mouthful of water and gave to their horses. The dunes had changed outline, the sand had effaced their tracks and thick dust obscured the sun. Each day they had started with the sun at their right shoulder and after noon kept it behind them to the left. Now they had to guess at their route and, making up lost time, to march under a starless light. Sky and earth were as though still uncreated. Only a grey, all-inclusive void, unchanged when they blinked or drowsily closed their eyes. They were back in the cretaceous period, gliding darkly like small fish at the bottom of the ocean. There was nothing stationary by which to measure movement, and so no time. Only the growing pain where their saddles rubbed and the ache in their jolted backs told them that night must be passing. Again and again they darted expectant looks to the right for a glimmer of dawn, but the grey remained unbroken. At last, morning crept up and ambushed them from behind. In alarm the riders swung round to stare, eyes narrowed, pulses throbbing, at the far glimmer of red.

Red with their blood, it seemed to Ghazan. They had ridden south-west instead of north-east. This mistake would cost them more thirst, perhaps their lives. What could they do? There seemed no way of fighting back. They stood in danger precisely of this nothingness, the naked desert which made all things conform to itself. Why should they be exceptions? Ghazan looked at the brown sand with loathing and fear.

That afternoon their minds no less than their bodies began to suffer from thirst. Ghazan felt a wild urge to spit at the sun, to extinguish it. Ahmad began to chant confused snatches of verses against jinns. Once more he spoke of riding towards the heart of the desert: now Ghazan shared his fear and knew what he was trying to flee. He attached a cord to the bit of Ahmad's slow-stepping horse, and held the end with his own reins.

Next morning, as Ahmad was mounting, his horse sank to the ground. From sheer exhaustion all four legs had buckled. Milk of the Moon was also weak: she hung her head and her eyes were dull. There was nothing for it but to lead the horses and stagger along on foot. The sharp gravel soon tore their cord shoes; their feet dragged naked along the blistering sand, each step an ordeal by fire. Ahmad began to

205

shout for water, then start to scoop up the sand. This tortured Ghazan as much as heat and thirst. It made the journey and its purpose seem idiotic. His throat was so dry, he could not speak the sane phrases which would combat the nonsense. He felt drawn into the delirium. Death, he thought—let that be, if it has to be, but without the preamble of madness.

By the evening of the eleventh day their mouths and throats had become raw flesh lashed by every breath of the salt air. Ahmad raved no longer—he had no more saliva; from time to time he grunted. Head to foot they flopped down on the sand, without fire or food, for they had finished their last dates that morning. Weary from hunger and the long day's march, Ghazan slept soon, but very fitfully. During the night he thought he heard one of the horses neighing.

At dawn he woke to find Ahmad already up. Nearby glowed the embers of a tamarisk fire. Strange, he thought, and strange too that Ahmad eyed him aslant. Then with a start he noticed behind the near shoulder of Ahmad's grey horse a wound, dressed with ashes. He was certain it hadn't been there last night. What could have caused it? He examined the wound: straight and deep, as though a vein had been opened. He turned quickly. Ahmad, who had been watching, dropped his eyes. Tense with suspicion, Ghazan unbuckled the saddle bag and found Ahmad's gourd. Brown with dry blood. He looked in horror at Ahmad, clothes ragged, beard unkempt, blackened by the sun. God forgive us, thought Ghazan, thirst has sent him sprawling down the centuries to this—worse than the worst long-forgotten orgies. He seized Ahmad's shoulder. "Not again—never," he whispered, shaking a fist.

Ghazan plodded on, conscious only of his movement, of the steps which sent his brain burning. No distance separated himself from things. He felt himself crushed into the sand, like a lizard, like an ammonite, and he thought, in death, as in the first unconscious stages of life, perhaps man reverts through the animal and vegetable kingdoms until he attains nothingness. He was astonished that the line of foot-prints gained ground, and wondered whether their apparent progress was not itself a delusion.

Through his dry eyes it became painful to see visions and nightmares struck from the burning sand and his burning brain. He closed his eyes and walked blindly, following the sun like some primitive organism without eyes, yet bound to move towards the light. He had become indifferent to their survival: only this twitching of his limbs continued, which he likened to the nervous spasm of a newly slaughtered sheep. Moments of clearness would intrude, when he sensed his predicament: unbearably intense but short. His breath seemed to him a two-handled saw, pulled this way and that, cutting down the tree of existence.

In one of these lucid intervals he saw what he took to be yet another mirage, a line of figures moving far away across their own direction. He pointed them out to Ahmad, who nodded as if he saw them too. Many times they had stumbled towards figures to find them cairns erected who knew when: but these past experiences were already blurred and did not check similar new ones. They were glad of a destination, even if it cost them dear.

It struck Ghazan that these shapes were odd. They cast no reflection. They moved. They were of different size: some high, long and humped; others lower and thin. A red daub, then a blue on the grey-brown canvas. Presently Ghazan saw the outlines of many camels, riders perched behind the humps, moving north, a long line of words writing their reprieve across the sand.

He felt no joy: only a painful transition to the key of hope. Their steps now had a purpose, but unless they hurried the caravan would pass without noticing them. Two days' fast had weakened their legs and their efforts at running were monstrous. They flung up their arms in grotesque scarecrow gestures, opened full their mouths and lungs and cried no louder than sparrows in the nest. Steadily the caravan filed past. They had not been spotted. So close, yet they had not been spotted. They were nothing, they were dead, they did not exist: this was the proof.

Walking, they could not catch up with the camel train, yet instinctively, like jackals, they followed the tracks, watching the figures seep like water into the desert, sink with all their hopes, with life itself, beyond the horizon. Ghazan wanted to weep. His eyes twitched but, as though pain had exhausted all stores of grief, not one tear came from his dry body. He was an empty coconut, hay, shell of a shellfish, dust: a wisp in the hot wind.

They staggered forward in starts, walking to the limit of their strength, then flopping on their knees to rest. The horizon was bare now except for one black patch. A cairn to mark their grave. As they approached, it bifurcated. Two cairns for two graves. They limped on, from surprise to surprise. One was too high, one too large to be a pile of stones. But this seemed scarcely to matter. Nothing mattered. Presently there could be no doubt at all: the cairns were a man and a camel, stationary. Ghazan waved and cried. The man turned and walked towards them. Ghazan saw eyes, nose and mouth take shape. Reality was too much for him. He fell reeling to the ground.

Ghazan woke lying pillowed on a blanket, a gourd held near his lips by a man's hand. He gulped at it for dear life, then recoiled. He seemed to be sipping fire. He thought with horror, this is another play put on by my mind. He held back, frightened when the gourd was again pressed to his lips. But the hand tipped it and the hand was strong. This time the drops hurt less. After a few mouthfuls the gourd was removed. He began to taste the liquid. Camel's milk, harsh and thin. Not, after all, the long-dreamed of water: but the milk had been water once.

Ahmad lay beside him, revived and drinking too. Other figures crowded round, blocking out the sun. Perhaps it was weakness which made him feel no curiosity about them. He was intent only on what had been enacted within him. He sensed it was important, but he must hurry: already a safety curtain was falling.

The illusions—those he recalled. But later he had been humbled still further. All accretions had been stripped simultaneously from both life and himself. Sensation, reason, will—these were husked, leaving a blind, moving object. And even movement had been declared super-fluous. The last state of all, he had fallen still with a whimper.

"Know yourself"—how often his master had urged him to that. With how many childish experiments he had failed and, failing, merely added brilliance to the hidden jewel. Now at last he did know. And if his knowledge were true of one man, it was surely true of all. Leaf by leaf, like an onion, he had been peeled away, and at the centre, which he had always imagined, held some secret too momentous to be spoken, some beauty too faultless to be gazed on for long, there lay not even a tear.

CHAPTER FIFTEEN

THE camel's milk made Ghazan and Ahmad violently sick. But it had given them sense enough to be conscious of hunger. The camel-herd offered them broiled pulse and dates. While they ate, he explained how he came to find them. He was suffering from dysentery: had risen late and assembled his baggage in a hurry. During the morning cords on one of his camels had slipped: his merchandise was in danger, so he had dropped behind his companions to rearrange the bales and tighten the cords. Anxious when he did not rejoin them, the caravan had turned back.

The camel-herd took an almost proprietary interest in Ghazan and Ahmad. He asked who they were and what they were doing. In reply to the same questions he said the caravan was bound for Meshed with carpets from Kerman and metalwork from Yezd. It comprised two hundred camels and dromedaries, and some forty cameleers and merchants. He offered them two of his camels, and said he would lead the Falqani horses.

The caravan set off. The camel's swaying motion made Ghazan feel sick. He was glad when they halted for the night. Again they ate broiled pulse and fed their horses with the same. The moment they lay down they slept.

Next morning Ghazan woke early, refreshed. As no one seemed astir, he did not rise at once. He lay watching the camels ruminate, musing on yesterday: how, precisely when life had become intolerably agonizing, in no way preferable to death, he had fought most frantically to preserve it.

These thoughts were interrupted when Ghazan saw a figure approach one of the more distant fires, a powerfully-built man. The lower part of his face was veiled, his hands gloved. In one he carried a bundle of twigs, in the other a piece of wood, which he laid with care on the embers. Taking a pace back, he waited for flames, then raised his hands and began to intone. Ghazan could not hear his words. After a few minutes the figure returned to the centre of the camp. Ghazan puzzled over this incident but could make nothing of it.

They set off again at dawn. The camel-herds fell silent: only at night, when the world had shrunk to human proportions, did they talk. To pass the time Ghazan spoke with his neighbour, a proud-faced man of about sixty, riding a finely-harnessed dromedary, who held aloof from the others. He took care to conceal his right hand; later Ghazan saw that it had six fingers, the smallest almost the size of the fifth and drooping a little.

"From where do you ride?" asked Ghazan.

"From Yezd."

"As a pilgrim?"

"No. I trade in metal, not in grace." He spoke with a sing-song drawl like some of the camel-herds. Ghazan took the drawl to be distinctive of Yezd. "For me Meshed is not a holy city."

Ghazan turned in surprise. "How can that be?"

"I am what you call a Guebre," said the merchant with dignity. That is, he practised the ancient religion preached by Zoroaster.

Noticing that the Yezdi was burly and sat high on his saddle, Ghazan put a question at hazard:

"Did you go to the fire this morning?"

"And what if I did?"

"I asked simply to know, not to blame."

Such an attitude was uncommon. The merchant's face softened. "Then it is well that we ride together."

Ghazan had never met a Zoroastrian before. By tactful inquiry he learned that about ten thousand of the Zoroastrian sect lived in Yezd, by far the largest group in Persia. Persecution had driven them to that remote city. Were they still persecuted? Ghazan asked. Not at present, the merchant said, but as a boy he had known persecution. His face clouded and, in a rankling tone, he recalled those days.

"Yellow, brown or grey—our clothes had to be one of those colours. In the town we had to walk, and outside, if we met a Muslim, we had to dismount. The walls of our houses had to be splashed white round the doors; double doors were forbidden and the height of the roof was limited. We had to wear a special shoe, with a turned-up toe, and twist instead of folding our turban. The tax on infidels: that we also had to pay." Now, he added, most of these penalties had fallen into abeyance, but the Zoroastrians were still a people apart.

"My tribe, too," said Ghazan, "are a people apart."

Having heard wild accounts of the Yezdi's religion, Ghazan said he would welcome a statement of its aims, for he believed that each faith contributed its own truths to the larger Truth. At first the merchant seemed unwilling, but learning that his companion was a Sufi, he became less reticent and at last agreed.

"How much," he asked, "do you already know?"

Ghazan said he understood that Zoroaster was their great prophet and had lived more than a thousand years before Mohammed. Their equivalent of the Koran was the Zend-Avesta. He had been told also that they venerated fire.

"All that is true," said the Yezdi approvingly. "Like you, we worship One God. His name is Ahura Mazda, Lord of Wisdom. He created the world and all good things. Sickness, pain and disasters were created by Ahriman, the Evil Spirit. Ahriman continually struggles against Ahura Mazda. We take part in that struggle: each of our good deeds helps towards the final victory."

He described two religious buildings in Yezd: a Fire Temple, where a sacred fire was fed with sandalwood, and a Tower of Silence, where the dead were exposed to be consumed by vultures. Burial or cremation were forbidden because dead bodies would defile earth and fire. Fire, especially the sun, was the source of life and most perfect expression of the Godhead. To fire, therefore, worshippers addressed their prayers.

Ghazan found himself both attracted and repelled. Reality in a perpetual state of war, man by each thought and action playing a prominent part—this greatly appealed to him. But why such importance given to fire? Only yesterday he himself had been newly created out of the earth. Water had been mixed with earth, and now he was distinct from the earth, could think about the earth and move over its surface. He thought, all that I am, my secret being, my mind and soul must be water, and death is an evaporation whereby the soul disperses to the sky.

"Surely," he protested, "Zoroaster was not a man of the desert. Otherwise he would have known that water, not fire, is the principle of life."

The merchant stared at Ghazan, as though he had blasphemed. "You are doubly wrong," he replied reprovingly. "Our prophet was born in Media, and that is hotter far than our plains. But he knew the power of the sun to create and shrivel up all things. If every drop of water in the world were evaporated—and mankind with it—the sun would remain. That is why we represent Ahura Mazda as the sun."

For a time there was no sound but the crunch of thick-padded hooves, as the long line of sand-coloured camels traversed the humped dunes.

The Yezdi's words prompted Ghazan to speak of a curious carving he had seen on the palace of Darius: a winged disc furnished with tail-feathers, streamers hanging astride the tail, out of which rose the upper part of a human figure, lifting one arm.

"That device," the Yezdi explained, "was borrowed from Assyria and ultimately from Egypt. It represents the sun as spirit, and also as a moving force."

Slowly and solemnly, as though in prayer, he raised narrowed eyes to the cloudless sky. The sun was like metal molten white, sending out concentric burning ripples. He tried to look straight at the sun, but his eyelids fell and after a moment he covered his face with his hands. Then he turned watery, dazzled eyes to Ghazan, with an air of triumph at this defeat.

"We pray also to lesser spirits," the Yezdi continued. "To Mithra, lord of bulls and horses, and to the undefiled lady of the waters, Anahita."

"Anahita!" Ghazan exclaimed. "That is the name of the girl I am going to marry."

The Yezdi looked incredulous. "But you told me you are a Muslim! We of the fire marry only among ourselves."

"This girl is not a Guebre. But her name is Anahita." Ghazan had always believed it meaningless, man-made and given for its sound. "Please tell me more about your Anahita," he asked.

The Yezdi said Ahura Mazda had assigned Anahita the work of guarding the holy creation, like a shepherd guarding his flock. It was she who gave rain to the parched earth. She wore a golden crown studded with a hundred stars, and her power was matched only by her mercy.

Ghazan listened attentively. To him names were important: they exerted an influence over the objects and people to whom they were given. More than that, the Sufi poets taught that, with men, the name of every thing is its outward form; with the Creator, its inward essence. In the eyes of Moses, the name of his rod was "staff"; in the eyes of God its name was "serpent".

Ghazan, leader of the Seljuqs of Central Asia, had become Shah of Persia in the thirteenth century. Often the Ilkhan of the Falqani had pondered on that: and his enemies too. Now a chance meeting had transformed the girl who wore his earrings, snatched her out of the simple present and mingled her with waters, with an ancient cult. Ghazan wanted to see her again in the shadow of her name. Because she had slipped out of the sun, he desired her more.

Water, trees, oxen, peasants: the objects were presented gradually, like simple food to a patient who has been gravely ill. About noon next day the caravan rode up a slope, to a high ridge called the "Hill of Salutation". Most of the cameleers added a stone to a large heap on the ridge. Ghazan followed their example, then rose to look at what seemed high-horned snails glistening through the haze: the minarets and gilded domes of the holiest city in Persia.

Meshed held for Ghazan and all Muslim Persians a significance, religious and national, lacking in Mecca: it summarized the whole history of the differences between Persia and most of the rest of Islam, between Shiis and Sunnis. Shiis (the name meant 'belonging to the Schism') rejected the traditionary portion of Mohammedan law based on Mohammed's words or acts, as interpreted by the great medieval doctors, which Sunnis, "followers of the tradition", accepted as authoritative. Shiis, partly influenced perhaps by the Zoroastrian and Nestorian Christian religions, which had left their imprint on Persia, supplied Islam with an infallible authority, in the words and actions of a group of sinless men: the twelve Imams or leaders by divine right.

The first and greatest Imam had been Ali, cousin and son-in-law of the Prophet. Each Imam named a successor until the twelfth, who never died but disappeared without a successor in the mysterious city of Jabulka: he would reappear on the day of judgment in the mosque of Gauhar Shad at Meshed, to fill the world with justice. The Imams were believed to have explained, infallibly, the occult meaning of the Koran: they were man's spiritual guides to set him free from doubt.

Meshed owed its sanctity to the tomb of the eighth Imam, Ali Reza. A century after the Arab conquest of Persia, the caliph al-Mamun, spiritual and temporal lord of Islam, ruling from Baghdad, paid a visit to Merv. Here he constituted Ali Reza, a pious and learned man of middle age, heir presumptive to the Caliphate. Already Persia was asserting her claims to independence, and this designation of the son of a Persian mother caused uprisings, especially at Baghdad, which proclaimed a rival Arab caliph. For two years Reza lived at Merv with al-Mamun, performing many miracles. He could indicate for which province every rain cloud was destined; during mid-winter he made grass grow and apricots ripen. In 818 he accompanied al-Mamun on a visit to the tomb of the caliph's father at Meshed. Here Ali Reza died from a surfeit of grapes. These grapes, Persians firmly believed, had been poisoned by champions of the rival Arab caliph-designate.

In the sixteenth century, with the rise of the Safavi dynasty, which claimed descent from the seventh Imam, the Shii doctrines were established as the national religion and Ali Reza's tomb at Meshed became the place of national pilgrimage. This change, occasioned by war with Sunni Turkey, gave official expression to certain long-standing differences between Persians and Islam to the west, between the Aryan and Semite nature, between the speculative, occult-loving imagination and the mind more apt for law and its rigorous methods.

Shii dogma underlay Ghazan's Sufism. Inferior in numbers and wealth, further east by twenty degrees of latitude and speaking a different tongue, the sect to which Ghazan belonged had nevertheless provided Islam with her most inspired mystical poets, some of her most subtle theologians and with her staunchest defenders against the Crusaders, so that the moon which had splintered from the sun could be said to outshine the parent body. Ghazan's relationship to the rest of Islam was therefore like his relationship as a Falqani to the rest of Persia.

Ghazan approached the walls of Meshed with growing excitement. His old master had been so sure this city would solve his problems. But how? Because it was ancient and holy, and the seat of authority? Ghazan wanted to reach the shrine quickly, yet also felt a certain anxiety, like a plaintiff going to court.

Meanwhile, the caravan passed crowds of pilgrims, not only among the living. The route was lined with cemeteries. A camel-herd told Ghazan that thousands of bodies were brought yearly from as far as India, Afghanistan and Turkestan to lie in the Imam's shadow, so many that the graves, each with its local granite or stealite headstone, changed occupants every few years.

They rode through the city gate into the main avenue, lined with plane trees and a canal. From the desert of nothingness to the bazaar of being. Mullahs in brown capes and white turbans, students and pilgrims speaking strange dialects, swarmed in the street, some patronizing the public kitchens (for pilgrims had a right to maintenance for three days), some the shops and stalls. Many wore a green turban and green girdle: seyyids, men whose descent from Mohammed gave them a right to alms.

Pedlars offered for sale rosaries, mementoes and amulets, promising to work miracles or communicate with the dead. Among them Ghazan found some of the peace he had expected to breathe only in the air of the sanctuary. Too long, he thought, I have cared about the future. Events turn out as they will. If I had died in the desert, this other world of buying and selling, of sin and prayer, would have continued.

The camel-train trooped through the archway of a caravanserai. Here the camel-herds began to unload carpets, kettles, bowls and metal jugs. Before turning off to superintend this work, the Zoroastrian said goodbye to Ghazan.

"If you are ever in Yezd, come to see me. I will show you our sacred buildings."

"Are you trying to convert me?" laughed Ghazan.

"We make no converts," answered the Yezdi gravely.

Ghazan gave him his hand. "That is good. Let each discover his own vision."

He and Ahmad stayed in a hostel for pilgrims off the main avenue. While eating a meal of bread and onions, they listened to the talk around them. Some had come to gain a reputation, to get away from a cross wife or responsibilities, but most in the hostel had crawled under the weight of suffering. Meshed: turning-point in countless spiritual journeys: the air heavy with sighs and light with prayers: to Ghazan it seemed to merit well its name "place of martyrdom".

Ahmad sensed a difference also. "It's not like Shiraz," he confided; "not like Isfahan. There they look at your clothes and shoes. In the tribe they look at your horse. Here they don't seem to notice you at all."

Ahmad delivered mullah Mahdi's letter to his friend the mujtahid. Then the two pilgrims bought new clothes and went to the public bath. They had their long black hair cut and their beards shaved. Afterwards they walked through the arched bazaar. Vivid silks from nearby Herat, Bokhara and Samarcand gleamed in the lamplight, the smoothest

215

Ghazan had ever touched. Just as the damask rose's scent was distilled in attars, so the essence of its petals and the petals of blue irises and yellow hollyhocks, of larkspur and pink carnations, was candied in these bales. They possessed all the virtues: seemed saints in the world of silk. Ghazan decided to buy a length for Anahita: enough to make a chador. He did not know her favourite colour, so he settled for his own: turquoise. That seemed appropriate, after what the Zoroastrian had said. While he was buying it, he thought of her mother, and for her chose a black silk mantle. For Dilbar Ahmad bought a small band of red silk to make a fillet.

Next morning the mujtahid sent his servant to escort Ghazan to his lodgings within the shrine. Removing his shoes at the Golden Gate of Nadir Shah, he entered a rectangular court pierced by two rows of alcoves, the lower occupied by artisans, schools, servants, the upper by high officials, including the mujtahid.

This doctor of sacred law, in white flowing robes and turban, was a tall, sharp-eyed figure of about seventy. Disease or fasting had revealed each fine bone in his face. He carried his head high, and those who passed him salaamed obsequiously. He greeted Ghazan warmly, questioned him about his journey, and then about Meshed. Finding only commonplace knowledge on this subject, he appeared disappointed. It soon became clear that his world was the shrine, its geography the very road to heaven.

He led Ghazan into the sanctuary, a whole town in itself, comprising courts, mosques, colleges, caravanserais and bazaars, all with their own discipline, enforced, if necessary, in a special prison. The mujtahid gave a few dry facts about each in a toothless voice which Ghazan had to strain to hear.

They saw the round dish on which the poisoned grapes were eaten, then entered a smaller room, adjoining which rose the dome of the mausoleum of the Imam. The interior of the small room was almost square, its floor inlaid with coloured marble, its walls covered with white, blue and gold tiles, hushed by a dim light from gilded lamps. In niches on the far wall lay jewelled swords and daggers and aigrettes. In one corner stood a bare stone tomb covered in gold.

Ghazan had prepared himself for the extraordinary, a sort of heaven after a lifetime's journey. He was disappointed, first with the bare tomb, then with his own inability to appreciate it. He felt remote, as though he had not yet arrived. He would have liked to approach and kiss the tomb as his master had kissed the black meteorite at Mecca, but three finely wrought grilles kept the living at bay from the dead. Following the example of others in the room, he shook the outer grating and kissed the heavy lock, praying to the Imam and remembering, too, all those who had asked for prayers on his journey. Meanwhile he began slowly to feel the aura of the shrine. Meshed—Mine of the Blessings of God—and he stood in the innermost seam: perhaps, all unknown to himself, undergoing transmutation into a less unworthy substance.

Presently the mujtahid led Ghazan through shadowy passages and halls which seemed prepared for Zoroastrian rather than Muslim rites: alone in the darkness, carved and chiselled in arabesques, according to the design of the arched lattice high in the wall, stood megalithic idols of pure sunshine.

From there to a world of blue, where it seemed that heaven itself had fallen to make a place of prayer. They had entered the mosque of Gauhar Shad, a large quadrangle, its central courtyard open to the sky, broken in the middle of each side by an arched hall. The most spacious, to the south, was used for public devotion and contained a wooden pulpit where the last Imam would one day appear. It had been founded over five centuries ago by the woman whose name it bore, wife of Tamerlane's son and greatest of Timurid queens. It was, said the mujtahid, the most beautiful mosque in the world, and here he left Ghazan alone to pray.

Nothing could be simpler than its shape—the four walls of a caravanserai—nor more complicated than the decoration and colouring of the mosaic tiles covering every visible part, even the squinches of the arched alcoves. Dark turquoise-blue dominated, the colour of the cloudless noon sky which seemed a dome crowning the walls. But the apparently simple turquoise effect was blended from a dozen shades of blue and its brilliance from the golden foliage and white Kufic characters spelling out quotations from the Koran, which formed a mosaic within the blues. These and geometric patterns were the sole permissible form of decoration, but a rule originally devised in order to avoid distracting the faithful, by its very strictness had stimulated the artist's ingenuity. In so complicated a pattern and foliage the eye was caught like a bird in tangled undergrowth.

217

Ghazan sat on a step of one of the open-fronted arched halls and looked about him. After the silence of the empty desert, the mosque sounded a fanfare, alerting every sense. Beyond the courtyard he could see a smooth turquoise dome, glowing silver where the sun was reflected, and twin minarets, garlanded like the dome with white and yellow tendrils. Elsewhere, nothing but the sky. Nothing to distract him from the Kufic design, looped this way and that round the blue like thread by a swooping swallow.

Slowly Ghazan felt himself become a prisoner of the place. None of the buildings he had seen that morning, rich and elaborate though they were, had this perfect symmetry of line and colour. It seemed to express, in another medium, the mullah Mahdi's teaching. Open to and imitating heaven; the foliage the intricate working-out of a theological system devised by one who had heard God speak directly and clearly the order "Submit".

"Submit." A hateful command. "Die to yourself." A form of suicide: so it had often seemed. But now—to drown in these blue waves, in this sea of perfection—almost lovable. To attain a new life—there might be truth, after all, in the trite phrase. Ghazan recalled his disappointment after the opium. True fulfilment, then, was it this: not to dream, but to be dreamed?

Ghazan stirred uneasily. His people were like leaves on a poplar, shaking the slender trunk. He was choosing also for them. He saw a vision of the future: the crumbling village, the hunchback, the blind potter, the sickly children. And yet, if the order was valid, absolutely authoritative, it was binding on every one of his people, no less than on him.

Ghazan stretched out his arms behind his head. Feeling the warm, hard faience, gazing at the ample line of the arch, he was aware of the weight of heaven and the consequences of setting his shoulder against it. Confront that absolute power, pit his will, however strong, against that—which was everything? If he swerved out of line, it would be like a falling star. He would fall into darkness, would become darkness himself.

"Submit." Why strain his ears for an improbable countermand? His parents' teaching, his schooling, the shrine, all said, Peace lies here within the system under the blue sky on walls of blue. His idea of the future, even if true, what did it matter, since in themselves he and all men were nothing? The myriad pilgrims, the Imams, men wiser and better than he throughout the ages had shown the way. Slowly, reluctantly, Ghazan bowed his head.

He felt the need to plant a commemorative tree, lest later he dismiss the moment as a dream. He had written verses since boyhood: all his friends did that—even Rohim: and he did not consider himself a poet. Words satisfied only one side of his character. He never kept his verses long and could remember only odd phrases from past compositions.

He took from his pocket a stump of pencil and the only paper he could find: the bill for the silk. On the back he wrote about the flower of submission which flourished in the climate of Meshed, of how all human life was an exile, and that to be exiled still further was to become nearer fulfilment. He sought finally to express man's submission before eternity, and found an image in the memory of a camel-press he had watched as a boy.

A dim room adjoining the bazaar, a single shaft of light falling aslant from a hole in one of the domes. A huge roughly square oak trunk lay in the far corner secured with iron fastening: at one end a pile of straw baskets containing opium seeds, at the other a capstan, which boys swung down with a daring leap, while the trunk groaned, and the baskets oozed.

All this served to show the continuousness of the main work. In the centre of the room rose a round stone floor, where an upright stone wheel to grind the seeds for the baskets was turned by a camel, its hide worn, the wool patchy and in places hanging loose. On the head thrust straining forward, where eyes should have gleamed, were two round wicker baskets the size of a palm attached with straps. They looked like huge bulging eyes from far. Only thus, temporarily blinded, could the camel endure the circular movement, walking away a lifetime without advancing one step. Round and round the camel plodded. A boy swept the ground seeds back into the stone's path. The smell of dung mingled with opium. In the backyard a second camel lay in the sun chewing: the two were changed at intervals. The press had been turning as long as anyone could remember, pausing only when the camels were changed or the ground seeds removed to baskets.

By night the wheel revolved at the same speed but invisibly, its motion attested only by the squeaking harness and the dry rolling of the stone, drawn by the blinded camel in order to make oblivion, the illusion of eternity, possible for men under the same destiny as itself. The universe seemed to move to just such a circular, inevitable repetition: everything came back on itself in the end. Sometimes the world might give the illusion of turning on the axis of his choice, but now, remembering the camel, Ghazan wrote that all men were as poppy-seeds under the grinding stone.

CHAPTER SIXTEEN

IF Ghazan had left Meshed immediately after composing his poem, the pilgrimage might have accomplished what his master had hoped. But next day the mujtahid again invited him to visit the sanctuary and explained its history in greater detail. He pointed out lattice-work designs in the minaret mosaics as of Chinese origin, for Gauhar Shad's empire had extended from the Tigris to the Great Wall. He showed filigreed swords made by a colony of workers transplanted by Tamerlane from Damascus. He told Ghazan that ninety thousand pilgrims visited Meshed every year.

"Most come to gain merit," he said. "To obtain forgiveness of sins, to fulfil a religious duty. But very few approach our saint as he should be approached," and the mujtahid looked challengingly at Ghazan.

"In a spirit of reverence?" he suggested.

The mujtahid dismissed this remark as obvious. "I was thinking more of the nature of the Imam. In Ali Reza was embodied the Divine Light which has descended through generations of Prophets from the time of Adam. Other sects of Islam by denying this render themselves poor—not only as regards the past. For the Imam's power is continued through time, in so far as he can answer prayer. Have you prayed to the Imam?"

"I bought a printed prayer from a pedlar."

"Much nonsense is sold. How did it go?"

Ghazan drew a card from his pocket and read the text: "Be thou for us a mediator before God on high, a saviour from hell fire, on earth a support, on the road of life an assurance, and in the grave a most intimate friend and companion."

The mujtahid nodded. "Just as I thought. That prayer would serve any Imam. But this is Ali Reza's shrine. He was a particular man with particular powers. We should pray to him, therefore, in appropriate terms to avert misfortune."

This line of thought was new to Ghazan. "Surely if a misfortune is written, it is written. Nothing can interfere with the Divine Will."

221

The mujtahid began to show interest. "No, no," he said, "you confuse eternity and time. We cannot be sure a seeming misfortune is written before it happens. Until then it is uncreated. And if uncreated, the Divine Mercy can be invoked to let it remain uncreated. Our invocations are sinful and earth-bound, but the Imams' soar, for they were sinless. Which brings me back to what I was saying: pilgrims to Meshed should call on the Imam Reza's particular powers."

Ghazan asked what these powers were.

"Very diverse," the mujtahid replied, in his most encyclopædic manner. "Stranger, Martyr, Bereaved: each title unclenches favours. For instance, the Imam Reza can grant a favourable journey; equally he can deliver pilgrims from the sufferings of exile."

Ghazan checked his surprise and eyed the mujtahid warily. "Do you tell me this for a particular reason?"

"A particular reason? No." He looked bewildered, evidently knowing nothing of events in Teheran.

Ghazan felt a stir of excitement. "Why should the Imam Reza possess these powers?"

"In virtue of his death far from home. Remember, he was born in Medina."

"In Medina." Abstractedly Ghazan echoed the words, thinking of something else. In the absence of the last Imam, the mujtahids exercised the highest spiritual authority on earth. And now, ignorant of his case, one of them was advising him to appeal.

This must have been fated, thought Ghazan, and it changed the meaning of the larger text he had read yesterday. His steps had been directed to the one saint whose power lay precisely in averting the evil which threatened him. The particular saint, not his conformity to the will of God: the living, interceding saint beyond the tomb, not the bare tomb itself, now became the focus of his thought. Despite the poem in his pocket, his whole conception of the pilgrimage changed. Only the dead could master the dead. He would call on the Imam Reza to unhorse Reza Shah.

With a zest he had not felt since the party at the palace, he conducted his appeal like a military operation. In the morning he entered the mausoleum and sent out tentative prayers to scout the lie of the land (which was really his own resources that day). Sometimes he had to hold back, awaiting reinforcements of grace—and these pauses, recalling his stillness in the mosque of Gauhar Shad, made him uneasy. For he was, in himself, both crashing wave and the yellow sand on which the wave broke. He could not be both at once, and now that he surged higher and more compelling, he thought with regret of still, smooth sand. But these hesitant moments were rare. Most often he led charge after charge of well-tried litanies and verses from the Koran, following up with thrusts of his own invention. Eyes closed and on his knees he fought the battle of Meshed.

Day after day for a week Ghazan revisited the shrine. But for all his fervour he could not spend every hour there. The bustling streets, the conflict of wills in the bazaar reasserted themselves. An unretentive memory made him all the more susceptible to change of place and mood. The white-streaked desert began to fade like a leprosy healed. He wondered whether his thirst, his fall, had not been mirages. The camel-herd who rescued him: was it he who had six fingers? With the diagram that had illustrated it, the theorem of resignation lost validity.

The week came to an end. Satisfied that he had prayed to the limits of his power, Ghazan booked a seat on the next plane to Shiraz. Ahmad was to ride the horses back by way of Gurgan, Teheran, Qum and Isfahan. Since the route was long, Ghazan arranged for an Isfahani pilgrim to accompany Ahmad in exchange for his food and three tumans a day.

The return journey concerned his body only. It was simply a movement in space. Ghazan left Meshed at noon and was back in Shiraz at four. Half an hour later he entered Garden of the Pines. At once he summoned his agent. What was the latest news? Had a countermand come from Teheran? The agent shook his head. Manœuvres had been intensified. Last units of the new division had just arrived.

Ghazan listened almost incredulous. He had been counting on an underlying harmony, a balance such as he had always known in the hills, to reverse the decree: even when he had not admitted it openly, or even to himself, this hope had coloured his outlook. It had taken shape in the Imam. The Imam had failed him doubly. For his prayer had shattered the symmetry of the blue walls of Gauhar Shad. That perfectly favourable moment might never recur. No harmony, only haphazard events. But the pattern of his life had been based on harmony. That too was shattered. His self, too; dissolved in the desert.

In this state of mind, the morning after his arrival, Ghazan revisited the mosque. In the arcade the mullah's grandson sat learning his lessons. Ghazan greeted him and asked where his grandfather was.

"Haven't you heard?" the boy said. "He is lying ill at home."

He offered to lead Ghazan there. The mullah had stumbled on steps within the school only a week after Ghazan's departure. He had fallen and injured his spine. Friends had carried him home and since then he had been unable to stir from bed.

Presently they entered a small house in the poorest quarter, a single room plastered grey and cracked. On a plain wooden table lay half a flap of bread and a bowl of oranges. In one alcove stood an iron chest; in others books were stacked. In the far corner on a straw mattress lay the old man.

Ghazan knelt beside him, shocked at how thin and grey his face had become. "I am sorry to see you so ill," he said compassionately, his own troubles forgotten.

"Save your sorrow," whispered the mullah. "I ask nothing better than to die. And so surely all would feel if they knew what awaited them beyond." Even to whisper seemed an effort. His neck was like a gnarled bough where the sap rose feebly. With weary eyes he scrutinized Ghazan. "You are not the same man who left me. You have suffered."

Ghazan was surprised. He had been conscious only of the goal sought and missed. The rest had been irrelevant. Then he told the mullah what had happened, starting in his rapid way, giving only the essentials, and analysing their implication; but the mullah interrupted, demanding news of his friend, changes in the shrine, until Ghazan was telling his tale slowly, while the little boy listened open-mouthed and puzzled, the sick man occasionally shaking his head.

"You did well to make the pilgrimage. And since your prayer has not been answered, you may be sure that what you call a move in a game of intrigue is nothing less than God's will. Lying here, thinking about you and your people, Cain and Abel came to my mind. The first generation born in the world. Their fate set the key for all. You too, Ghazan, must accept a seeming evil."

Ghazan listened, disappointed. He had searched the mullah's eyes for an image of himself and found Abel's. Why wouldn't his Master see him as he was? Nevertheless, the analogy held his attention.

224

"Can it be true," he murmured, "that they hate us because our hills touch the sky!"

"Cain found he had killed not a rival but a brother, whose vigour was needed to defend his own possessions. His punishment resulted from the nature of his crime: he gave up his land, became a fugitive over the earth. Your brothers may suffer too, but it is not for you to make them suffer."

"Abel was not warned," objected Ghazan. "Had he been warned, he would never have gone down to the fields."

The mullah looked shocked. "You say that—coming from the Imam's shrine!"

Ghazan conceded the point. Imams were gifted with perfect knowledge. Ali Reza knew that the grapes offered by al-Mamun were poisoned. Yet one by one he lifted the fruit with the dusty bloom of death and crushed their purple pulp on his palate.

"But Moses," he said on an impulse. "Did he not combat evil? Did he not lead his people out of slavery?"

"Moses was given signs: the burning bush, the stick which became a snake, and the hand tainted with leprosy. Have you been given signs?"

Ghazan dropped his head. "No. I have been given no sign."

"Look at me, my son. If I am resigned to death, cannot you accept a living death, your own and your people's?"

Ghazan studied the pleading eyes, the pathetic bald head, the wasted flesh. Already the mullah cast a faint, almost invisible shadow. He would glide away. The moorings had long ago been untied. He would feel no sorrow at leaving his grandson. All his life he had been dying to himself—had he in fact ever lived? Could I attain his state, wondered Ghazan. He doubted it, yet felt no regret. He loved people, objects, the very air he breathed with a passion shared by none of his friends in Shiraz—or anywhere in the plains. The narrow streets constricted and circumscribed, denying movement, denying life. Ghazan refused to deny life, the fullness of life. As for his resolution in the mosque of Gauhar Shad: it had been exacted under pressure. But the old man's eyes were suppliant: that sort of blunt message could not be given to the dying.

Ghazan simply said, "I don't know what I shall do. When I do decide, your example will weigh with me—perhaps heaviest of all."

He tried to fix the scene: the drab, bare room, the oranges gleaming like the old man's soul. Admiration fought with revolt: was there only one perfect way: to pour the wine out on the sand and turn downwards the cup?

"Ghazan—to you I have expounded any wisdom I have learned. Grant me one dying happiness. Promise to accept."

His voice was tremulous and more urgent than ever. Why were the dying such tyrants? It was little to ask—one disciple—and it would be so easy to promise. And such a deliverance. A tired camel, its back bruised by the saddle of free-will, its heavy panniers sagging from this side to that. Now, even now, he could let the ill-balanced load drop from him and browse in the meadows of peace. Yes, but a promise to a dying man: sacred, unbreakable. Somehow, he felt that he could not take a wholehearted decision here in this mud box, far from his own habitat. But how refuse? To gain time, he asked:

"Why do you seek this promise?"

"I want to depart glimpsing rain-bearing clouds. I want to be sure my life will yield a harvest."

As Ghazan weighed the point, in the distance rifle shots rang out: manœuvres continued.

"It seems I may have no choice," he answered with a wry smile. "You hear the army firing."

"Do not turn my question, Ghazan. Tell me whether you accept in your heart."

Taking a deep breath, Ghazan said gravely: "Old man, it would be worse for you to die in an atmosphere of untruth than of despair. I cannot give you that promise."

The mullah closed his eyes with a barely audible sigh. He lay very still. Unbidden, two lines came to Ghazan: lines he had read once with the mullah:

> I taught him archery every day
> And when his arm grew strong, he shot me.

Ghazan felt suddenly immense pity for the tired, drawn face. Going as far as he could, he said:

"All my life I shall try to imitate your virtues."

"Virtues? I have none." His voice was flat, but what he had said seemed to strike a chord. He opened his eyes and raised himself on his elbows: "Tomorrow is the ninth of Moharram. For my sake, Ghazan, go to a passion play."

Moharram was the first month in the lunar year, by which religious holidays were reckoned, the civil calendar following the solar cycle. In every large town, on the ninth day, plays were performed, emphasizing an incident in the death of Hussein, Persia's great martyr, followed by processions on the tenth, anniversary of his martyrdom. Ghazan had not attended a play since boyhood. Seeing no reason to refuse, he agreed to the suggestion.

The mullah seemed pleased. "This poor body fails, but Hussein, the virtuous Hussein—he will perhaps convince you."

He fell back on the straw. After a moment he turned to his grandson: "My mouth is dry. I should like an orange."

The boy lifted one from the bowl and began to peel away the tightly clinging skin in small pieces. The white remained, and this he removed in strips. He divided the orange and put one leaf in the Mullah's mouth. The thin lips twisted as though it were sour. He took a long time to eat the leaf. Then the boy gave him another.

As Ghazan watched, with a start he thought, the old man asked for this orange. A small thing, but nonetheless a desire. He claims indifference—but his desires are not quite dead. Ghazan's own thoughts appalled him. Monster that I am, shall I judge this saint on his death-bed? I who am a bundle of desires, shall I condemn this pitiful thirst caused by speaking to me? But a voice insisted, all the same, I must pierce to the truth.

The mullah's wish to influence him, to assert his will after death: these too were desires. He wanted truth to prevail, his life to achieve good. But these were precisely Ghazan's own desires. And he thought, take away the orange and you take away life. Take away the desire for good and you take away the person. Certain loyalties are necessary for identity. Since desire has to exist anyway, let it be for something more than an orange.

The boy's hands were empty. The mullah closed his eyes as though in sleep. For a long time Ghazan waited, wondering whether he would speak further. But no: he had entrusted his pupil to the martyr Hussein. Ghazan understood that it was finished between them: they had said all that had to be said. All his life the old man had taught resignation by word and deed. No one could go further than he in self-denial. And

227

then, asking for an orange, a sour orange, he had shown that resignation could never be total on this side of the grave. And it struck Ghazan as extraordinary that the last and most important lesson should be unrehearsed and unconscious. As with flowers: only at sundown did one catch their exact fragrance.

Next afternoon Ghazan drove to the southern quarter of Shiraz and at the end of one of the poorer streets found the black flag which announced a play. Part of the street had been cordoned, and on a raised platform covered with carpets stood a tent. The walls behind were strung with black cloth and inscriptions praising the martyrs. On the right stood a pulpit with five steps. Sometimes plays were reserved either for men or for women, but this audience, already assembling, was mixed: men on the right, women on the left.

Ghazan took a place near the front, in the most crowded part, and learned that *The Marriage of Kazem* was going to be performed. The title gave him no particular pleasure or annoyance. This episode, like others in the history of Hussein and his family, he had imbibed with his mother's milk. It was beyond objective criticism: true and fundamental, conditioning many of his reactions, colouring his thoughts.

The historical background was a dispute between Hussein, grandson of Mohammed the Prophet, and Yezid, eldest son of the Governor of Syria, for the supreme spiritual authority in Islam: the caliphate. The scene was the desert plain of Kerbela, near the Euphrates, where Hussein, his family and followers, numbering ninety, were surrounded by several thousand troops of the usurper Yezid. Most of the passion plays showed, in one form or another, the heroic resistance and final massacre of Hussein and his family.

In hushed groups Shirazis assembled, many red-eyed with weeping, until the platform was surrounded with a dense, black-clothed crowd. About an hour after Ghazan's arrival a mullah mounted the pulpit and the play began, with the entrance of Hussein, in a loose tunic but without accoutrements, on the plain of Kerbela.

For Ghazan, Kerbela was remote neither in place nor time. In his pocket he fingered a tablet, hard as stone, baked from Kerbela dust, inscribed with praises of Hussein. When he prayed, he laid this before him, so as to prostrate his forehead on holy earth. Neither was the play remote, and Ghazan strained his ears to catch every word, not out of curiosity but hoping, just as the Shirazi actors lost themselves in their parts, to lose himself in the action and hear across the centuries a voice speaking directly to him.

First, Hussein announces that his own daughter is to marry one of his followers—Kazem. Preparations for the wedding take place amid fighting in the besieged camp, but blood instead of the usual henna is splashed to adorn the hands and feet of the wedding guests. While women of the court bejewel and perfume him, Kazem, with a cry of exaltation, promises as dowry all the rubies in the treasure-house of his body. Hearing this, Hussein laments,

"The tomb will be their bridal bed, the shroud her wedding gown."

As Yezid's troops surround the camp and hurl insults at the besieged, Hussein announces his intention of fighting to the death.

The declaration drew from the mullah in his pulpit this comment: "Hussein does not shrink from suffering in the cause of justice." In vindication he read from the Koran: "Permission to fight is accorded those who take up arms because they have been unjustly treated." A passage familiar to Ghazan, which had weighed with him nine years ago when he attacked the Kazerun and Shiraz garrisons. He would have liked to reflect on it further, but the actors went immediately into the next scenes: battle, bloodshed and still more battle against insuperable odds; wailing of women and massacre of children, whose blood mingles with the waters of the Euphrates. With no signs of regret or reproach, the Prophet's family, young and old, go out to meet their death.

Kazem has led the fighting. At last, when the tents are on fire and the besieged cut off from water, he strides out through the barricade of reeds and tamarisk, crying:

"The moment has come for my life to merge with Eternal Life. It is time for this isolated pearl to leave its shell and lie in a corner of the crown of Eternal Being."

But Kazem succeeds in killing the Syrian general. He returns and asks Hussein for a reward.

"What reward shall I give you?"

"Water," groans Kazem. "For every drop of water, I shall kill a soldier of the Syrian army."

One by one the goatskins are reversed—empty all.

229

"I am dying of thirst," cries Kazem, seizing his sword again. "I will quench it in the waters of Paradise."

With that he rides away, leaving his mother, his bride and Hussein to weep his death.

Their tears ended the play. For three hours the wailing and bloodshed had been unrelieved by a syllable of joy or hope. Ghazan felt exhausted. Never had the story seemed so urgent as now, enacted before his eyes. He found himself almost welcoming Kazem's death, since it put an end to the pain.

He tried to stand back from what he had witnessed in the hope of isolating the lesson which the mullah Mahdi wanted him to learn. Certain meanings were clear. Hussein, whose wife was a Persian princess, represented Persia ravaged by her traditional enemies: Arabs, Turks and Afghans, who recognized the legitimacy of Yezid. The play, like all the others in the cycle, was peculiar to Persia; it satisfied an instinct for suffering, perhaps the result of centuries of oppressive rule, and for a vicarious death which orthodox Islam could not supply. For that reason most canonical mullahs opposed the plays. Scholars' ink, they claimed, was more sacred than martyrs' blood.

With this view Ghazan totally disagreed. He admired Hussein and Kazem, who had fought to the death for their rights. And yet the play's presentation of their deeds and motives revolted more than it attracted him. It seemed to Ghazan less an act of remembrance than a wallowing in blood for its own sake. Death was the hero: all the characters seemed to be courting death. But no one, surely, behaved like that in everyday life. Or were the players portraying the ideal, to which commonplace men ought to be exalted? Did the mullah Mahdi intend him to add his voice to this grisly chorus in praise of death? With sudden revulsion Ghazan vowed he would never do that, never collaborate in his own defeat.

Afterwards, the mullah preached endurance of evil, illustrating his point from the play. Ghazan thought, this may be the lesson my dying teacher sent me to learn. But, another voice whispered, Hussein and Kazem fought to the death for their rights. A parable making clear your duty? No. Hussein and Kazem fought because they were attacked. Their courage was merely a specific form of resignation. They had no choice to make, no decision calling on steel to blaze from four thousand rifles. They were holy men taking orders direct from heaven. Ghazan looked up at the blue sky—so high, so far, so silent. This unanswerable, unfathomable silence, this blue surface beneath which he struggled, trapped.

The longer he wrestled with the play's two morals, the more clearly did Ghazan see that neither one could be eliminated in favour of the other. Wearily he left the closed street. The play, he considered, was not strictly tragedy, for a martyr received an immediate place in Paradise, but the men around him could not or would not look to the unacted hopeful epilogue: crying "Hussein! Alas, Hussein!" and beating their breasts they trooped barefoot to the nearest mosque. Many wept: an angel was believed to collect their tears and show them at the Last Judgment as proof of devotion.

This passive commiseration, which had lasted since the beginning of Moharram, on the following day became active; as though the Shirazis had been learning parts they now began to perform. From the quarter where the stage had been Ghazan watched a procession take shape and begin to parade the town. It was led by a trumpeter and horses richly caparisoned, followed by drummers and a man holding on his head the model of a fountain: boys accompanied him, serving water from gourds to those who watched. Next walked a group representing the martyrs: one with an arm hacked off, another with an arrow in his eye, another's body cut open by a sabre: draped in white profusely stained with red. Others held cardboard replicas of human heads on lances. The white horse of Hussein followed, caparisoned in black, pierced by arrows. The corpse of Hussein himself was covered by a boy disguised as the panther which had protected it from profanations. A broad-shouldered giant of a man carried on his head a cell representing Kazem's nuptial chamber: inside knelt a boy arrayed as a bride, applying henna to his hair.

Last walked the flagellants. These made no play with imitation wounds and blood. Stripped to the waist, they lacerated their bodies with chains and knives to the rhythmic beat of cymbals and their own groans.

"Ya Hussein, ya Hussein," a man near the front recited. The crowd repeated the words, swaying their bodies to the responses. Black-clad women shrieked as the procession passed, but their tears seemed to elicit from the flagellants still wilder excesses.

Ghazan recognized shopkeepers, tinsmiths, gardeners: ordinary townsmen, back and breast streaming blood. Was it, he wondered, mere sympathy that led them to reproduce Hussein's sufferings? Or bravado, a desire for new sensations, even scars to break the too-smooth skin of existence? Perhaps they were mourning their own future death. Despite an instinctive revulsion, he found himself watching the flagellants closely, and even for a time following the procession, as a hunter his wounded quarry.

Into the dusk they marched. Great iron cressets filled with burning wood were carried, showering fiery fragments which fell to earth with the drops of blood. There, in the dark, Ghazan picked up the clue. These flagellants were cringing to their own exalted selves, submissive to their cruellest instincts. This was resignation carried to the limit. Goodness could go too far, could curdle. Having formed that conclusion, Ghazan would not follow any longer: he returned to his house alone, sickened and uneasy.

CHAPTER SEVENTEEN

THE days shortened, and for the mullah Mahdi ended altogether. Ghazan was with him when he died: having exchanged no further words of importance. For four days after the burial Ghazan felt such a sense of loss he did not stir from his house. Never again to hear that broken voice echoing eternal truths, to meet those placid eyes which had the air of having seen heaven. To control his sorrow Ghazan found himself drawing on the maxims of the very man he was mourning.

But he was aware, all the time, that he must return to his people. One task remained. On the fifth morning, having announced his visit to Anahita's mother, he was driven down to Garden of the Orange Grove and shown into the same drawing-room with mirror alcoves where he had taken tea that spring.

On the mantelpiece stood a framed photograph of a girl, an enlarged snapshot taken against an orange tree. He lifted it. The girl looked about Anahita's age. Her stance was oblique and shy, yet she held a long-haired cat to her breast with firm hands. Her face was oval, with large eyes—pretty. She was smiling into the sun, with a strange slightly self-conscious expression. Could this, he wondered, be Anahita? He gazed intently at the face. Lady of the Waters, crowned with stars, shepherding creation: this schoolgirl. He replaced the picture thoughtfully. One instant of one mood plucked from the living tree, one line from a poem he did not know.

Presently her mother came in, wearing a black chador, in her hands a black rosary. After exchanging politenesses, she said,

"I have good news, Ghazan. Can you guess?" She swelled proudly. "All the wedding arrangements are made—even the sweets ordered! You are so busy, and without your poor mother have no one to manage these things. So I bought all your gifts. Ten yards of white sheeting for Anahita to wear on the day: that's ordered from the brothers Sardeh. The shoes: I drove specially to Isfahan and bought twenty pairs, five embroidered with gold thread. Rather expensive, but durable. Mirrors and silver candlesticks are being hand-made to my own design."

233

With a show of being casual she added, "I suggest the bills be sent direct to you."

"Yes, have them sent to me," he echoed, his thoughts elsewhere. Marriage—he had wanted to look forward to it, savour its meaning. Too much had happened. He had hardly thought of it. And now it was too close, a matter only of shoes and sweets.

"The marriage deed is being drawn up. Are you staying here long?"

"I leave tomorrow."

"It won't be ready by then. But you'll have time to glance through it before the ceremony."

She paused. Only then was he able to tell her what he had come to say. Her chador fell about her face, veiling her anger. In a cold, commanding tone she said:

"You must hurry to Teheran, rally your friends."

"I have been to Teheran. There's nothing more to be done."

She looked at him wide-eyed.

"Ghazan Falqani—does he think of bowing meekly."

"Not meekly. Perhaps not at all. I don't yet know what I shall do."

He watched her nervously twist the folds of her chador. She was very upset. He broached his subject.

"If I go abroad, Anahita and I—we shall make some sort of life."

He was prepared for a demur, not for her outburst. Eyes flashing with scorn, she cried, "An alien life in an alien world. Anahita a castaway from home, from country! My girl was born for better than that!"

These claims were familiar—his own soul's claims on himself—and as difficult to refute.

"You shall visit her," he said appeasingly.

"Visits!" She bit at the word as though to prove it counterfeit. "Is it so easy to leave the country? And so far. To find Anahita at the end with new interests, new ideas. I should arrive to find a stranger. We should not meet at all."

Anahita, who had been going to live so near, within easy range of love. Ghazan felt a little sorry for the mother.

"And the children!" she continued, more fiercely than ever. "Would you dare breed men to disinheritance?"

Here she touched him. Among the Falqani marriage was contracted for the sake of its children. Marriage only to satisfy longing Ghazan had been brought up to believe a dual selfishness.

The mother swept forward on a broad front. "Exile will bring passivity, despair, eventual hatred of life. Will you use love to renew what you hate?"

"That decision lies in the future," he answered coldly.

His tone provoked her still further, "You toy with more lives than one, Ghazan. Let her leave me—my only daughter? To cringe beside a deported political prisoner. What do you think I am made of?"

"If she chooses to come, she will come."

The mother swept back her chador and faced him. "It is time for frank words, Ghazan. I betrothed my daughter to the Ilkhan of the Falqani, and none less than the Ilkhan will she marry. If you are stripped of rank and wealth, give up all thought of Anahita."

Ghazan looked at her in astonishment. A challenge like this—from a woman. But she had Falqani blood: even here it raced fast and furious. Then Ghazan recalled other things she had said, other incidents. He answered accusingly: "My emerald grass—you covet that for her!"

"Yes," she said fiercely. "All the open emerald mines along the Zagros: those must make her crown. She is a diamond, Ghazan: rarest of the rare. Beauty must be given beauty; splendour, splendour!"

Ghazan leapt to his own defence. "And a girl a man. Am I less a man, poorer by half a Persian province? Possessing less, the more I'll win. Disinherited, I shall hack myself a new kingdom."

"Better keep the one you have!"

Flushing indignantly, he retorted, "Did you choose for her my turquoise tunic—or the man beneath?"

"It is more than a tunic, Ghazan. By guarding it, you prove the man you are."

"By guarding *her* I prove the man I am. You should be glad that on my bare stage she will play every part, win all my applause. She will be the sole possession of one stripped of possessions."

The mother thrust forward her chin. "And Anahita," she almost cried, "What will she possess? Praises pall and kisses spoil. She who should lose count of all her servants, all her snow-tipped hills, will wake in a far country, on a stranger's plot of land."

"She shall have her own land. I shall buy her land!"

235

"Some bantam-run squeezed between others. To queen it there—in her pocket principality!"

"Acres she shall own—all she desires."

"And would it be your fathers' land? Would you be rooted there? No more than she. A play-act against tinsel scenery!"

The land, the land: he held no higher card. And the mother saw this.

Softening her expression, she said more quietly, "I spoke out, Ghazan, to show what you stand to lose. Things have not come to the worst. You are still free, still on Persian soil. You have friends, money, guns: I believe you will do all in your power to remain Ilkhan—for Anahita's sake. Have you forgotten her slender figure—like one of your own cypresses? Her quick fingers? So many things she can do, make sweets and jams to sugar any mood, and gay, always gay. Like a musical box, this big house—and she is the music."

Jam—but it was a question of Persia, man himself. Then he thought, only Anahita can resolve this conflict. It was for her to choose her life, say whether she would follow him abroad. She was of an age to obey her mother: was she by nature dutiful?

"If it can be arranged, I should like to speak to Anahita."

Betrothed though they were, they could not meet alone.

"As you wish." She smiled, but he thought it cut against the grain of her face. "You see, Ghazan, I'm being very fair. But loving Anahita as I do, I must protect her happiness."

"This evening?" he suggested.

She agreed to that. Shortly afterwards Ghazan walked out by the open French window into the garden, back to his car.

All afternoon Ghazan sat in the shade of a cypress. Heat had burned the grass of his garden brown. Flies buzzed in the scentless air above the pool, where the last fallen rose-petals floated. He thought of the image he had formed of Anahita. Now that he might lose her, he wanted her more. With her beside him, a Shirazi, half a Falqani, he would never altogether leave Persia. But how would she see it? She had never been abroad: it might hold a romantic appeal. On the other hand she loved her home, and him she had met only once. Yet he had no way of making himself and his claims better known. And he had nothing to offer but a piece of silk from Meshed. He was despoiled like his own garden: as part of his garden, for he could not commit

236

himself as an individual. Even towards Anahita, he rode in rank, one of many.

Before dinner he bathed and washed his hair, then dressed carefully in a white shirt, new plum-coloured tie and dark blue suit. At eight he returned to Garden of the Orange Grove.

Anahita was sitting opposite the window on the couch. A rose-red chador allowed Ghazan to see only her profile: a straight nose, lightly lifted at the bridge, a rounded chin—the girl of the photograph. Her mother sat facing Anahita on a stiff upright chair. He handed each the present from Meshed. He watched Anahita unknot the string. Her fingers were white, free of henna or nail-polish, girl's fingers.

With a little cry she raised her hands.

"Thank you, Ghazan. It's so pretty." She turned to her mother. "See what Ghazan has brought."

Her mother admired it and thanked him conventionally for her mantle. Anahita sat down on the couch, her mother on a chair. He took a chair, making the third point of an equal-sided triangle.

The mother knitted. Ghazan wondered how to begin. These were not tribal tents. Anahita seemed so self-contained in the cool room. And he must burst in, with his hot demands. He watched her pick up a piece of loose beige material from a cane-work basket, the centre held in a wooden ring. He asked what it was.

"A piece of needlework. Won't you come and look?"

He walked across the room and sat beside her on the couch. The mother watched him closely. He felt hampered.

Anahita spread the canvas-work out on a low marquetry table in front of the couch. Ghazan looked at the design, marked in various shades of brown, difficult to distinguish clearly. To the left was a garden. A few stitches of green lawn had been sewn in. On a stone bench sat a girl in a long dress, a lute in her hand, dogs running towards her. Behind vague trees and flowers, as yet unrealized in colour, lay the sea and a ship. In the centre was a horseman, to the right other mounted figures.

"It's imported from Paris," the mother explained. "Anahita happened to see it this afternoon, liked it and bought it."

"And it was you who taught me how to stitch in the wools," the girl smiled back. Half-turning to Ghazan, she pointed to the horsemen, then to the figure in the centre.

237

"This one's their leader. His horse is going to be white. I chose the design specially."

Ghazan looked up, but could still see only her profile. She had emphasized that last word. Specially chosen; the white horse; the girl in the garden. Had she planned this, so that they could speak discreetly, with her mother in the room, by way of the pattern?

"And the figures—have you chosen colours?"

"Colours depend on the story. Will you tell me the story, Ghazan?"

"Surely the story comes afterwards, when we know what each person is."

She considered this. "Perhaps you're right." Then, more eagerly, "Take this one first—the leader. He's a knight, I feel sure. Tell me something about him."

He wanted to catch her eye, have done with obliqueness. But still she looked at the canvas-work. Ghazan, too, looked down and tried to adjust his words.

"He is a wanderer—that much I know. All his life he has ridden the brown hill. His face is burned by wind and sun: his narrowed eyes peer forward to the horizon, looking for something—or someone."

He paused, wondering how she would take it.

"I think I shall like him," she said. Her warmth decided him to go on.

"This spring he glimpses the girl in the garden. But at twilight. Her name is whispered, her face veiled. He thinks his journey may be over. But much depends on the girl."

Anahita picked up several small skeins of wool from her basket.

"Then let's embroider the girl." She held out magentas and aquamarines, yellows and greens. "Choose, Ghazan."

He looked from the wools to the design, to the sea behind the garden. He still saw Anahita in terms of what the Zoroastrian had told him.

"The girl should be the colour of the sea," he said. And when she asked why, he told her the meaning of her name.

Puzzled, she said, "But I am Anahita, not that spirit no one has heard of."

"Since you bear Anahita's name, you inherit from her."

He felt she was laughing at him. "What have I to do with water and stars?"

Then she appealed to her mother: did she know anything more about the name? No. It was just a girl's name which she and her father had happened to like. When Ghazan insisted, Anahita laughed at him and said firmly:

"I know what I am."

Ghazan left it at that. Tonight, he thought, everything turns not on what she means but on what she is and does. But he was surprised that she should be so definite.

He looked at the wools. Green? Red and yellow—tribal colours? But what was he trying to match? Lowering his voice, he said, "To choose faithfully, I must see the face of the girl."

For a moment Anahita sat quite still. Then she turned to him and drew aside her chador. The butterfly swept free of its chrysalis, fluttered and came to rest. Ghazan saw black hair falling almost to the shoulders, large grey eyes, but not too large for their expression: calm without being inattentive; shy but not without strength; the nose fine between high cheekbones. She rose for Ghazan like the new moon, and all his thoughts of her, his expectations based merely on her name, dwindled like stars. She was butter, and they tasteless as skim milk; dry crumbs beside new, fragrant bread.

Anahita looked down at her multi-coloured skein. "And the wools, Ghazan?"

None, he answered, was vivid enough. Mulberry juice and bloom of apricot—only such colours as these would fit. She would find them in her garden, a garden with all the flowers, all the fruits, the herbs that cured every ill.

"But will she deign to give them?" he asked. "Will she sing to her lute this snatch of a rough ballad, give this wild rambler a place in her rose garden?"

As though playing with her skipping rope, she slipped under his words.

"The garden isn't there yet. Shall we make it?"

Threading a green wool, she pushed the sharp needle through the edge of one of the brown shadowy trees. Fumbling a little, she drew it out. Ghazan could see she was unpractised. He looked from Anahita to the figures of the pattern, in which, with every stitch, he felt himself more involved.

"I remember—perhaps ten winters ago—climbing to the high rock above Shiraz called the Eagles' Eyrie, where the Old Man of the Hills

239

sat cross-legged in his tiny stone cell, a copy of Hafiz on his knees. I asked him to cast me a lot. He looked me up and down with his glazed old eyes, asked me where I was from and the day of my birth. Then, closing his eyes, he opened his book and pointed with his finger. There was my fate: the first line at the top of the right-hand page: 'Rubies of wine and music in the garden.'

"That verse puzzled me, but the old man must have seen the girl with the lute, his sharp ear heard her strike the first chords of the dance."

All the time he watched Anahita. He had come, hardly knowing her, to ask her to follow him into exile, should that be his destiny. But now he had seen her face. She was no longer an image and a name but a person.

Each stitch of her embroidery pointed the contrast between this person, her garden: actual, present, visible; and her dark surroundings. Ghazan thought, everything I love is threatened or fallen. The mullah Mahdi is dead. My people stand on the brink of destruction. If I let Anahita drift into that uncertain future, I shall lose her altogether. Lose her, the moment he had found her? But they were betrothed, united by promise. He would stand no more pillaging. He must keep Anahita beside him, make her his certain future. He must. He would.

"I see now what is happening," he said, pointing to the figure of the horseman, then to the dogs. "His greyhounds race up and lick the girl's hand. They bark, urging her to follow their master." He met Anahita's questioning glance. "To leave her garden." His voice was quietly persuasive. "Let her leave at once—tomorrow."

Anahita drew back. "What are you saying, Ghazan?"

He remembered that the arrangements were made: her mother had said so.

"The betrothed shall be married. She shall ride out with the horseman—either into the free hills or the thick wood, what does it matter, as long as their way is one."

He was aware of her tenseness. After a silence she said in a wavering voice, "She cannot ride—and she has no horse."

"She shall be mounted before him on the white mare, steady in his arms."

Still she tried to twist free. "But who is the rider, and what are his colours?"

"Does it matter? You can trust him."

"You said yourself we must see what each figure is, before we could know the story."

He looked at her, wanting an answer. Her eyes were two grey doves in flight, and he held back. She must have time to consider.

"You said he was a knight. So he must wear his lady's favour. A rose-red ribbon high on his breast."

She drew out a wool of that colour from her basket and threaded it. Then she asked, as though the question were important:

"And shall I show him with armour and lance?"

"Why should he be armed?"

"To fight battles for his lady."

A shadow fell across Ghazan's face. He thought, battles, what does she know of battles? The epic poems of Firdowsi. He recalled his tribesman shot in the arm that spring: torn flesh, contorted face, groans of pain.

Then Anahita turned to look at him appealingly. She swept in on Ghazan: his people, like a scattering of cockle-shells, were covered and hidden by the tide.

"And fight for her, no matter the cost?" For a moment he felt he could launch on that course. Perhaps it was disapproval in her mother's glance which made Anahita draw forward her chador. With that gesture, silently, the tide turned and Ghazan, half-disappointed, half-relieved, saw once more the profusion of cockle-shells.

Very seriously he answered his own question. "This is no knight errant. He rides at the head of many men." Ghazan indicated the figures at the right of the embroidery. "Though he rules from a sheep-skin throne with goats as his suite, he tries to be a scrupulous king. And so he serves his people. He must act on their behalf: even yield his arms for them. So do not depict the knight in armour."

"A knight without arms!"

"Single-handed in tournament, he would arm himself for that. He would fight and win. But many lives, many loves hang on a battle."

All the warmth gone from her voice, Anahita asked, "Then how shall I depict him?"

"Do not depict him at all. He must be free to be what the occasion demands. You see, he is not alone." After a pause, he continued more softly. "But the girl in the garden, she is alone."

"No, Ghazan, she is not alone. There is another figure in the garden."

"I see none."

He watched her spread out the design on the table and point to a figure he had missed, standing in the shadow of trees behind the girl. He looked at it in silence, listening to the mother's knitting-needles click regularly.

"You could leave that figure out."

"Could I?" she asked, as though seeking encouragement.

"Say the girl will leave her garden, say she will leave tomorrow. The moon must follow its planet—don't you see: the stream the slope of the hills."

Her hands with the bright needle fell quite still.

What did her eyes say? That he was asking an upward course, calling the salmon to leap the falls, falls that were too steep? Still he tried to persuade her.

"After waltzing in the ballroom, is the knight to be led down stone steps into the dungeon? After two days of spring, are the trees to be stripped and the fresh fountain to fall in the salt sea?"

He had raised his voice, and now her mother came to them.

"You've stopped sewing, Anahita?"

"Just for a moment, while we decide."

"Decide what?"

"How the design is to go?"

"It's all marked out. You have only to follow the pattern." She looked down at the stitches and nodded approvingly. "You have made a good start."

Her words, her tone, her presence beside them: more than ever Ghazan sensed the threat of separation. When the mother had returned to her chair, he looked reassuringly at Anahita and, with all the persuasion at his command, asked again.

"Will the girl come with her knight, come tomorrow wherever he wills?"

Anahita's eyes were like the scales of a balance, weighing a love of two meetings and many dreams against another love, long as her own life. He watched the light in them tremble, then come to rest.

"She cannot." A whisper, but firm.

"No?"

242

She threaded her needle with a black wool and began to sew in the second figure in the garden, with faltering fingers.

"No, Ghazan."

Still he could not believe it. Only when he saw the black wool spread like a stain behind the girl with the lute did he begin to realize. Not misnamed Anahita, he thought. She had drawn down in a single breath a new and more terrible deluge. All his stars were splashed out: they hung in the black night like shot crows, frightening away the sun.

From this darkness he appealed to her, using every argument he could think of. But she did not look up: she continued to embroider: the grey doves brought no sprig of hope. He saw his earring, like a hook, in her right ear, but felt no line in his hands. Was there no way of drawing her back?

Finally she looked up, eyes swelling, lips trembling, silently pleading for him to stop. But he held his course.

"Will you banish the Ilkhan a second time? Expel him to a cold world, to drag out his days like a Laplander? Leave him to drive his reindeer herds through calf-deep snow to a scattering of lichen and moss—and he alone the months-long darkness of an Arctic night?"

With a little cry she dropped her work. Ghazan drew up short.

"What is it, my dearest?" her mother asked.

"I've pricked my finger." Tears formed in the corners of her eyes.

"My poor baby," said her mother, coming to the couch.

Anahita looked at her left hand. A tiny red drop formed slowly on the smallest finger. From his breast pocket Ghazan drew a white handkerchief, folded it into a strip, then wound it twice round the finger and knotted it at the wrist.

Anahita turned to her mother, seated on the other side of the couch, and laid her head on the black-draped shoulder. She was crying. From time to time her mother patted her back and stroked her head, looking at Ghazan in silent reproach.

Ghazan sat motionless, dazed. Why was she crying? Had he driven her too far? But they were betrothed: he had a right to ask her to come. He felt angry at her refusal, sorry at having hurt her. These were two vultures hovering remotely above the remnants on the empty plain: the sense of loss, of irreparable loss.

Slowly the sobbing subsided. Anahita sat upright again, but her face was hidden in her chador.

"Does it still hurt?" Ghazan asked, looking at her bandaged finger. "It's nothing. It's finished now." Still her face was hidden. A new page: text without illustration. In a whisper she added, "I'm sorry, Ghazan."

With an effort he smiled away her apology. "Sorry for crying!" "Sorry for everything."

He had not expected this. Did she, after all, feel a little regret? But the words arrived too late: like a reprieve after the execution.

Slowly Ghazan came to himself, to a new self near despair. He had to blame something. The decree, that was it. Because of the decree, she stood so near and far, belonging to him yet not belonging. He had wanted to ride up a broad open avenue, to find Anahita in the sun. But how could he, when he himself brought twilight?

The mother spread the design on the marquetry table.

"One tree in the garden: and the beginning of two figures already. How well you've worked. And the stitches are neat and small, just as I showed you. What a clever girl you are!"

Ghazan looked down at the two figures, the girl with the lute, the other, black—behind; at the rider still shadowy. Was Anahita deliberately choosing her garden, he wondered, or bowing her head to an irresistible force? Impossible now to ask, and useless: no woman could answer that sort of question.

Himself he could not guess, she seemed such a mixture of strength and weakness. And yet it mattered, for her decision was the one he would have to take—though hers was written small.

Ghazan saw there was no more to be said or done, only drag himself, wounded, back to the hills. He asked permission to leave.

"It's early yet. Must you go?" So said the mother, but she rose to lead him to the door. Anahita sat still. He thought she would not come. But as he stirred, she followed her mother out of the room.

They stood awkwardly near the door. Neither offered him a hand. More than ever Ghazan felt loss, emptiness.

The mother said, in a friendly enough tone, "May your shadow never grow less."

"May God protect you, Ghazan," the girl whispered. Still he could not see her.

"May God protect you."

With that farewell he walked out into the night, down the avenue of orange trees, bare of blossom, bare of fruit. After a few paces he looked back at the two of them: the new moon lying in the arms of the old.

CHAPTER EIGHTEEN

NEXT morning, Ghazan began the long journey back to the tribe, not at the pace of goat and sheep, but as fast as his whipped and spurred-on horse would carry him. His own tribal clothes, tattered by the desert trek, he had discarded at Meshed. He now wore fawn trousers, a loose white tunic and winged brown felt hat borrowed from one of the Falqani servants. He slept out at night rolled up in a single blanket, his feet turned towards the embers of a camel-thorn fire.

The first night he thought of Anahita. He now felt shame at having, as he imagined, blundered and hurt her by demanding too much. The plains and the hills: was that, he wondered, the fundamental gulf between them? Her mother had chosen to settle. The choice had been then, a generation back. And from the different upbringing had come the disunity of thought, so that now the tribe's blood could not stir Anahita's.

His pilgrimage ended, his master's death, his preoccupation with Anahita: these had conjoined to throw in the shade the dilemma posed by his master's counsel of resignation. But only to light up another which Ghazan considered himself still less fitted to confront. Neither Meshed nor Shiraz occupied his thoughts, but Teheran. He felt he had lost much by going there. Already his schooling abroad had given him too ready an understanding of "the other side". Now he had come to know his enemies' point of view too well. Phrases in Teheran lingered: "We must march with material Western civilization if we are to avoid being exploited"; "Next time precautions will be taken to ensure the welfare of the tribes". There were, indeed, arguments in favour of settlement and his exile: he knew them agonizingly well, and wished he did not. They were backed by the strongest, most strident and cocksure part of the world. Ghazan felt that, like a cosmopolitan port, he had allowed sailors of all nations within his gates. In an emergency the gates still shut but did not exclude.

Besides provisions for five days, he carried two parcels of books in his saddlebags. The smaller, bought in Teheran, contained an Arabic work on horse-breeding and Moussu's *Les Maladies du Mouton*. They were for Rohim, who wanted books on those subjects. The larger held paper-bound Arabic texts, some in manuscript, which he had studied as a boy and found in his room at Garden of the Pines: al-Ash'ari, with his curious notion of man 'acquiring' responsibility for his actions although they are willed by God; al-Ghazali, in revolt against dry formulæ, seeking truth through all the Muslim religious systems of his day and finally becoming a Sufi; Muri'ite philosophers, stressing the sufficiency of faith, irrespective of a man's actions: fifteen books altogether were in the parcel.

It seemed to Ghazan that he was faced with a choice between two evils, or, if evil was a negation, between two possibilities, each containing only a few grams of good. The distinction between good and evil— that was easy: the power had been given to Adam and all men. But this other choice he sensed would prove very difficult. Foolish then to disdain the best authorities. Moussu for sheep, al-Ghazali for man.

Slowly he worked his scathed spirit into the scabbard of hill and sky. On the fourth evening he approached the southern outskirts of his tribe: half a dozen black tents alone. These would belong to huntsmen apart from their section. Ghazan knew all the headmen by sight and where possible stayed in their tents. But tonight he preferred to be with the ordinary tribesmen. He would learn what they were feeling, bring his jangled thoughts into harmony with theirs.

He dismounted at the first tent and called a blessing on the people there. Two men came out, one about his own age, the other old and wrinkled, with patient hawk eyes steady above the ravine of a long nose and jutting jaw. His thin, deeply lined face was eroded of inessentials. Ghazan felt a lift of pride: all his months away he had seen no finer head.

The two men did not recognize him. His big white mare distinguished the Ilkhan, and the horse Ghazan now rode was a small tribal grey. He washed in a nearby stream, beside which grazed three or four hundred sheep. When he returned two others had joined the group squatting before the unskirted black tent. He sat down beside them. They gave him a friendly nod. Probably they assumed he was a messenger from the court or, like them, out hunting. He had addressed them in Turki and his distinctive hat marked him as a Falqani. Politeness dictated that no questions be asked till after the meal.

The older man's wife served a platter of barley and curds. They broke their fast in silence, then began to talk about the day's shooting. Only one hunter had been lucky: he had shot a yellow ibex. The older man, who was called Kutlugh, remarked with scorn:

"You youngsters couldn't hit a camel at ten paces."

"There's less game now," the others retorted.

"Ibex are still thick as plums on a plum tree," said Kutlugh. "It's fighting for his life makes a man a marksman. In the old days we were forever skirmishing—with troops or the Khamseh or Bakhtiari. We kept our hand and eye in. But now . . ." he struck an attitude of good behaviour, then asked with a sniff, "If you miss a partridge, does it ever fire back?"

The hunters had climbed many of the higher peaks looking for mountain ibex. Ghazan asked if they had met any snow leopard. No, they hadn't seen one, said Kutlugh. After all, thought Ghazan heavily, I shall never glimpse the snow leopard. But this seemed to him just and appropriate. Truth, his own self, he was further than ever from finding. And these he identified in his own mind with the snow leopard. Only as the expression of these, he believed, could the snow leopard appear.

They continued eating in silence. Later Kutlugh said to the man who had killed the ibex: "You'll be taking that head up to Ghazan Khan."

Tradition decreed that every ibex head be offered to the Ilkhan: Ghazan usually gave the hunter a present of money for his prowess.

The young man said, "I was up at court two days ago: they said he was still in Teheran."

"Not possible," one of the others contended. "Months he's been gone."

"Trouble—you can be sure of that," muttered Kutlugh. "Ghazan Khan wouldn't stay away for a trifle."

"Supposing they've captured and poisoned him?"

Kutlugh looked scornfully at the questioner. "You don't know what you're saying."

"And if it's true, as some claim, that the Ilkhan's to be exiled?"

"Then he'll find a way back—as he did before." The others looked at Kutlugh doubtfully. "I remember Ghazan Khan as a boy," he continued with conviction. "We were settled in a village of tents near

248

Farrashband. All our donkeys and most of our horses were dead. It was spring, just before barley harvest. One morning we woke to find an army sergeant prowling about—the one nicknamed Squint Eyes."

"I knew him," growled one of the men. "We used to gather acorns to mix with our barley flour. Squint Eyes made us pay a so-called 'tax' on the acorns."

"That's the one. He went to the headman. 'A donkey's missing from my stall,' he said, cracking his riding whip—he liked to do that. 'I've traced him here. In your village the tracks come to an end. Where have you hidden him?' The headman couldn't explain the hoof-prints but denied the charge. 'Lies,' cried the sergeant and searched the village. 'Clearly the donkey has been removed to the mountains and hidden. Which of your men is responsible?' No one would own to the theft, so the sergeant said, 'Ten of your men come with me to Shiraz: the courts will arrive at the truth.'

"Now the standing barley was all our food for the year. With our young men gone, we'd never have entered the harvest. Even if cleared of the charge, they would be away three or four weeks. And they would leave their wives unprotected, with troops stationed an hour's ride away."

"I could tell you a tale or two," muttered one of his listeners.

"So the headman began to bargain. How much would it cost to indemnify the sergeant? He asked about five times a donkey's value. I forget the sum: with rising prices it wouldn't seem much now. Our women had to unsew their skirts and count out their last coins. The headman was just going to hand over the money when who rode into the village but Ghazan Khan. He couldn't have been more than twelve. It was afternoon by then and he'd returned from school. Seeing trouble, he said to the sergeant. 'Explain what you want.' The sergeant told him. He'd stopped cracking his whip. When the lion appears (be he only a cub), the jackal falls silent.

"'How old was the donkey?' asked Ghazan.

"The sergeant thought awhile. 'Three months,' he said.

"Ghazan examined the prints carefully, twisting in and out among the tents, on hands and knees. It was spring, remember, and they were very clear on the soft ground.

"'Strangest colt I've ever known,' he said. 'It walks on one hoof, and that hoof is the size of a one-month foal.'

249

"Squint Eyes was getting very restive. 'If you give me my money, I'll be getting back.'

"But Ghazan said, 'Wait. Tell me more about this donkey. One of mine was also stolen—two months back.'

"'I'm not sure of its age. All I know is, it's gone from my stall.'

"Ghazan said, 'You can't claim money on that evidence.'

"We were all astonished Squint Eyes didn't protest. He simply shrugged and went to his horse. Ghazan was watching all the time and as the sergeant mounted he saw a great long bulge in his trouser pocket.

"'Wait a moment,' he cried. 'What's this?' Squint Eyes dodged away, but Ghazan grabbed at his pocket and pulled. Squint Eyes galloped off in a cloud of dust. We looked at Ghazan. In his hand lay the front hoof of a donkey, cut at the fetlock. It was clear Squint Eyes had stolen the donkey and made the prints himself. Later we learned he had pulled the same trick in five neighbouring villages. But Ghazan Khan didn't know that." Kutlugh looked round like a trapper springing his snare. "Don't tell me that Ghazan Khan will be made a fool of, in Teheran or anywhere else."

Ghazan listened uncomfortably. He recognized the long-forgotten episode as true, but it annoyed him to overhear it like a spy. As others recalled incidents from the days of Reza Shah, a crude brown arack made of fermented dates flavoured with aniseed was passed round: a drink to make the head swim. To appease their consciences they called it 'cold tea'. Voices grew louder and gayer. Now that he had been accepted, Ghazan told them he had returned from Shiraz, that the army was massing and intended to try and disarm the Falqani.

"Which would you choose," he asked, "to yield your rifles, or take your chance, outnumbered?"

They looked at him in surprise, then Kutlugh said, "Men like you and me—it's not for us to decide. Ghazan Khan will issue orders; we will follow."

This blind trust ruffled Ghazan in his present mood. The Ilkhan would know best, but supposing the Ilkhan didn't know?

He said to the old man, "If you were Khan, what would you decide?"

Kutlugh seemed confused. "But I'm not Khan, so how can I know?"

250

"But *if* you were," Ghazan insisted.

"Ghazan Khan decides. I follow," said Kutlugh. The others agreed and changed the subject. They began to question Ghazan. Which section was he from? Why was he riding alone? Ghazan wondered whether or not to reveal himself. At first he did not want to disturb the easy atmosphere of equality, then he thought, they will confide their wishes to me only if they know who I am. He took a deep drink of arack, and said, with a ring of challenge:

"Don't you know your own Ilkhan?"

Some of the drinkers cocked their heads.

"Haven't you been listening?" Kutlugh retorted annoyed. "Just because I do know him, I leave it to him."

Smiling now at the confusion, Ghazan cried, "You call yourselves Falqani! I am your Ilkhan!"

A puzzled silence, then they burst out laughing. Kutlugh leaned over and snatched away his bowl of arack. "You've had enough. One half-sip more and you'll be saying you're the Prophet himself."

After his first astonishment Ghazan joined in the laughter.

"By the life of this fire, what I tell you is true. I am on my way back to court."

"From Teheran by way of Shiraz!" they mocked.

"Twenty bowls of arack wouldn't turn my head," Ghazan protested.

"Even if you hadn't drunk," said Kutlugh, "I shouldn't have believed you."

Half laughing, half incredulous, Ghazan retorted, "If your own mother handed you a gold coin, you'd say it was copper."

"Another time," continued Kutlugh, "if you want to take us in, choose a better horse, and bring a servant, and ride on till you reach the headman's tent."

One of the younger men added, "True, you've got the same cast of head. But the Ilkhan's cheeks are much fatter."

A third said, "Do you think Ghazan Khan would ask *our* advice? It's clear you don't know his ways."

They thought he had pulled a good joke, and liked him for it. They were so convinced he was trying to trick them that Ghazan said no more. The reversal of rôles amused him. It scarcely mattered who they believed he was, and the arack was a difficult argument to refute.

An hour after they had emptied the bowl, conversation petered out

251

with the fire and Ghazan, wrapped in a blanket, stretched out with the four shepherds. Though he had enjoyed the evening, he felt uneasy. Kutlugh knew more about him than he did himself: recalled a lost boyhood story: yet failed to recognize him face to face. Was it because of his trappings or because he had changed? They knew him from his actions as a determined leader. But the polemics, the groping behind a decision—not a fitting of pieces within an accepted jig-saw puzzle, but a decision where one man alone confronted the universe—to change the course of blood and lymph, as they might be the Tigris and Euphrates, the sinew's first stirring like the stirring of Eve in Adam's rib: of these they had no experience. For them action was reflex action; tomorrow did not exist. As an ignorant boy confronting the sergeant, his decision had been impulsive. He had not questioned fundamentals then. Now, freighted with facts, a course was harder to hold: every minute, on the bridge, he must fight for leeway.

But his men had given their answer. They were extras who had not read his part. He must decide the problems himself: his own and the tribe's. To be Khan meant to carry alone knowledge and doubts which others could not bear. And he thought, only I am acquainted with both points of view. Neither Tughril, nor Rohim, nor the others look beyond the Zagros. To consult chieftains no less than tribesmen would be to falsify the issues. Only I have this special knowledge; I alone can take the decision.

The Madaleh had shifted their tents often in the last months, but Ghazan knew the limits of their moves and by noon next day glimpsed red, yellow and blue canvas. On the last stage he had visited headmen: messengers had been sent to announce his arrival. Riding up into the last green valley, he was welcomed by the women gathered in two lines to form a long avenue. Vibrating their tongues, they made a shrill, quavering cry, like a quail's, now soft, now loud and continued for a long while. They seemed to voice Ghazan's own joy. On each stage of the ride his spirits had risen, almost in direct proportion to the physical ascent. To regain the wide bare slopes, the oblong black tents, the flocks, his people moving against the skyline: this was to multiply life, to take eternity in his stride. Seldom had he savoured each sight and word as now, returning under the threat of returning no more. Last rite of welcome, amid the shouting crowds, some firing jubilant shots, a servant slit a ram's throat and spattered his master's sheepskin boots with blood.

At his homecoming feast that night Ghazan told what he had done and learned. The scattering of elders and chieftains who happened to be in the Madaleh camp listened between anger and dismay, then voiced their opinions. Some were for yielding their rifles and hoping the army would be content with that. The summer had been dry, the gadfly arriving late, doubly rife. Their flocks were thin and depleted. They claimed they had trouble enough already. Others, the younger, argued for resisting, by force of arms or by braving winter snows in the uplands. Rohim raged to cut down the army like a field of yellow corn. Tughril said nothing. When they turned questioning glances, Ghazan held them off.

"When frost ices the winter pails, then I shall give my word. For now it is enough that we eat again together."

And because they were glad to have their Ilkhan back, they questioned him no more that night.

Instead they told him of their hunting achievements, of births and deaths among men and beasts. One piece of news Ghazan received with mixed feelings. Rohim's marriage—to a princess of the Adashuri, a federated tribe—was a project which had been in the air for some months. Always Tughril had delayed it, saying that Rohim was too young and impetuous to rear a family, but during Ghazan's absence Tughril had shown himself unusually good-tempered, and Rohim had prevailed on his father to fix a date before the autumn migration.

Later, to Manuchehr the elder, Ghazan spoke in a different vein.

"This spring and summer," he confided, "I think I caught a glimpse of the face of Persia."

"How was it, this face? Wrinkled as mine?"

Ghazan looked at the old man, his skin like bark. Stump of a gnarled oak: but standing against the skyline a landmark, reassuring. He cast his mind back to Teheran.

"The thin, bright-eyed face of a wandering dervish, poor in possessions, but rich in spirit. He has met a man with the opposite characteristics, who dresses in silk and feasts on pilav and passion fruit. This man offers hospitality and entertainment. The dervish accepts gratefully, thanking God for His mercy. Next day the dervish wishes to resume his journey, but his new friend presses him to stay. The dervish

253

agrees. This continues for a long while. Then the dervish says, 'It is time that I leave.' His benefactor replies, 'Don't go. Stay here always. Give up your old habits, live with me. Let feasting replace your prayers, and yellow wine your topaz beads.' 'Your kindness is slowly destroying me,' the dervish says. 'If I stay longer I shall cease to be a dervish.' 'What of that, since you will be well fed and clothed till the day you die?' 'It is not my own death I fear, but yours,' answers the dervish. 'For the goods I have come to expect will cease and, as for me, no longer a dervish, I shall have no claim on the bounty of God. Will the desert yield me passion fruit? In my fine silk shall I stoop to draw a wooden plough? I shall die with my face downwards and none will turn it to Mecca.'"

Pausing, Ghazan looked abstractedly at the elder.

"And with that the dervish leaves," Manuchehr concluded with conviction.

"He has one bare foot on the threshold," said Ghazan gravely, "but he has not yet left."

Next morning Ghazan was told, on his return from a tour of the camp, that an army officer was waiting to see him. Accompanied by Rohim, he approached the court tents with misgiving. But even before he distinguished his visitor's face, Ghazan recognized the dumpy figure and smiled: it could only be Major Shami.

He was the son of a slink-butcher whose brother had commanded the quartermaster section at Shiraz. During his period of conscription the young Shami had been well looked after by his uncle, and had proved a good hand at diverting trousers and boots to the nearest bazaar. Finding it more profitable to dye khaki than pass off wasted meat as fresh, the young Shami joined as a regular and, having learned to read and write, presently bought a commission. When his uncle retired at an early age, with a fortune which built him one of the biggest houses in Teheran, he saw that his own coveted command fell to his nephew. The younger Shami had continued the family tradition of selling army property to local merchants and the tribes.

Ghazan watched the quartermaster waddle like a partridge across the camp clearing, khaki uniform stained and creased, black shoes matted with dust.

"Peace be upon you, Ghazan Khan and on you, Rohim." His style and expression were dignified. The hand he offered was as flabby as his cheeks. Only the small, restless eyes suggested energy.

They entered the court tent and after the usual greetings tea was served. Ghazan watched Shami closely, wondering what he would offer for sale this time. Once it had been five huge drums of plastic-covered electric wire. When Ghazan had asked what use the Falqani could make of that, Shami had suggested, in all seriousness, "Bridles."

Presently Shami broached the reason for his visit.

"I have on my hands a great deal of surplus equipment. Tiresome, but there it is. It goes against a soldier's conscience to destroy good material. Would it be any use to you?"

Ghazan gave his usual reply. "Fortunately we have all the equipment we need, for hunting and the protection of our flocks."

Ghazan spoke firmly, but Shami was nothing if not persevering: "No one can foretell the future; no one was ever too well prepared."

The offer held little appeal for Ghazan. Falqani weakness lay in their flocks and women, and these no amount of material could totally protect. But Rohim listened more closely.

"Machine guns?" he asked. Rohim had an obstinate belief that superior weapons brought invincibility.

Shami seemed genuinely sorry. "Machine guns are scarce this year."

"Automatic rifles?"

"Hardly enough for ourselves."

Seeing Rohim lose interest, Shami turned back to Ghazan.

"Straight-pull Mannlicher rifles—three hundred. Fifty cases of ammunition, some of it tracer.'

"To shoot low-flying owls by night!" laughed Ghazan.

Shami smiled politely. His expression seemed to say, You Falqani will have your little joke. Cajolingly he said:

"The Khamseh would snatch at an offer like this." After a silence, he continued, "Surely you're not so well supplied . . ."

Ghazan, aware that Shami hoped for information regarding Falqani stocks, answered purposely off the point.

"Sheep and goats yield according to the rhythm of nature. Nature's profits are small."

"Being surplus material, the rifles can be offered especially cheap."

"We must think about it," said Ghazan indifferently.

The silence which followed was shattered, without warning, by a loud volley not far away. The major, tense and pale, clambered to his feet, brandishing his revolver.

"An ambush! An ambush!"

"It's nothing," said Rohim. But he asked Shami to be careful. The pistol was pointing directly at his chest.

"Didn't you hear the guns? A full-scale attack!"

"Only on quail and francolin," said Ghazan and explained that a hunt was in progress.

"You're sure?" Shami peeped doubtfully out of the tent and saw the hunters for himself, while the cousins watched with growing amuse- ment. They guessed Shami had been terrified not only by the shots but by their implications. A chance army patrol, and his presence in the Ilkhan's tent would take some explaining.

A few moments later he turned, affecting to be quite unabashed, with furrowed brows and a show of disappointment. He had hoped, he said, for a little excitement. Nothing he liked better than a rough tussle with brigands. A pity, he sighed; then with an air of dignity sat down and replaced his weapon.

Ghazan took the opportunity of changing the subject.

"What is your illusive General doing these days?"

Shami seemed pleased. "Looking for a horse. Or rather, he has asked me to look for one." Pulling down his sleeves with a flourish, Shami continued, "For some reason, General Bahrami seems to have taken a fancy to me. I intend to get him the very best, and still further improve our friendship."

Rohim said, "You are doubtless an expert on horses?"

The Major pushed unruly black hair back from his temples. "I am a soldier and a quartermaster. I should say I know more about horses than most."

The cousins exchanged glances. Major Shami never admitted ignor- ance, no matter what the subject. As the proverb had it: "His jug held a lot of water."

A gleam came into Rohim's eyes. He turned to Shami with an amiable smile.

"Talking of horses, perhaps you can help. A stock-breeder paid us a visit this spring. He spoke of a German manual on the diseases of foals. The best of its kind, he claimed. Doubtless you know the book?"

"I seem to recall it." Shami's tone suggested that the manual lay in a corner of his well-stocked library.

"I want to order the book direct. I know a little German and I'm trying to write the letter. Pferd is horse, I remember that. Do you happen to know the German for foal?"

Rohim leaned back and waited. It seemed he had caught Shami at last. The Major passed stubby fingers over his brow and pondered for several moments.

"The Germans have no word for foal," he finally announced.

"No word for foal!"

Shami smiled easily. "They wait for the foal to grow into a horse, then call it Pferd."

The cousins looked at each other, open-mouthed, speechless, scarcely able to contain their laughter. Ghazan was the first to recover.

"A horse," he said casually. "Is General Bahrami really in need of a horse?"

"He is shortly to inspect advanced gendarmerie posts. The country will be too rough for jeeps."

"Our horses are the finest in the world," said Ghazan. "You cannot do better than get him a Falqani Arab."

"Purchase from the tribes! I could never do that."

"Why not?" asked Ghazan, with a show of displeasure.

"The army's implacable enemies! Or rather, his former enemies. That would never do."

"He need not know. It could be your gift. One does not ask the origin of gifts. This afternoon," concluded Ghazan, in a tone of finality, "you shall see one of our Arab thoroughbreds."

After the midday meal, when their guest, according to his unalterable rule, had retired to an empty tent for a short sleep, Ghazan told Rohim of a plan to dupe Major Shami. This desire to score off his enemies, even a single point, had been growing since the sad-eyed captain had read that unanswerable document in the Ministry of War. For months now he had suffered in silence at their hands, and their image was beginning to haunt him. He felt it must somehow be smashed. He must fight back; for once, no matter in how small a degree, prove his power to retaliate. Shami was a particularly appropriate target, for a friend of Ghazan, a certain Arghun Khan, leader of a small neighbouring tribe called the Shishbuluki, had recently tried to humiliate Shami and had had the tables turned on him. It had happened like this.

A company of infantry had raided the Shishbuluki and seized some two thousand cases of Mauser ammunition. The Shishbuluki used ·433-inch ammunition for their old Mausers, while army rifles at that time had a bore of ·256-inch. As the captured cases were useless to the army, Major Shami was ordered to blow them up. Instead, he approached Arghun and offered to sell back the ammunition, asking two hundred thousand tumans, payable on delivery. Now Arghun had no immediate need of ammunition; moreover, he had particular reason to hate Shami, who was forever instigating these profitable raids. But he hid his anger and agreed to buy. After much haggling he beat down Shami's price. They arranged that the money should be handed over one night the following week at an old quarry where Shami had hidden the cases. Meanwhile Arghun sent an anonymous message to the General commanding Fars province, pointing out that irregularities were occurring within his command and that he should come, well guarded, to the quarry, without telling any of his officers. The night for delivering the ammunition arrived: Arghun and Shami made their way separately to the rendezvous.

Arghun succeeded in prolonging the transaction until the General arrived with a detachment of troops. Shami guessed what had happened but saw no way out. He tried to conceal his embarrassed alarm, while Arghun told the General of Shami's proposals.

The General turned to his quartermaster. "Is this true?"

In desperation Shami retorted, "No, sir. This is a trick. You can never believe a Shishbuluki."

"Then how," asked the General, "do you explain these hundreds of Mauser ammunition cases?" and he pointed to the wooden boxes, neatly stacked against the quarry face.

Shami began to stutter an excuse.

"This is the very same ammunition he captured four weeks ago," snapped Arghun, and the General shouted at Shami:

"I thought I gave you orders to blow up those boxes."

"There must be some mistake," wavered Shami. "If you and I could talk this over together . . ."

He hoped to bribe the General to disregard the matter, but in front of Arghun and the detachment of troops that was impossible.

The General dismissed the suggestion. As a last resort Shami tried bluff.

"Surely you don't imagine, sir, that I would be guilty of selling materials of war!"

The General had his doubts, but declined to argue. Instead, he ordered his men to open the cases. Major Shami, more alarmed than ever, pleaded for delay. The wooden cases were prized open with bayonets: four of them: each revealing a neat row of brass and nickel. Shami closed his eyes in horror.

"A hundred and fifty thousand tumans was the price he asked," said Arghun, picking up one of the rounds. He glanced at it and frowned. There followed a long silence. Then Arghun said:

"This isn't Mauser ammunition."

"Not Mauser ammunition?" repeated Shami in amazement.

"It's half the size. Useless for our rifles."

The General took the round.

"One of our cartridges," he announced in a puzzled voice. He ordered more of the boxes to be opened and tipped over. Wood snapped, metal grated on metal, as the boxes were reversed. On top were a few ·256 rounds such as the army used, underneath nothing but sand.

All three looked at the sand, stupefied. Shami had believed the boxes were full of Mauser ammunition: he prided himself on giving value for money. He did not pretend to understand, but he saw a chance of escape.

"*You* arranged this?" the General asked, and interpreted Shami's bewildered look as modest assent.

"Then where is the Mauser ammunition?"

Shami answered, like one inspired. "Blown up, sir, according to orders." A faint note of reproach crept into his voice. "My plan was to collect the hundred and fifty thousand tumans from Arghun, thus weakening tribal power. This money, of course, I should have handed over to you in trust for the Government. But," he added with a sigh, "it's too late now."

The meeting broke up. Arghun considered he had been made a fool of, while Shami discovered later that one of his own lieutenants had removed the Mauser ammunition and was himself conducting negotiations with another tribe for its sale. The Major was furious at losing his hundred and fifty thousand, for which a commendation from his General for astuteness certainly did not compensate.

When Ghazan had explained his plan, the two cousins went to see the chieftain of the Pardalun, a federated tribe which used horses as pack animals. They asked to buy the oldest he had. The chieftain went to fetch a skewbald of fourteen weary years, suffering from glanders.

"This horse is so lazy," he said, patting its thin neck, "it has been known to try and mount its rider."

At first he was puzzled, but learning the cousins' plan he offered it free to Ghazan, who ordered the animal to be washed and groomed and its tail rubbed bright with mallow petals, then led to his tent richly caparisoned.

Presently he and Rohim were joined by the Major.

"We have been to see the chief of the Pardalun," said Ghazan, with an air of triumph. "As a special favour, he has found you a rare and wonderful animal."

"A horse?" asked Shami.

Full of enthusiasm, Ghazan replied: "The very essence of horse-hood. Your heart's desire. Come and see it."

Outside the tent the skewbald was paraded before them. Its brown and white coat gleamed in the sun; a thick saddle-cloth of purple damask hid its sagging back.

Ghazan turned to Shami, his expression between awe and wonder. "Have you ever in your life set eye on such an extraordinary creature?"

"On al-Burak," said Rohim, "the blessed Mohammed ascended to heaven. On this celestial steed you too can follow him." With a pilgrim's fervour he approached the horse. "Look at those fetlocks, like the wrists of a juggler, that gait, like the touch of a lute-player on strings: that tilt of the head—no king ever carried himself with such pride."

They both looked at the Major. To their relief he did not examine its missing teeth or its withers. As they expected, then, he knew nothing about horses. He was well aware that the Falqani were experts, and the horse, of good breed and carefully groomed, looked passably well.

Not to be outdone, Shami said, "To ride such a horse would indeed be a foretaste of Paradise."

"Look at that back," Rohim continued. "The curves are like velvet hangings."

"Like a houri's outstretched arm," said the Major.

"And that tail—a cascade of amber. Not even Rustam's horse had such a flowing tail."

"A tail to end all tails," Shami concluded.

"And so calm now, you would never think he was fiery as arack." Shami's eyes flickered. "Not too fiery, I hope?"

Like initiates before a venerable idol, for some time they vied to festoon the horse with far-fetched compliments. Finally Ghazan turned to Shami.

"Although we cannot afford your rifles or ammunition, we do not wish you to have made your journey in vain. Is this horse not fit for a General of the Persian army?"

"Indeed it is," said the Major, with conviction.

Ghazan turned to his cousin. "What is the horse's value?"

Rohim pondered. "An Arab thoroughbred? Five thousand tumans at least."

"But I cannot buy it," Shami protested. "The General's money passing to tribal hands!"

"We will accept no money," said Ghazan in his most magnanimous tone. "The horse is yours."

Shami looked at Ghazan in astonishment. "You give me this rare animal?"

"Why not? You can present him to the General if you wish: he will make a most suitable mount."

Five thousand tumans. The cousins saw Shami repeating the figure silently to himself. He looked again at the horse; then, a little doubtfully, at the cousins.

"You wouldn't have a pedigree?" he asked mildly.

"*Pedigree!*" cried Ghazan. "Why, this horse has its pedigree written in every curve of its body." Then he made a show of being offended. "Of course, if you decline . . ."

"No, no," said Shami. Fearing lest the gift be withdrawn, Shami did not trouble with explanations. He accepted the offer and took his leave almost at once. The last they saw of him was mounted on his donkey, headed for the hills, the skewbald on a leading rein, already lagging behind.

261

Ghazan had to wait ten days to hear the sequel, which included a second unforeseen twist. The agent who brought his letters from Shiraz told Ghazan it was the talk of the town.

Shami, reluctant to lose an opportunity of making money, discovered the highest market price in Shiraz of an Arab thoroughbred and, leading his new acquisition to General Bahrami, announced that at last he had acquired the ideal horse. The General, after a cursory inspection, discovered the horse's age and noticed the swellings below its jaw and its U-shaped back.

The General stared at Shami. "You spent how much on this animal?"

Shami decided to make the most of what he believed was the General's pleasurable surprise. "Seven thousand tumans, sir."

"Out of army funds?"

"Yes, sir."

"Are you tired of life that you dare bring me such a nag?"

"I assure you, sir, it is an Arab thoroughbred."

"A thoroughbred! It isn't worth killing for its flesh. It's the most dejected jade I've ever set eyes on. Where did you buy it?"

The Major had intended to say nothing of its origin but, stupefied by this disappointment and stung that the General had turned against him, he tried to put some of the blame on Ghazan. He blurted out that he had bought the horse from the Falqani. How was he to know that Ghazan had tricked him?

"You idiot! First you deal with those Turki chiefs. That is expressly forbidden. Then you allow yourself to be cheated. There are no words to express what I think of you. You yourself shall forfeit the seven thousand tumans."

Shami pleaded, but in vain. The General was exceedingly cross.

"Furthermore, you shall be degraded a rank. No, it is useless to protest, the matter is settled once and for all."

The threat was fulfilled. Shami had to return his major's crown for a captain's three sunbursts. That was bad enough, but he had already spent seven thousand tumans from army funds—his hoped-for profit—on a new car. One horse for thirty horsepower, as Shami put it. This too had to be returned, and the garage gave him two thousand tumans less than he had paid, leaving Captain Shami in debt.

Hearing this sequel, Ghazan was elated out of all proportion to

Shami's discomfiture. In their offices these soldiers might be impregnable, but not on the hills. Once already in battle he had made them lick his boots. Ten times the numbers they might have now, but they were not thereby irresistible. Clever tactics and bluff could always turn the scales. Back with his men, his blood was up; the dice were in the shaker, a hundred thousand of them: if only he had a fixed prize for which to throw, if only he could be demonstrably sure that settlement was at all costs to be avoided.

With Ghazan the whole tribe triumphed. It was the sort of incident they appreciated. The good news spread from tent to tent; by the time it reached outlying sections, Shami was held to have been dismissed the service and imprisoned. Even the unexaggerated victory partly compensated for dark memories, and one more incident was added to the sagas told round evening fires.

CHAPTER NINETEEN

GHAZAN reintegrated himself in tribal life. He superintended the collecting of gum from spiny tragacanth bushes. The gum was sold in Shiraz at a good price and sent abroad to be used as a thickener in textile printing and as a protective agent in medicines and cosmetics. Ahmad was not yet back from Meshed, and Ghazan found the Ilkhan's sheep in poor condition. The roll of fat at their tails, which weighed up to thirty pounds in spring, had been reduced by drought to a third that size. A flock of six hundred, infected with foot-and-mouth disease, had to be treated with salicylate of sodium. The rutting season was about to begin, in the sign of the Balance, and Ghazan had to choose ewes to be covered.

With a touch of unreasoning scorn, Ghazan had expected the ewes on which the stock-breeder had experimented to miscarry or yean two-headed monsters. In fact, both bore big healthy lambs. The shepherd who attended the ewes viewed the births with gaping eyes. Since no rams had come near the ewes, the lambs, he claimed, had been fathered by a stroke of lightning. Ghazan drew a less startling conclusion. The experts were not such fools as he had thought. And the experts favoured settlement.

Once again he had to give judgment in judicial appeals: untangle knife-fights and thefts, award damages and punishment. One case was particularly knotty: a marriage childless after six years, and the husband claiming a second wife, despite the protests of the first. Tradition was clear on the point, and Ghazan had to allow the husband's claim. The protagonists withdrew satisfied.

Under the silent sky, on the hill which served as witness-box and judgment seat, Ghazan was left alone with his secret case adjourned. Justice had issued from him, in however minor a form: now he remained under the shadow of injustice. So easy it proved to decide these cases brought from the grass and beasts: why could he not solve his own dilemma? Because it related to the future, to values not easily weighed? Or was it impossible to be one's own judge? This he refused to admit: always he had believed that life was a seeking of truth and that the search was not vain. Perhaps justice entailed coming fresh to a problem, seeing it new, without desire or preconceptions. He resolved to climb still further into the mountains, scatter inessentials like chaff to the cold wind, and only when he returned to camp reconsider the future.

The chieftain of the Galanzi, who had ridden over for an appeal case, had glimpsed, two days before, a grey-striped shape on the western slopes of Kuh-i-Dina, one of the high peaks of summer quarters. He was almost sure it had been a snow leopard. Ghazan considered the opportunity too good to miss. If he were destined to leave the Zagros, what could be a more appropriate last gesture? He could keep the pelt and head by him wherever he might be.

Next morning he rode over to the Galanzi encampment. From afar the tents seemed slabs of jet, mined out of the grey mountain, and the dark flocks clambering up its sunlit sides exposed seams. Snow still lay entrenched on the arrow-headed summit, a garrison in temporary difficulties, soon to break out and overrun all the surrounding hills. Some peaks were cloud-swept. The Galanzi chieftain gave Ghazan a special warning to beware of mist on the Dina; men had been lost for days in that mist.

During the early afternoon Ghazan questioned shepherds who thought they had seen traces. Several sheep had been killed, and Ghazan noted the position of their bones. Others had been stolen without trace. Remains of hares, a favourite prey, had been found on the western slopes. One old man said he could remember when the mountain was teeming with snow leopard. They had killed a hundred sheep a year. He believed that when the migrations stopped most had died for lack of food. Now there might be less than a dozen in the whole Zagros range. They were rarer even than brown bear.

Ghazan started off in the late afternoon, alone and on foot. He planned to climb half way up the mountain on the eastern slope, then circle to the western side. He carried his favourite ·400 rifle with walnut stock, a leather sling and ten soft-nosed bullets. His experience was less adequate. He knew that snow leopards were afraid of man but when wounded by a poor shot would attack and kill. They emerged towards dusk to roam and strike by night. This one probably had a lair in one of the many rock caves that pitted the upper western slopes, two thousand feet above his starting point. Size alone offered no clue, for a leopard could squeeze into very narrow clefts.

Ghazan began to climb. The slope was not steep, but his cord shoes continually slipped on the gravelly screes. The skidding rumble reverberated from rock to rock, like a system of beacons. There were no trees and few bushes. The mountain itself must yield him cover, and for this reason he had dressed in grey shirt and trousers. It was still too early to reckon with the east wind. Hugging the highest rocks and steepest bluffs, he took the line of least resistance upwards, like lava in a threatening volcano.

He crossed to the western slope and began to spoor, on a zigzag upward course. He walked stooping and sometimes sank to hands and knees. He questioned the position of every pebble, the lie of every stick on the stony, wind-swept surface. Nothing could be taken for granted. Each mark had a meaning. Prints of Falqani sheep and goats, these he found in plenty, and occasional paw-marks of dogs. Once he crossed the cloven path of a yellow ibex. But of larger animals he saw no sign.

He reached a sheer gash in the mountainside and sat to rest in its cover. With a sense of achievement he looked down. An hour's climb had reduced tents to the size of beetles, sheep and goats to flies. He could see, beyond, the green valley where his own tents were pitched. They were invisible. Further still, on all sides, ranges of fawn hills sloped away to the blue afternoon sky like scalloped sand to an ebbing tide.

His attention wandered to the exposed rocks where he sat resting: layers of limestone, clearly defined as the circles in an oak trunk, each line marking not one year but many millennia. In the shelf nearest him Ghazan noticed two fossilized fish: grey ovals, plum-sized, their backbones exposed. How long, he wondered, had they been stranded there in the rocks, minnows with one of the highest mountains in Persia as their mausoleum? He chipped out the fossils with his hip-knife and put them in his pocket.

He began again to stalk, crossing a patch of juniper and cranberry into less stony ground. He moved alone except for an occasional hawk wheeling overhead, searching too. But so well did his clothing blend, so smoothly and quietly did he climb, that the hawks did not swerve away in alarm. For perhaps a thousand paces he continued like this. Suddenly he caught his breath and stopped. In some fine earth that had sifted down between two big rocks he saw a strange mark, as though the flower of a large tulip had been trodden deep, then removed. He touched the edge with one finger. It was quite soft. A giant, deeply embedded paw-print the size of his own palm. Its outlines were still sharp: it could hardly be more than a day old. Twenty paces higher Ghazan found a second. Again he was struck by its size, its suggestion of mass. The snow leopard must be larger than he had imagined. He tried to visualize it, but even with this new evidence he could picture only a grey misty shape without distinct form.

This moment of distraction lost him the sequence of paw-marks. Slinging his rifle, he sank to his heels and edged his way slowly forward, checking his excitement, again reading the hieroglyphics made by lizard and scorpion, spider and ant. So many lives on the bare, silent, seemingly dead slope: all claiming his attention. But he forced himself on. In a few moments he found another of the big paw-marks, then two close together. They pointed towards a high escarpment two hundred yards directly ahead.

Ghazan chose a line of approach up a dry torrent-bed, well sheltered by boulders. He crawled on hands and knees, sweating, grazed and cut, breathing fast in the rarefied air. He had to move quickly. He could count on one hour more of day. He had neither food nor covering to sleep out at such a height. If this trail came to a dead end, he would fail. And not once had he seen his quarry: he had simply followed signs, and the word of a few tribesmen, the snow leopard's prophets.

Reaching the base of the escarpment Ghazan began to crawl on his belly. He felt completely on the animal level, edging into the cold wind. So alert were his senses, he half-believed his nostrils would pick up the scent of fur and flesh. Sand and grit worked their way into his clothes and hair, under his fingernails. His eyes became swollen with dust. Half-way up he stooped to tear a strip from his shirt. Screwing up the cotton, he made a stopple of it and rammed it into the rifle barrel. Again he slithered forward, silent as a snake. By the time he reached the top the front of his shirt and trousers was ripped to shreds.

Very slowly Ghazan lifted his eyes. Ahead lay a line of grey rocks and clefts, interspersed with thorn bushes. He scanned them anxiously. At first he saw nothing unusual, but as his smarting eyes became adjusted to the distance and shades of colour, he felt a stir of excitement, and, as though in direct response, the blood throbbed in his wrists. In the branches of one spiny bush hung the red and white carcase of a half-devoured sheep. That was said to be a likely sign of a lair. The leopard kept the carcase in sight and ate the flesh when it became high.

But the bush lay two hundred yards away. At that range he could not be sure of hitting the heart. He must halve the distance. A difficult task, because his present approach was devoid of cover. He dragged himself down the escarpment and crawled to the left, hoping to find, as it were, a seam leading into the mine. After half a mile he came to a shallow ravine. He darted up this to a vantage-point protected from sight of the clefts by boulders.

He lay sprawling behind the boulders out of breath. Carefully he removed the wadding from his muzzle, brushed the sights clean and set them at a hundred metres. He opened the breech, took out the cartridge, examined it, then replaced it in the breech: grey bullet for grey quarry. He cocked the rifle. When his hands were steady again he lifted the muzzle between the boulders.

Ahead rose the snow-tipped peak, ridged and gashed. There were three clefts near the bush with the carcase: two were narrow, about a palm wide, the third about Ghazan's own height and width. In front, on the side nearest him, was a flat clearing of stone, silhouetted; to the right a precipice—impassable; to the left thin bushes below a ridge. If his prey emerged onto the clearing, it would be visible for a moment only. Ghazan swung the bead on his muzzle up into the centre of the clearing and brought the shoulders of his sights round to enclose the bead. Then he began to wait.

The day's sweat and torn flesh, hunger and thirst had culminated in a passionate desire to kill, to carry his enemy's head and pelt in triumph back to the encampment. Ghazan's eyes, his whole being, were centred on the clefts, willing the beast to appear.

But the beast did not appear. His presence altered nothing, brought nothing to birth. As before, grey stone outstared the blue sky. A worshipper without an idol. His tension, in spite of himself, gradually relaxed. He preferred stalking to lying in wait. But he had to match silence with silence. He continued to lie stretched out on the earth, absolutely motionless.

For a long time he remained alert, thinking of the unseen beast. But as the moments passed his attention began to wander. The slow, arduous search, vestiges in the earth leading upwards, the unique grey, ghostly shape: they reminded him of something. Of what? Not for some time did he remember. They were stages in the Sufi ascent to truth. His clothes, torn to shreds, his body cold in the cold wind: those recalled a particular stage: the 'grave exercise', an elementary method of self-renunciation the mullah Mahdi had taught him long ago. The initiate had to imagine himself stripped of every shred of existence: dead, washed, wrapped in his winding sheet and laid in his tomb: he had to picture the departure of mourners, leaving him alone to face the Judgment.

Lying on the scree, facing the snow-tipped peak, Ghazan wondered whether he was still capable of that exercise. How selfish, how depraved had he become, he who had dared to judge a saint on his death-bed? He resolved to try. But groping his way up the mountainside he had passed through many existences. Deep in the earth he had been stone and seam of silver; resting he had been a juniper bush swept by the wind; lizard-like he had crept between rocks; forward he had bounded like a greyhound: steadily upward. Now he lay alone, facing south-west, facing Mecca. He had to shuffle off all these lives, and last of all his own. As man had gained in stature by dying to each of the lower evolutionary stages, so by a final death he must win yet greater gain: a vision of the Beloved's face.

So ran the doctrine: it remained to implement it. Ghazan's eye was still trained on the stone clearing. Any movement there would rouse him. Reassured, he gradually consigned the cuts and bruises on arms and legs to oblivion; with a firm hand he wound himself in the shroud of indifference. He noticed with pleasure that he had complete control of his feelings, his thoughts, his will: and this pleasure he also deliberately ground to dust. One by one he stripped away the petals of desire, until he became as scentless as the cold wind.

Something stirred. Not on the stone clearing, but above to the left on the ridge. The bushes darkened as a great shape moved up beyond them. Ghazan raised his eyes slowly, at the same time edging his rifle up. The shape emerged from the bushes, in profile: massive, giving the impression of great weight. Ghazan looked covertly, avoiding the beast's eyes, for the glint might give him away. He saw the arched neck, its muscles apparent even through the thick pelt, grey, tinged with yellow, beautifully marked with a pattern of dark rosettes fused together on the back into three longitudinal stripes. Like no other beast he had seen. The snow leopard, at last. All this Ghazan thought, swinging his rifle up and round until the still-moving shoulder lay between the sights. His finger curled on the trigger. Like something from beyond, not of this world. He sensed the magnitude of its life, of its death. Now, it must be now. Why did the trigger resist? The beast moved out of the sights: Ghazan's eyes followed the rippling flanks as they passed behind the rocks. Gone. His one chance was gone. Sweat broke out on his hands and a prickle crept over his scalp. He examined the safety-catch: yes, it was off. He fired at the rocks. The explosion seemed to rend the mountain. He heard the bullet ricochet with a whine. Far down the slope he could glimpse the snow leopard, the size of a cat, of a kitten: out of range. And, to his astonishment, he felt no anger: all his desire to kill seemed to have disappeared. He felt only bewilderment—lying there in the last sunlight on the high mountain.

He thought: I crawled up this mountain in order to kill a snow leopard. I could have killed it. But I did not. I let it live. Ghazan pondered the incident carefully. One by one he went over his impressions while the grey shoulder had lain in the groove of his sights. He bowed his head on his chest and closed his eyes, concentrating on that moment. No, he had ordered no last-minute reprieve. A sort of safety-catch had come down, deep in his own flesh.

Nothing like this had ever happened to him before. It was so extraordinary that Ghazan told himself he had imagined the whole affair. He stood up and walked to the three clefts. He pulled the stinking sheep's carcase down from the spiny bush. He climbed to the ridge. There was another cleft there, behind the bushes. He went in. The rock floor was littered with sheep-bones and fresh dung.

A thin mist was beginning to fall. Slinging his rifle, he walked down the mountainside. He had always believed that meeting the snow leopard would elicit some secret. It had always been the unattainable, charged with mystery. And now the secret was laid bare: a revelation not about the universe but about himself, dark and unpalatable. In the moment of crisis he had done the opposite of what he had always intended. Ghazan became aware, with something like panic, that the decision had been issued not by headquarters, not by his mind, but by a hidden agent. And so the decision had been no decision.

Even as he stood aghast before this conclusion, his mind, very precise and matter of fact, hurried to fill the vacuum with likely hidden motives. This had been like no other hunt. Quail or gazelle were flushed and shot on the instant. But all his life he had been tracking the snow leopard, thinking about it, giving it imaginary form. The snow leopard had been his dream. One did not kill one's dream. More than a dream, its image was a silver thread binding together his past. Snapping it, he would have snapped his life in two. Self-preservation: had that pushed down the safety-catch?

Ghazan thought so for a moment. But his mind quickly took another line. During the grave exercise he had stripped himself of desire. When he turned to the snow leopard, had the mood persisted—as a boat glides awhile after the oars are shipped—so that he could no longer will even the squeezing of a trigger?

But desire had been very strong. It had driven him up the mountain. A desire for the snow leopard, or only for the chase? Had his desire faded when he saw that the prey was mere flesh and blood? He remembered his disappointment in face of the boar.

But disappointment came after the kill. He had not felt that. Awe he had felt, and the sense of something beyond. Had he projected his own expectation of the Beloved's face onto the beast, treated the snow leopard, for a crucial split second, as a sort of God? This explanation also seemed to him possible: but neither more nor less probable than the others.

Ghazan tried to frame his present attitude. Strangely enough, he did not now mind losing the ghostly pelt, the snarling head. He had sweated away an afternoon in vain, but that did not rankle, for he knew he could have killed. Why did he feel no regret? Because the leopard was rare, and species, once extinct, were never resurrected? With extinction threatening his own people, had he faltered at wiping a beast from the earth? Had that been the hidden motive?

All these keys fitted the keyhole, and there were doubtless many others on which he could not lay his hand, but Ghazan thought in sudden despair and humility, I can never know which one actually turned the lock. At the moment when my finger lay curled on the trigger, my carefully laid plans, my knowledge of the snow leopard and how to shoot through its shoulder to the heart, my will to destroy it, were irrelevant in face of some force within me which I can never know. And last of all, Ghazan thought with a shudder, perhaps none

271

of these many keys turned the lock, perhaps the door of escape was opened by a golden master-key, cast and cut at the moment of creation.

Struggling with this hornet swarm, Ghazan passed the first Galanzi tents. Supposing he told the tribesmen simply the externals? They would assume their Ilkhan was averse to take life, no longer a hunter. Had he, and the tribe with him, grown soft? Was the ending of nomad life implicit in themselves, not arbitrarily imposed by Teheran? From his gestures that would be a valid conclusion, but his gestures gave a false picture. This much Ghazan knew for certain: he had not shrunk from the actual killing. Inside and out, the way to truth seemed blocked.

He entered the Galanzi chieftain's tent. A tall, sleek man of middle age, his left cheek scarred by a bullet, looked from Ghazan's eyes to his empty hands.

"You left the brute to the vultures?"

Ghazan muttered a curt No.

"I heard your shot." He put the words like a question.

"It hit the rocks."

A gleam came into the chieftain's eyes. "Didn't I tell you? Mist on the Dina plays queer tricks."

"No mist had fallen," said Ghazan flatly, "and the light was good. I came very close. I saw three lines of rosettes on his back. But I did not kill him."

The chieftain seemed neither disappointed nor puzzled.

"It was certainly the mist. Many times it is there when you don't see it. Many times I have lost an ibex on the Dina."

Ghazan's empty hands justified past failures. Every happening on the Dina explained by a blanket of mist. The incident neatly tabulated. No mist in the mind: windows, doors hermetically sealed. So thought Ghazan, more than ever upset.

Talking of other matters, Ghazan rode back to the court tents with the Galanzi chieftain. The camp was preparing festivities: coloured flags flew above the black squares, huge fires were lit in front of cairns, before which a space had been cleared for dancing. Rohim's marriage. There would be three days of feasting, of which tonight was the first.

Two court tents had been pitched adjoining to form a single hall, hung with multi-coloured saddle-cloths. White linen was spread on the thick rugs, and the base of the tents lined with carpet bags stuffed with grain. Here Tughril was giving a dinner for all the chieftains.

Already Tughril had played his part in events. Among the tribesmen a marriage was arranged by a third party, but because of Rohim's rank Tughril had made the proposal to the bride's father and arranged payment of a tenth part of Rohim's possessions.

Ghazan, as chief guest, sat at the centre of the long cloth, When all were assembled, three servants entered and handed round copper basins, cans and towels. In turn the guests washed their hands in running water. Tughril helped everyone to hare-flesh on gold plates, while the guests served themselves individually with rice and waffles.

Ghazan tore hungrily at the meat. He was sick of preying on himself. Like the others, he ate only part, then handed the rest over his shoulder to his personal aide. He in his turn ate only a part, before passing it to his servant, who stood behind: so at great feasts the dependence of the tribe on its lord was symbolized.

Glasses were filled from a goatskin of red wine. Ghazan swallowed his at a mouthful. He wanted to forget, to centre himself in the warmth, the flavour of hare-flesh. Why think ahead or backwards? He gave a friendly glance to his cousin directly opposite. Rohim was being teased mercilessly by his father, and seemed unusually glum.

"Only yesterday you were playing hopscotch in the women's quarters. A wife, you won't know what to do with a wife!"

The chieftains laughed in deference to their host. A servant passed Rohim a plate of eggplant stuffed with partridge: when he declined with an abrupt twist of his hand, Tughril continued:

"You'll have to be sweeter than that, my boy: women like to be baited with a smile. But she'll soon break you in."

Rohim scowled and round his glass pressed his right thumb hard against his forefinger, revealing the sinews. Ghazan recalled how, as a growing boy, every so often Rohim would proudly announce the discovery of a "new" muscle on chest or calf. He had been teased for that, too.

"Clothes and horse-blankets sprawled over your bed," Tughril continued, "those days are over. Trousers and tunics will have to be neatly piled. And no more muddy riding boots inside your tent. She's bringing you silk slippers."

Again his guests laughed. Rohim had several times announced he would make no concessions to domesticity.

Tughril was enjoying his success. "Your father married an Adashuri girl; now you are doing the same." He looked round the company. "What is the moral?"

Someone replied, "Why, that the Adashuris have almond eyes."

Another said, "They own fat flocks and bring good dowries."

"Not at all: it means the son has inherited the wisdom of his father. Part of it, anyway." With his huge oaken hand Tughril tousled Rohim's hair in a rough, scalping sweep. "If Rohim weren't here, I'd swear no more than five years had passed since my own marriage feast. You remember, Manuchehr?" he shouted to the elder, near the end of the cloth. "You remember the sherbets? He doesn't hear. My father spent much money, but it was famine-food compared to this. Lamb pilav. And tea in the glasses. Not a drop of wine. Drink up, my lucky guests." And he led the way.

Tughril's boasting jarred on Ghazan. Pointing a finger in mock accusation, he said:

"You've quenched the fire in this wine with water."

Tughril held his glass to the light. "Water this colour?"

"Rose water."

Tughril laughed. "By salt and earth, Ghazan, this is the pure juice of grapes."

"Pure as the morning dew!"

The charge evidently amused Tughril. He had drunk a lot and was in high spirits. Tears of laughter ran down his cheeks.

"I paid two hundred tumans the barrel."

"In counterfeit coin, I should hope."

"Oh, that's good!" Tughril doubled up and tears dripped from his cheek into his wine-glass.

"Ghazan is right," cried the guests and laughed anew.

But the tears set Ghazan brooding. At the heart of laughter, sorrow. Behind Rohim's bride, Anahita; behind this crowded feast, his own empty tent. Lepers in ancient times had been deported from Persia. Tainted, was he, with some such plague, invisible to himself, from which his bride, his countrymen, even the snow leopard shrank? But it was I, thought Ghazan, who recoiled from the snow leopard. Lunacy then? A wandering—a sort of occupational disease of the mind; an alienation? And so to the asylum of aliens, to the aseptic sanatorium called Switzerland.

With an effort Ghazan gained control. His gloomy frown would

274

spoil the others' evening. He drank up and refilled his glass. But Rohim had noticed. He knew from Ghazan's silence that he had had no success on the mountain and thought he was brooding on that. He asked what had happened. Ghazan gave a brief account.

"The chase is enough," he added, shrugging his shoulders, "without the booty."

"Hardly the words for a wedding feast," laughed one of the chieftains.

Rohim said thoughtfully, "To seize the booty is to end the chase. But do we hunt, Ghazan, for the chase or for the booty?"

Looking at his cousin, at the assembled chieftains, Ghazan felt sudden exaltation. After all, they were still one, still united. "For something beyond both," he cried, raising his glass. "And so we drink, not for the wine or the exaltation it brings, but for something we glimpse beyond."

With a dry laugh Tughril said, "I wish I'd been there. The Ilkhan and the snow leopard meet on the mountain, eye each other, sniff, snarl and go their separate ways. There's a strong strain of mercy in you, Ghazan. You have it from your mother."

Ghazan looked at his uncle coldly, without replying. Another explanation, he thought: but wide of the mark. A split second had given him no time to feel for the beast.

"Happily I didn't spare these hares," Tughril continued. "Fifteen with twenty shots on yesterday's hunt. Quite a feat. No, Tughril never returns with empty hands."

"My hands are not quite empty." From his pocket Ghazan took the fossilized trilobites and tossed them on the cloth. Tughril picked them up cautiously and looked at them. "Won't you taste my present?"

"Cooked, I might."

"They've been barbecued in the sun for several thousand years."

"Too long," laughed Tughril.

"It's true they've merged with the spit. But the spit too is made of fish and their shells."

With a puzzled expression Tughril turned the fossils this way and that. "I wonder how they got into the rock," he murmured.

Ghazan said in a meaning tone, "Perhaps they leaped higher than was good for them."

A little ruffled, Tughril handed the fossils back. Ghazan pocketed them with a laugh. "You spare the little fish?"

Along the purple carpet they meandered to a pavilion of verses. Ghazan recited two lines of Firdowsi in praise of hunting. Tughril found an apt return from the *Gulistan*, beginning with the last letter of the last word in Ghazan's quotation. Then it was Rohim's turn to parry according to the same rules, and so on down the double line of guests. Again and again, antiphonally, they launched quotations across the red tide of wine.

Finally, as custom ruled, Ghazan improvized an epithalamium. "Three springs ago Rohim spied the gazelle. Now he has run his quarry to earth."

This put Rohim in too good a light for Tughril. "The bride sings quite another song," he retorted. "Something like this: 'I tossed my black ringlets like lassoes. Now I drag Rohim behind my mare.'"

Another said to Rohim, whose tent colour was red: "At last two fruit on the pomegranate tree. At last a body to perfume the flowers on your bed-rug." These verses set the tone for the rest of the meal.

Afterwards they went to watch the dancing. During the past week relatives of the bride had ridden out to issue invitations, each receiving as a present a lamb dyed red, blue or orange. The guests had arrived that day, bringing timber to feed the huge bonfires, and now sat around the level space where camel-drivers provided music on surnay, hare-skin drum and stringed instruments; while the rice-pounders—unmarried girls of the Madaleh—sang tribal love-songs in chorus.

At Ghazan's appearance the dancers, women and girls dressed in red and blue cottons, a white veil tied back from the face and around the head by a scarf, began to form up in a circle. Tentatively they tripped a few steps, like pennants fluttering in a half-breeze. Their long, heaving, pleated skirts scarcely lifted as they circled the central fire, at first raggedly, loosely, but steadily tightening with the increased tempo, tossing their hands, their arms, their heads, until no part of themselves held out to the music. The spectators clapped in time. The drum beat like rain, the dancers rose like flowers from the earth. Above their heads they waved coloured handkerchiefs; their red and blue skirts unfolded; the flowers bloomed. The music grew louder, the intervals shorter. The women's feet beat the earth like a hare-skin drum.

Each of the twelve tones was named after a sign of the zodiac. From listening and watching Ghazan drew a three-fold pleasure. The sounds in each arrangement pleased his ear, set in motion their associated months, and expressed a conjunction of signs which, by applying the rudiments of astrology, he was able to interpret for good or ill. The circling women, their lithe bodies now bent, now outstretched, became, for the dance's duration, the signs themselves. casting a horoscope for Rohim and his bride.

Men with staves and sticks entered the arena to perform their dance. They paired off, one carrying a heavy wooden staff of almost his own height, his partner a willow branch. They strutted round, the music martial now, the spectators clapping more slowly, until the holder of the staff turned and placed it in front of his body, resting one end on the ground, shielding his ankles and calves from the attacker's willow. Both jumped about, feinting and dodging to gain an advantage— muscles tense, eyes sharp, for a clout on the ankles could lame a man for several days—until the attacker, who was allowed only one blow, finally struck. Then rôles were exchanged and the parade continued. The dull knocks were reminiscent of male gazelles wrestling with interlocked horns in the mating season, while the does watched approvingly. As the Falqani proverb put it: only a man who struggled daily was worthy of life; only a man ready to fight for her was worthy of his wife.

Again the women danced. From time to time a girl, unable to find full expression in the common rhythm, began a lyric of her own, the accompaniment growing softer, the dancers holding back, while she lamented a love which was not returned.

Ghazan listened. The quick beat of the drum was the beat of the blood in his wrists. The voice of the singer seemed his own voice: one of several in counterpoint. Why were problems not simple? This three-dimensional geometry was beyond him. Why this conflict of loves: of the Absolute, of his people, of Anahita. Feeling the need to share his thoughts, he leaned across to Rohim and spoke of Anahita: in a lop-sided world of ovals and ellipses, the one perfect circle: her hair a wave breaking at midnight; its surf her teeth and white hands; its phosphorus the glitter in her eyes, her dove-grey eyes. Up on the hills he had discovered more worlds than a patient astronomer, brighter worlds than exist; and saved them for her. Glittering galaxies Anahita should have been first to disentangle; stars like white currants on an unpruned bush; comets she should have caught like darting fireflies: all these he would have plaited as a diadem and set in the dark night of her hair.

It seemed to Ghazan that her power had never been stronger. Her presence was multiplied, for he saw her in everything. Ghazan felt a sudden urge to seize this one certain feeling, ride down to Shiraz and say to the girl, "I am a lover even more than a leader. I shall fight for you, the one certain good. You shall ride on your white mare, and every winter walk with your mother under the orange trees."

The singer ended her song. Far away the fire crackled in the silent night. Beside him Rohim laughed at a friend's joke. A tribesman passed, whistling. As the official in charge of water turns the supply from one garden to the fields of the whole village, so now Ghazan's impulse was diverted. He remained where he was.

He listened to the camel-herds retuning their stringed instruments. At first they jarred, like the bleating guts they were, gibbered, stuttered and finally articulated. His mother used to play that falling tune. Sad as boats stranded at ebb-tide. He had sat by her knees and watched her long, agile brown fingers against the brown wood and transparent strings. She had sung it in a cracked voice. An old tune from before the great migration, from Turkestan. The notes were stepping-stones across Ghazan's life. He remembered other nights he had heard that tune: while snow pelted the canvas and wind thrashed wilder music from the guy ropes; under a full moon in Garden of the Pines, to the scent of roses and resin. Even though the tune seemed to him so plaintive, Ghazan felt elated by his extension backwards in time. This effect of music Ghazan had discussed more than once with his friends. Some claimed it was the response to an echo of angelic praises heard before birth; Ghazan believed it quite different; a sinister form of self-love. Music seemed harmless, took nothing from anyone: an undiminished stream no matter how many drank. But the waters swelled without appeasing: they added a new dimensity to his being, an unjustified swagger, the fictitious strength of past selves.

Usually Ghazan sipped warily: tonight, however, he drank deep. The camel-herds' fingers seemed to be plucking down leaves from an autumn poplar. How the notes sobbed, like an ebbing wash on the seashore. They expressed his own feelings precisely.

The tune ended. Rohim called out: "Play that again." He leaned over to Ghazan and said happily:

"It's my favourite tune."

278

Ghazan looked at his cousin in astonishment. The musicians obeyed. Smiling, Rohim began to swing his head and with one hand tap his thigh in time to the melody. Ghazan thought, this music is Rohim's joy and my sorrow. Yet it cannot be both. The composer long ago on the steppes of Turkestan—what had he felt? Perhaps it had been just a chore, or a game: piling notes as a child piles wooden blocks, regardless of colour. He recalled records—jazz and negro spirituals—which some of the boys in Lausanne had played on Saturday evenings. To him they had seemed ugly as a landscape of jungle or swamp. Music of earth, like this, but of another part of the earth, and so for him discord. Was there, then, no order in music except that imposed by familiarity? Was music itself an invisible gut, and past hearings the beads which made it a necklace?

Ghazan looked beyond to the shadowy hills. Did the same apply there, in the natural order? Night and day, spring and autumn: an orderly procession. But perhaps that order depended on the spectator's lack of attention, his disorderly observations. Like it or not, man had to cram the universe—its nebulæ, its constellations, its mountains and oceans—into his tiny bone-walled attic under the gables: how else but by simplification and arrangement? But supposing he were able to catch and note every demi-semiquaver played by drum and horn, pipe and flute, the difference of size and colour and texture between two beetles of the same species, between the leaves of two poplars, might he not be forced to exclaim Disorder? If repeated hearings imposed both order and mood on music, might not man in a similar way, from the very beginning, have imposed his own essence—mind—on a neutral world? And to attribute it to a Perfect Mind was again to read sorrow into a succession of notes.

Ghazan thought of his encounter with the snow leopard and applied the same hypothesis. Supposing in the last analysis all so-called decisions were like his own that afternoon? Supposing cause and effect, motive and action, were not really father and son, not even distant cousins? Ghazan put a hand to his brow. His head was throbbing: the day's unsolved events clanged there like the clapper in a brass camel-bell. Supposing his body were a harlot, who named any chance vagabond as father of her brood. Or worse than a harlot? Supposing from himself any prodigious decision could come to birth? Closing his eyes tight, Ghazan shrank back like a magician who, from a harmless-looking bottle, has conjured up a violent jinn, a jinn whose rôle it was not to transport his body to Basra or Samarcand, not to steal his money or metamorphose his bride, but with fingers hard as steel totally to eviscerate him, wrench out his reason, and then introduce him as a eunuch slave into the palace of madness.

Before midnight dancing and music ceased, but for the two following days festivities continued. On the third morning a thousand Shalguli horsemen rode to the Adashuri camp. There they took lunch with the bride's family—a feast which lasted several hours. Late in the afternoon they set the bride, a cloak of red printed cotton falling from her head, on a white horse, which was led solemnly three times round the family hearth, before setting off to her new home. During the ride Rohim's horsemen honoured their princess by showing off their skill, galloping and wheeling round the bride, like gulls round a yacht on her maiden voyage. Within a short distance of the groom's tent, a three-year-old boy was set on the white horse behind the bride, as a promise of male children.

Ghazan stood beside Rohim within the threshold of his tent, awaiting the bride's arrival, his thoughts on a piece of embroidery in a house in Shiraz. Shots of welcome sounded far off. Until then Rohim had affected the greatest unconcern, but now he fidgeted like a colt being broken-in to rifle-fire. When the bride was a few paces off, he stepped forward to meet her and, as the custom was, lobbed an apple into her lap. She stretched forward and caught it.

Ghazan helped her to dismount. She was a slender girl with a pretty face. Lifting her down Ghazan caught the sweet scent of *ambar*, a black-coloured perfume made of musk, ambergris and oil. The little boy, left alone in the saddle, began to cry: Ghazan grasped him under the shoulders with one hand and swung him to the ground.

The bride handed Ghazan a present: a leather riding-crop. He thanked her and, in his capacity as Ilkhan, led her to Rohim's tent, where a bowl of water and a mirror stood on Dilbar's rug as symbols of their new happiness. Beside them the bride set a third symbolic object: a jar containing strains of ferment from the curds eaten in her own tent that day, which tomorrow she would add to milk from Rohim's goats. Continuity would be unbroken.

An hour later Ghazan led Rohim to his tent. The couple had not stood together since their betrothal. Placing the bride's right hand in the right hand of his cousin, Ghazan said to Rohim:

"This woman is entrusted to you until the day of Resurrection."

And again he caught the sweet scent of *ambar*.

Next, Rohim and his bride lightly scuffled, each trying to place a foot over the other's feet as a sign of who should rule the new household. Three times Rohim almost fell to her slipper, embroidered with silver thread. Three times he drew away and at last brought down the leather sole of his riding boot squarely over her silver slippers. At that they laughed, and Ghazan noticed how her little purling laugh was lost in his.

Ghazan handed Rohim and his bride two sugar-loaves which had been used at their betrothal ceremony, inviting them to sweeten each other's lips. Having broken the sugar, Rohim circled the bride's neck with his arm and placed crumbs in her mouth, while she did the same to him. Then they were left together. Outside dancing and music rose to a final burst of triumph. And Ghazan—he was left alone with the scent of *ambar*.

CHAPTER TWENTY

NEXT morning Ghazan sent a servant to tell Fatima the astrologer that he wished to consult her that evening. Besides her other accomplishments Fatima could become entranced and speak in a strange tongue believed to be Hindustani; she could read omens and sometimes predict the future. It was prediction that Ghazan now required of her.

Ghazan did not believe in occult powers all the time, but a mood of belief hung over him now. It had been gathering like a storm since his encounter with the snow leopard. Since man's own motives could not be known, since each imposed his own pattern, then the way to discover truth was not to trace links backwards or forwards (for there could be no telling how the mind worked, or at the bid of what motives), but to slip free of earth and time, look down on past, present and future as one. If choice were impossible, decision a jest of nature, he would try to look forward with Fatima's eyes beyond the so-called choice, and see his own self in action.

Rohim considered Fatima a fraud and had tried in the past to dissuade Ghazan from consulting her. Ghazan justified his recurrent belief in her powers along these lines.

Animals had a sense or senses most did not possess. A horse knew a boy's confidence or fear even before he mounted for the first time. More than once Ghazan had heard a dog whimper when his master—perhaps a day's ride away—was dying. Only that spring crossing mountains deep in snow, an old sheep leading a flock of three hundred had stopped dead before a harmless-looking patch of ice. Ahmad had tried to drive it on, but it would not move. When he probed with his stick, he almost fell headlong. The ice covered a sheer crevasse.

Men and women in the tribe had sometimes shown similar direct knowledge. Ghazan believed they had this power because they lived close to animals and the earth, and that a similar power underlay the magic of prehistoric peoples. To dismiss that magic out of hand, to sneer at it, seemed to Ghazan, in a new sense, provincial. He considered that magic applied a sense or senses different from the normal five and now usually atrophied. A spear transfixing a bison—by drawing that on his cave wall man concentrated himself on his prey, imposed his own predatory mind, weakened the bison's will and made it easier to kill, just as an angry man, looking daggers at another, could destroy his morale and even decide the battle before ever a blow was struck. The magic called sympathetic magic was not based on mistaken premises, but on a real sympathy. In support of this Ghazan argued, could man, for millions of years, at a stage of his development when he could least afford mistakes, have indulged in the luxury of a method which did not work?

Ghazan had been given too many proofs to doubt the primacy and pervasion of mind. Between the mullah Mahdi and himself had often passed unspoken thoughts, which only telepathy could explain. Ascetic dervishes could bear without wincing the insertion into their flesh of burning needles. And if the mind could act outside space and on distant bodies without intermediary, it was surely powerful enough, under certain conditions, to slip from present to future like a carrier pigeon and return with a message.

Twice, at least, Fatima had seemed to accomplish this. The first occasion had been before Ghazan left for school in Switzerland. He had asked her his future, and she had described, as though seeing it before her eyes, how a sick man fell into a deep faint. He lay still and cold and silent. His family, believing him dead, buried him in a shallow grave. Darkness fell, but next morning the sun rose bright. Its heat revived the buried man. He tunnelled his way out and stumbled home to his family.

On the second occasion also Fatima had spoken parabolically. After Ghazan had taken his decision nine years ago to attack Shiraz—a choice which circumstances forced him to make overnight, with the utmost speed, and therefore comparatively easy—Fatima had told him that he would hold the turquoise ring in his hands, but not slip it on his finger, for he would be given a jewel which he desired even more than the ring.

In the plains, also, Ghazan had consulted magicians who opened a copy of the Koran or Hafiz—Tongue of the Unseen, Interpreter of Mysteries—and pointed to a vague verse as answer. He preferred Fatima's way. She more directly touched the beyond and, so it seemed to him, was all the less capable of error.

As darkness fell, Ghazan carried his question to Fatima's tent. She was a widow of nearly sixty and lived with a daughter and son-in-law. As a herdswoman she was stupid and rather clumsy, with no special powers over animals, and Ghazan believed stupidity was a condition of her power. She was inclined to unpredictable outbursts of temper and knife-drawing. Some believed she was the daughter of a camel. She had a human mother too, but to the tribe many things had a double aspect. Worn coins in ruins, for instance, were also a few drops of a subterranean silver sea. And Fatima, as a girl, had been observed many times followed and nuzzled by a cow camel.

She sat alone in front of her brazier, head bowed, plucking a newly-killed fowl. When Ghazan entered, she rose to salaam. In her brown wrinkled face the eyes, not specially large, were set wide apart. They glowed in the flames. Her grey hair was hennaed, she still retained white teeth, and her wrists, when she lifted her tunic, were small.

"And how is Fatima the astrologer?"

The old woman flushed with pleasure. She liked that title.

"Chilled in the cold dawns. I long to move south."

"Soon we shall strike tents." Ghazan motioned her to sit, and placed himself opposite on the rug. "Much depends on you, Fatima."

"On me, Ghazan Khan? A poor old woman!"

She was very vain: it was she who had washed her hair in a dye made from the red poster.

Ghazan looked at her steadily. "The future of the Falqani is in your eyes."

With a cackle she laid the tips of her hennaed fingers above her cheeks, pointing.

"These poor spiders in their web of lines—they're too old to catch anything now. It is you, Ghazan Khan, who hold our future."

"To act I must see. And this summer I am dull of sight. So I come to see through your eyes."

Fatima bent her face, suddenly tense and alert, to Ghazan's: "To see? To see—forward?" she whispered.

Ghazan felt his heart speed into a canter. His strained nerves seemed to tighten a notch. Here in the black tent crouched over the fire secretly to steal the still unknotted rug, to unroll it, to see the perhaps terrible blood-stained pattern: to usurp the prerogative of God! But he choked down his guilt. He had to know.

"This autumn our people face storms," he answered quickly. "Not the life-giving equinoctial rains, but storms of fire and steel. Must they fight or flinch before the fire?"

Fatima wrinkled her brow. "Ask the poor old woman simple questions," she whined.

Ghazan thought, she knows nothing of army plans and the tribe's vulnerability in the Guyum plain. Life stretches no further than gossip with friends, the health and sickness of children and beasts. And yet she is in touch with something: her tent is open to the stars. In touch, perhaps, like a tree, with earth and sky.

"Peer forward and see what the Ilkhan is doing, when the grass has turned brown."

"When the grass is brown! Autumn-brown?"

"Yes, autumn-brown."

Putting the fowl aside, slowly, with creaking bones, Fatima stood up and from the corner of her tent lifted a small wooden box. From it she took a pinch of rue and scattered grains on the fire. Rue kept evil spirits at a distance. Presently a sharp perfume enveloped the tent. Then from five leather pouches in the box she began to mix powders and clotted lumps into a bowl of milk, telling them off aloud: iris root and acorn and the tail of a scorpion, wild celery and grease from a lamb. Ghazan watched the white milk turn yellow, then greyish-brown and tried to imagine the power of each. Or did Fatima only know their effects as a whole, a formula learned from her teacher? These arts were jealously guarded, handed down to those with manifest powers. Her enemies claimed one of the ingredients was hashish.

Squatting over the fire, Fatima raised the bowl to her thin lips and drank slowly, noisily, while Ghazan studied her face. She remained still and impassive, eyes fixed on the fire, taking the drink into her blood, into her brain. Suddenly closing her eyes, she shivered and hissed like boiling water on cold metal. Beneath the hennaed hair the brows arched like a crupper-strap. More than a change of character, a metamorphosis seemed to be taking place. But into what?

She began to sway from the hips, backwards and forwards, as though rocking an unseen milk into butter, until the movement forced her to rise. Still she swayed, like a tree in a storm. Her hands opened and closed all the while, her face was contorted. Ghazan believed something had entered into her, not gently, and was now

285

effacing her womanhood. Though her arms hung loose, she seemed to be wrestling. It was so painful to watch, Ghazan wanted to cross over beyond the fire, help Fatima overcome that unseen clawing beast, but after a moment's thought, he beat down the impulse. To speak, she must be overcome.

But she did not speak. Her mouth gaped, then dribbled weak sounds which, like desert streams, soon gave up the struggle, stopped without end. She began to gibber like one of those idiots, witless but without evil, whom every tribe supported. Before the ugly mask of her face, the oozing nonsense, Ghazan dropped his eyes, nauseated. Was this the approach to truth, this degradation? Yet why not? Soaring upwards or tunnelling downwards, it scarcely mattered so long as he knew.

But this struggle was only an embryonic stage in Fatima's trance. Next, she began to pronounce words Ghazan understood, though still unconnected: like the inventory of a dead man's possessions. Some were long and complicated. Yet she was illiterate and could not know their meaning.

As she spoke, every nerve of her arms and legs began to vibrate, and her whole body moved very slightly upwards and downwards, like a tin humming-top whipped to life. She opened her eyes but seemed to see neither the flames nor him nor even the darkness beyond. By searching her pupils, would he find what she saw? Or, if the vision came directly to her brain, why open her eyes brimful, as though to contain in a single glance the whole universe? Fire, sun, garlic, claw, jackal: so she laid the foundations of her vision. Sweat trickled through the jubes of her wrinkled cheeks. Molten, she seemed: only when white-hot could iron truth be hammered out as words.

Ghazan clenched his fists in unbearable impatience to know, coupled with anxiety, as the dark moments passed, that the storm-cloud, the lightning would go without yielding rain. Involved though he was in her struggle, part of his mind stood cautiously aside, trying to put a rational meaning on Fatima's movements and sounds. Every word he scooped up, turning it this way and that for an inscription he could not find.

For a very long time Ghazan listened to this nonsense. From the embers of despair anger flared that he should be dependent on this stammering soothsayer. The fragrant rue had become a stench. He wished he had not come. He thought of leaving and at once heard Fatima groan. Then he realized the two of them were, for good or ill, linked in the descent. He himself was changed no less than Fatima: from Ilkhan to drudge.

In the brazier a thorn branch slipped down on sagging faggots, crackled and became sparks. To that slight sound Fatima seemed to respond. She began to speak in a new, authoritative voice. Her eyes were intent on a remote scene.

"I see, I see!" she cried, and Ghazan turned, only to find the long black goatskin strips of the tent. "A long dark arcade covered over to hide the sky. On both sides stalls are set up, with apples and bales of cotton for sale. And at each stall stands a bearded man, silent, staring ahead."

Her cavernous voiced seemed to issue through layer upon layer of rock, from mountain depths, echoing slightly and at first not easily distinguishable. But it gained in strength.

"Now I begin to walk down the arcade, on, on. Listen: a voice. Someone is speaking far away. Harsh and confused—a man's voice, yet not quite human. It seems to come from a courtyard off the passage. Here is the door." With a slow, dreamy movement Fatima lifted her arm. "I push and go in." Her eyes looked up and round. "I am standing under a blue sky. Round the walls copper basins and cauldrons are stacked, trays and lamps. In the middle is an old tree with big jagged leaves, brown at the edges. A plane tree. And there on one of its boughs hangs a small iron cage. The voice comes from there. Inside the cage is a wooden perch and on the perch a bird. A lovely bird. White head, blue body and indigo tail. And a fat hooked beak. A parrot. He keeps flapping his blue wings.

"The parrot pecks with his big beak at the iron bars. 'Let me out! Let me out!'" Fatima screeched the words. The parrot seemed there in the tent. Then she looked round with narrowed eyes. "There is no one else in the court. Softly, softly, on tip-toe I walk up to the cage—to open it. Locked." At this Fatima shook her hands violently against bars which were not there. "And the lock is too strong to break. The parrot is squawking, 'Open my cage! Let me free!' But what can I do?" Fatima broke off with a sharp wail so heart-felt and keen it made clear to Ghazan the importance of what she saw. After a moment she lifted a hand to her eyes. "Now a man enters the courtyard. He is wearing a leather apron—a coppersmith's apron. He empties a handful of seed into the cage. The parrot pecks at a grain, begins to eat. The coppersmith caresses the bird with his fingers and speaks soft words. Now he is leaving. Once more the parrot frets and cries to be released. He dashes his blue wings against the bars. Again. Again. He's going to destroy himself unless I help. I walk over to the cage. He looks at me and cocks his head. I bend and whisper, 'Be still, little bird, still and silent. When your master comes back, lie down at the bottom of the cage. When he offers you grain, do not accept it. When he speaks to you, do not repeat his words. Be still and calm and silent.' The parrot shakes his white head. He seems to understand but he answers nothing."

Fatima closed her glazed and staring eyes. As though with painful effort she swallowed several times quickly. Under the sunburn Ghazan saw her face was mottled. Her shoulders were hunched and when she resumed her voice had fallen to a whisper.

"The sun is rising. It strikes the parrot's body, lying at the bottom of the cage. And the coppersmith walks up. He scatters grain round the bird. He speaks to it. Will the parrot move? No, no, it remembers what I said. The coppersmith tries to stir the parrot with his fingers, but cannot reach it. Quickly he takes out a key and unlocks the cage. He lifts the parrot out in his open palm. His cheeks are pale. He cries, 'My parrot is dead.' He turns over the blue body, looking for a wound. With a wail he lifts his hand to cover his eyes. And the parrot flies up, up, out of the courtyard, away into the blue sky.

"The coppersmith looks round, angry. Will he see me?" Fatima cowered, and for a moment hid her face in her hands. "I step back into the shadow, through the door. Softly I begin to walk away, up the long dark passage, with apples and cotton for sale, past the silent bearded storekeepers, back, back all the way . . ."

Fatima's voice tailed off; she put a hand to her eyes, she staggered. Ghazan rushed to support her, then helped her to squat down in front of the fire. Her head fell forward and she breathed heavily. It was finished.

Tensely Ghazan had listened and now stood over the fire, staring into the clear future, exultant. Not, as he had feared, obscure or irrelevant, but crystal-clear. As though they corresponded to watermarks in his soul Ghazan divined the meaning of her terms: coppersmith, the army;

cage, settlement; the blue-feathered parrot, the Ilkhan. And the meaning? No matter the difficulties, the Ilkhan must yield to the army's guns: then, in the moment of seeming defeat, he would triumph. How, he did not know. That had not been foreseen. Only his acquiescence had been foreseen. Still and calm and silent. When the time came, he would be shown a way.

He wanted to shout out his thanks to the old woman who had foreseen his release, make her a gift—but she sat slumped, an emptied sack, her triumph hidden in the posture of defeat. She had travelled through time, probed deep in the earth and beyond the earth—to return with the metal of truth gleaming in her hot palms. Now let her take her rest.

His body seemed suddenly light, almost porous, as Ghazan left the tent and the sleeping woman. Sky and earth were one blackness, but for the dying tribal fires. Ghazan gazed up and read the plough, the lion, the hunter. Order on earth and in heaven: a star-set course. All was well: the future had been foreseen and found good. With his men he could take his rest now without anguish. He passed a herd of unsleeping camels, like tumuli; one of his greyhounds bounded up and licked his hand in recognition. On the hills a jackal cried, and a camp dog barked defiance.

Ghazan reached his own tent, removed his boots and stretched out to sleep. But this new-found peace excited him more than new wine. He turned over the scene with Fatima. Often he had watched parrots in the Shiraz bazaar, squawking, forever snapping their beaks in anger. And their cages with intricate locks. Strange, that bird which could speak only what it heard. Yet not so different from man.

Ghazan wanted to sleep, not think. Usually he slept at will but tonight the mattress, stuffed with partridge breast-feathers, would not fly him away. He found himself picturing the copper merchant, saw him with a thick black beard. The merchant said the parrot was dead. The master should know. Then he remembered that it had flown out of the courtyard up into the sky. Its soul, then: not its body. Parrots never soared like hawks or larks.

All at once Ghazan's peace was gone. He had misinterpreted the vision. Fatima had acted out the truth, but he had misunderstood. He thought back to his first reading, that too seemed convincing. What could have killed the parrot? Yet Fatima had not said it was dead.

How could he know? For a long time he lay puzzling in the dark, finding the vision fissured with quibbles. And the vision was his own life. He had to discover for certain. He rose and ran out, past the ruminating camels, past the greyhound which nuzzled but could not help, to Fatima's tent. She was still sleeping, and he shook her awake. She became alert at once, as all Falqani were trained to be, and stood up to face him, a little frightened.

"The parrot," he demanded breathlessly, "when the merchant took it out of the cage, was it dead or alive?"

Fatima looked blank. Perhaps she had not heard. He repeated his question word for word.

"What parrot, Ghazan Khan? What are you talking about?"

For a moment he was taken aback: he must have mistaken the tent and the woman. Then he recognized the perfume of rue.

"The parrot you saw tonight." And he explained, all the while astonished to see the woman's eyes blank. She cowered from him as though he were mad. She recognized nothing: it had been some other force speaking inside her.

Fury rose in his throat, at first with Fatima, then at having been cheated, trapped. He strode out of the tent as though from a net. And there were no more constellations in the night. The hunter, the plough, the lion were so many vagabond sparks from the dying tribal fires. He had been given the future—with no means of understanding it. Fatima had spoken the truth, but truth was a conundrum.

Ghazan left the tribe for a world of books. Day after day he sat in his closed tent and declined all invitations to hunt. His latest failure had thrown him back on the issues raised by the snow leopard, and chiefly whether choice itself was a chimera. Having drawn only blanks in his own search, he now consulted the authorities.

First he opened his copy of the Koran. Here was Truth unchallengeable. He turned to those verses attaching merit to prayer and alms-giving, describing the blessed in paradise and the damned being fed with boiling water and the fruit of the zaqqum tree, like molten brass. Merit and demerit entailed choice. Yet how square that with verses praising an Absolute Power, inescapable Divine decrees, all things determined by God's foreknowledge, unalterably written on a tablet? Ghazan compared the verses and tried to reconcile them. But they seemed irreconcilable. Therefore one group must be true, the other hold a hidden sense. It was necessary to choose. Confronted by this conclusion, Ghazan thought with dismay, I am trying to discover whether choice is possible and at the very outset I am faced with a choice between texts.

To aid him in this choice he turned to the commentators and philosophers. Their well-defined words, the syllogisms, the closely argued paragraphs: surely these straight, neat lines would act as a grid.

Drawing back the flap of the cover, Ghazan opened the first book. The feel of the rough, deckle-edged paper, and its dry, clean fragrance, as though of wisdom itself, brought back days of study in Shiraz. Lovingly, with that reverence for books inculcated by the mullah Mahdi, Ghazan turned the hand-written pages.

In this first book he read that only the dispassionate man was capable of choice. His rational will judged the results, good and bad, of each possible course and chose the one most likely to produce the greatest general good. Ghazan liked this view because it gave the primacy to reason and he wanted to believe it. But it did not tally with his own experience on the Dina. And this rational will, pictured as a judge— did it not form part of himself? Therefore not aloof and disinterested but of one blood with the plaintiff, and the case to be judged was a case of life and death.

Ghazan put this book aside and opened another. Here he read that only the good man has the power of choice, which is really a co-operation with grace. In a third he read that individual choice does not have eternal consequences, for the only immortal soul is the world-soul, from which individual souls go forth, and to which they return.

In a fourth book he found that all men are predestined at birth either to heaven or hell, that their actions are not chosen and count for nothing. This argument seemed unassailable, because it had infinity, the Absolute on its side. But for Ghazan it counted less than others because elsewhere in the book its author condemned many harmless pleasures and violently assailed all who held different views. Ghazan thought, this philosopher is cross and cold-hearted. I do not like him as a man: why should I take him as my guide?

This line of thought led Ghazan to analyse the characters of the other authors from their writings. He was vexed to discover that each based his argument on certain premises, stated or assumed. And these premises, because they suited a particular temperament or seemed expedient, must, consciously or unconsciously, have been chosen. His question, far from being answered, had simply been pushed back a stage.

But now his quandary was worse. For all the arguments, on whatever side, were so powerful and so cunningly reasoned that when he found himself disposed to adopt one view, a host of objections shouted him down. The answers to these objections were complicated and could not easily be carried in the head. He had to turn back to the books. And, as he thumbed the pages, the first view seemed to require modification in the light of a chance phrase that happened to meet his eyes, and at last seemed altogether untenable. When he tried to move forward, on the simplest errand, one or another of the texts snatched at his elbow and held him back.

Meanwhile, Falqani barley had been cut, threshed, winnowed by hand and stored in carpet bags. The days grew shorter than the nights, and the nights colder. On the surrounding mountains snow fell and as though by mutation the piebald peaks, and some of the animals who wintered there, became pure white. The hunters found little game. Herds of ibex had already started for the plains. The cropped, burned mountain grass was the colour of sand. Ghazan felt all his people's eyes on him, felt the pressure of his people and the changing weather: but his mind was like an ill-laden camel, reluctant to rise.

Meanwhile, Ahmad had safely returned from Meshed. Each morning he came in with the same refrain.

"The tent is stiff with frost. The sheep are growing braxy. When shall we start, Ghazan Khan?" and each morning his master answered, "Soon."

Each morning until a midnight blizzard swept the camp and Ghazan rose to find the ground white, the tents roofed with snow. So early a fall meant winter would be long and severe. One course of action—to remain immune in the uplands all winter—was rendered unfeasible. Even to delay a few weeks would injure the flocks.

For Ghazan it was as though from a clutch of eggs, among which lay a cuckoo's, one has been discarded as addled. With a sense of relief he set the day for his own tribal following to strike camp—next full moon. Other groups would leave on successive days. Dances were held on the eve of departure, and on the morrow, to the surnay's skirling call, the city of a thousand tents was folded and transported across the earth.

Not as in spring: then they had risen with the sap to their mountain stronghold, where none might enter against their will. Now they were returning, in the year's old age, highlanders to the lowlands, to the scene of sufferings and disaster, to the plain grass. Their horses stepped languidly, the men's expression was set, their songs were few and pitched in a minor key.

Ghazan had little time now for books. Though the moment for decision or the show of decision was approaching, he had much less a sense of urgency, moving now in habitual actions to a seasonal rhythm: riding ahead, the cleaving arrow-tip; mingling with his men, listening to their talk, joining in their ballads; watching with pride one small girl manœuvre two or three hundred goats down the mountains' ravined flanks. Over the mountain peaks and down the foothills the Falqani streamed, now cascading, now flowing smooth, at night dark, star-reflecting pools. For eighteen days they purled. The herds found enough to eat. Messages from the other groups brought Ghazan good news. Then, from a blue sky, struck another migrating force outnumbering the Falqani ten thousand to one.

A glint on the north horizon, like a silver clasp unlatched. A grey shadow, like the lifting of a lid; a grating sound, as though the wood of the grey box were warped. And as it rose the shape became yellow-grey. Stars hidden in the blue seemed to fall in sudden ambush. A cloud of chaff flying from the winnowing-stone, up and down, in and out, a patternless gyration in three dimensions. Before he saw them distinctly Ghazan felt whirling edges against face and hands, catching in his clothes, rubbing against his flesh. Locusts. One or two Ghazan caught in his hand and examined their rough bodies: the male yellow, spotted brown; the female larger and leaden-coloured: wings glassy, They were dry and thin: poor products of the end of the year—but capable of as much damage as the plump spring brood.

Chaos in the air was extended to earth, as two myriad forces met and fought. So thick they thronged—a river of dryness. Surely they would suffocate the tribe and their beasts. No time to pitch tents for protection. The herds, already frightened at the noonday darkness, panicked when the locusts dashed against their bodies, flicking their eyes with rough wings. The men ran to head off the bleating, straying flocks.

Children in arms shrieked and would not be calmed, dogs barked and snapped at the dodging pests, asses brayed; but these sounds were dimmed by the whirring wings. Only the boys enjoyed themselves, each trying to make the biggest catch.

The swarm followed a haphazard course, moving in all its parts, like fire or water: unassailable and, obeying no certain laws, the less to be resisted. For about an hour it flew steadily south, though each group for a while might hover or retreat. Then the dark veil became tattered, rent and finally frayed to pieces. The winged sandstorm passed. The sun issued from eclipse. A cock on one of the horses crowed.

With the swarm vanished the grass. The sky was once again blue, but the valleys were no longer green. The plains had been withered and dried by this destructive rain: all the essential green evaporated into the whirling, strengthened wind. The herds wandered among the scorched boulders, they bent again and again to the brown earth, but their teeth found only dust to crop. All that day they moved over a temporary desert. At night when they halted the animals were bleating and yielded little milk. In some tents locusts were roasted and eaten, in others singed and salted for the morrow. And so a few paid for the swarm's plunder.

Two days later the Falqani had still discovered no grass. The locusts had followed the tribe's intended route, leaving not a desiccated stalk behind. An unusual occurrence, but in no way connected with their late departure. The herds had altogether ceased to yield milk, so that the tribe had nothing to eat. To slaughter animals would be to trade future for present: to touch their slender supplies of barley equally rash. They must march on until they found grass. And many of the elders murmured that a curse was on the Falqani.

On the third day, towards noon, the ranks broke. A donkey loaded with tent-poles fell in its tracks. Its owner coaxed it, whipped its thin haunches, then tried to drag it on with a rope. Reluctantly Ghazan ordered its burden to be transferred to another. Hardly had this been done when vultures swept down, gorging the donkey's flesh, carefully leaving the entrails intact. An hour later the sun would be bleaching its bones.

Thereafter many goats and sheep, especially pregnant ewes, fell from hunger. Howling children, moaning dogs: the procession of pain chanted its own dirge. Only the camels, dry as locusts, did not suffer.

Ghazan, who had eaten as sparsely as his men, could gauge their weakness. He could not hold his rifle steady in his shoulder, could not have hit a partridge at a hundred paces. The locusts had pillaged their manhood. But he heard no complaints. They had suffered before, and if suffering took a new form—well, they had lived through the other pain. "It was written." Something would always be left for them in a cranny of the great earthenware platter.

On the next day some women had no milk for their suckling infants. Ghazan ordered a little ground barley with water to be distributed, and six of his own rams killed and roasted for nursing mothers. The earth, he thought, has refused us her milk. The earth in which we trusted has rejected us in our hour of despair, sent locusts to signify that the Falqani have no privileged place on her breast. Just when he needed strength, for himself and his people, strength had been taken from them. It had been a mistake to see favouritism in the brown, uniform, impartial earth. And yet on the earth they were totally dependent.

How make the earth yield? Whip it, as Xerxes had lashed the white horses of the Hellespont? Implore it, kneeling down, prostrating his brow in the dust? Offer sacrifice? But he and his men were already poured out like milk, curdled like cheese. Threaten to leave? No, not that. Ask pardon? For what? Not once had they failed in gratitude for all its gifts. And they in turn had treated the earth well. Their sheep, by loosening its roots, disposed the grass to spread, by biting off short shoots promoted an increase of stronger blades. Where water flowed, Ghazan had planted trees. Summer and winter he had slept on its breast. Never had he branded its flesh to prove it his slave. He had loved the earth well. His joy in that love had hidden its full extent. Now, by his pain, Ghazan measured its height and depth: and it was higher than any mountain, deeper than any valley.

Only on the fifth day after the swarm passed did the Falqani reach vegetation: at first a few stumps of camel-thorn disdained by the gorged locusts, then coarse stems of yellow grass from which the sweet blades had been stolen. The herds cropped greedily, but this first dry pasturage, at the point where the locusts had swerved westwards, did not appease their long hunger, nor swell their udders with milk. Nor did the rediscovery of grass appease Ghazan's sense of rejection.

CHAPTER TWENTY-ONE

THE Falqani passed through the village of Ramjird. A few houses with mud roofs, like a herd of buffalo drinking at the flashing jube, and, further along, an open bazaar: stalls of strong cord shoes, little mirrors, coloured rugs, confectionery, sugar-loaves, bowls of cummin, cloves, cinnamon and aniseed. And, above all, the wonder of electric light along the main street, outside the gendarmerie and one or two houses, lights that needed no oil and hung like civic stars. Each shop, too, had its petrol lamp, casting a strange white glow, not flickering like the tribal mutton-fat flame.

So many objects! Even the chairs and tables were novelties, to be admired and appraised. A world of possessions, a fairy-tale world that did not move, where you could put something down on the ground, leave it for days, weeks, months and still find it in the same place. To live among tables and chairs: to be an object like them: no, the Falqani didn't want that. But they loved walking on level flagging stones under the glass eggs that gleamed, watching the little chugging engine which lighted the stars, seeing a car pass, touching the smooth metal body of the car as it rattled by. The riches of a hundred cities: strong blue trousers with metal buttons, bales of cigarettes, tin kettles, needles and filigree jewellery for their women. In one open store unleavened bread-dough was being wound on a spade-shaped iron, thrust into the oven to cook a few minutes, then pulled out and unfolded—hot, flecked-brown pancake. The luxury of bread! In another store china cups with roses on them, caskets of tea, gleaming chests. These were made of imported beer-tins nailed together, but to the tribesmen they seemed pure silver. Strange, static, lifeless wealth.

The sharp-eyed shopkeepers encouraged the tribe to buy, finding choice epithets for the shoddy goods, but cautiously, lest they excite desire to the pitch of robbery. Just as in a rippled pavement of desert sandstone old seas were visible to the far-seeing eye, so Ghazan, watching the tribe's passage, saw his ancestors sweeping through jewelled Herat and Samarcand—cities truly rich—on that first long migration from Central Asia.

The tribesmen lingered wide-eyed before the lighted stalls. Many held part of their tunic across their noses: accustomed to pure mountain air, they were strangely sensitive to the rank village smells. Among them Ghazan caught sight of Ahmad, surrounded by his sheep. He had sold a skin of clarified butter and now held a few coins in his hand. He was haggling for white sugar-loaves, in shape like five-pounder shells, which hung on a string above a basket of eggs. Ahmad claimed they were nibbled by rats and brought down the price to sixty rials the *man*. The grocer, a small, rabbity man of Ahmad's age, put two loaves on the scales, struck a balance and waited for the sixty rials. Usually three middle-sized loaves made the *man*.

"Weigh them again," said Ahmad.

The grocer did so, Ahmad watching closely.

"You've got your thumb on the scale," he cried.

The grocer flung up his hands in annoyance. "Of course my thumb's on the scale! Do you expect me to give my sugar away?"

The grocer vented his anger on Ahmad's father, and Ahmad returned the compliment for several generations further back.

"You Turki bandit," the grocer cried, his little nose quivering like a rabbit's. "What do you know of the price of sugar?"

"You village trash—what do you know of the value of money? We mine the silver ourselves in the far hills, while you squat here all day in the cool shadow, laying your thievish schemes."

The grocer drew himself up. "Pure sugar I offer, at a fair price."

"Then sell me pure sugar—without throwing in your thumb."

"A mere flick of the thumb! And you argue all night."

"A thumb for a thumb," Ahmad retorted, putting his down firmly on the side of the weights.

"Give me your sixty rials," said the grocer, holding out the two loaves invitingly.

"Give me my *man* of sugar."

The grocer tossed his hands in the air. "Take what's weighed, or nothing at all."

Ahmad looked the grocer up and down, then at the sugar. He wanted it badly—but not at any price. Attraction and revulsion mingled in his face, then, deliberately, he spat on the ground.

"That for your sugar! May the rats make a banquet of it and you!"

He swaggered away with his sheep in train.

Ghazan had witnessed such scenes so often, he knew Ahmad's attitude to the sugar, to the village: the temptation of a settled life: the possession of things, a fruitful harvest, the certainty of daily bread; above all, a house: man turning to the earth as to a nurse, a mother. But stronger rose the revulsion. Man was the male, the conqueror; he must march over the earth, tread the earth down, not submit to her chores, to the sowing, the watering with the sweat of his brow. Man must continue master of his own work and life.

Further along the street Ghazan met Dilbar haggling at a stall, Hussein in her arms. She held a pink celluloid comb in one hand.

"One tuman," the stall keeper was saying, a stocky middle-aged man with a growth of beard. Like other villagers and townsmen, he wore a brimless felt skull-cap tight on his head: duller brown than the Falqani hat and without its distinctive wing-like flaps.

"Eight rials." Her accent made the offer sound more.

"Look how strong it is. Two tumans it's worth at least."

Ghazan valued the comb at about two or three rials; the stall-keeper would get five from a villager.

"Eight rials," Dilbar repeated.

The man said no. Dilbar walked to another stall, fingered some lengths of green cotton, then returned.

"That pink was made for your cheeks—for your red scarf." He held the comb up to the light. He thought she could understand. "You'll never find another so pretty."

She ran the comb through her thick black hair, then looked at it, drawing it away as her child snatched as though at a toy. The crown of her dreams. But she showed with gestures how flimsy and feather-light it was. The man held firm, watching her half-greedy, half-afraid: with these nomads you could never tell. Dilbar picked up a blue bead bracelet. Tents had to be pitched and a meal cooked that night.

"Two tumans," said the stall-keeper. She tossed up her chin and returned to the comb.

"Eight rials." A year's pride hung in the balance.

"You Falqani!" cried the stall-keeper in disgust. "But I'm the victim of my kind heart. Nine rials."

She opened a square of knotted material folded into her skirts. Ghazan saw her count out two five-rial pieces: there remained one more. The Falqani never accepted paper money for their milk-products, deeming it worthless. Dilbar gave the coins to the stall-keeper and took the comb. He handed her a one-rial piece. Dilbar put it between her white teeth, bit it several times hard and tied it in her skirts. Then, flinging him a scornful look, she turned on her heel and strode away like a queen.

Still the Falqani gaped and marvelled. Only Ghazan looked with unwondering eyes at the stalls. Possessions like this, at the lowest scale, seemed to him to betray the whole system, showed it unworthy of man and his striving. To have one's dreams, which could enclose the universe, reduced to a pile of gimcrack pink combs: to long for these, to covet them, to make them one's end and glory; in his eyes the settled life stood self-condemned.

Wildly he thought, my people came from the heart of Asia. For seven centuries here in Persia we have been exiles, all of us exiles. I shall lead them back to our original home, to Turkestan, to steppes bare in trees but rich in grass, to steppes bare of idols, to steppes idolatry can never touch. I shall lead my free people to yawning spaces where the only time is eternity. And all the while on his white horse he led the Falqani out of the village of Ramjird southwards, away from Central Asia.

A few moments later Ghazan thought, I spit with Ahmad. But Dilbar bought the comb. She wants her man to march in glory across the hills, but even more she loves the pink comb. In fairness I must take account of the women, their instinct to build a square of stones for the fire, and round that a larger square for the house. But this notion aroused in Ghazan only distaste. He thought, if I am honestly to give it its due, I must feel it as well as think it. But for that I should have to be both man and woman. The whole thousand-cursed affair, he decided, was beyond anyone's powers.

Meanwhile tents were being pitched beyond Ramjird. And the brown irregular stony space within the skirts blossomed as flower gardens—the only sort of garden tribesmen were privileged to enjoy: there they had been born and hoped to die. Dilbar had killed a chicken for dinner. It was served boiled with barley and saffron. Cross-legged in his tent, Ghazan pushed the dish away. He felt no hunger. Food! Why feed his dreams? Already his mind was overspiced. Puppies lapping the milk of Falqani women, the stalls with the small-eyed vendors: over against these images, a tired old man on his deathbed, the sad-eyed captain saying "Careful plans have been laid to protect their health and give them arable land", the poem still in his pocket.

Clearest of all, especially now at night, he saw Anahita's grey eyes, beckoning him to battle. To give her all he had promised, to lead her in triumph up into the Zagros, to ensure the succession—and her sons, what a brood they would be! But precisely because her image acted with such power, Ghazan suspected the course for which she stood. Since motives were masked, disguised, could act on a man all unknown, he must take double precautions. To be strictly honest, to make a dispassionate choice, not as a man in love but as Ilkhan, he must give the benefit of any doubt to the other course.

Ahmad entered and took away the untouched platter.

"This chicken," he laughed, "enjoys life after death." Looking more closely at Ghazan, he asked, "Are you ill, Ghazan Khan, that you eat nothing?"

"I have dined off dishes of doubt."

"What doubt, master? The locusts have passed: all day the flocks have cropped."

As Ghazan explained, simplifying the issues, Ahmad drew in his lips, very concerned. With feeling he said:

"You will card yourself thin on that fine comb, and all to no purpose. Whether we throw up or down, left or right, the dice will fall as they are destined to fall. What can we do by ourselves? Nothing, nothing."

"Ahmad takes care to guard his sheep," Ghazan replied. "If he slept, and jackals stole two new lambs, wouldn't Ahmad blame himself?"

"Not for long," he answered lightly. "And if I decided to sleep, I wouldn't think about staying awake. I'd say, supposing I watched all night and not the stir of a jackal?" Seeing Ghazan unconvinced, Ahmad squatted beside him.

"Did you never hear of Malik the Kazvini? Like all Kazvinis, Malik was very cunning. He stole gold and jewellery from his master, then ran away. Near a caravanserai along the road he saw a party of horsemen behind him, among them his master. Malik said to himself, 'Shall I hide here in this caravanserai?' No, he decided. It is so obvious my master will be sure to look. I'll continue my journey; while he searches the caravanserai, I shall have time to escape. Malik ran a few paces, then drew up. He thought to himself, 'My master knows I am not a fool. He will say, 'Malik will avoid so obvious a hiding-place. Useless to search the caravanserai. I will continue along the road.'

"So Malik turned back to the caravanserai. He was getting ready to hide under a pile of loose bedding, when a new thought struck him. 'My master may foresee this cunning. Perhaps I should go one better and continue my journey.' While he was still debating, the horsemen rode up. His master seized Malik and carried him off to prison."

With a laugh Ghazan asked, "Would you have been wiser, Ahmad?"

"Not wiser, Ghazan Khan—but with less time to take decisions. I should have shaken the cup once and let the dice fall. But even if you shake for months, the destined number will still turn up. Meanwhile you grow sick and thin."

He could not help laughing with Ahmad. Was this the truth at last—seen in his servant's mirror? Was he nothing more than a cotton kite in the wind with a tail of gaudy dreams, a would-be bird; now swooping to earth, flat on his face? A clown attempting the juggler's act: Seven, eight, nine coloured balls—and the tenth brings them all to the ground? It was true: true for the spectator. But the clown had a heart. He could laugh at himself in the intervals, but the intervals were soon up. The act was beginning. Only a dress rehearsal—Ghazan tried to reassure himself—but if he couldn't balance the balls now, how would he do so on the day?

The leading sections reached a point forty miles from Shiraz, ten from the Guyum plain. Every autumn, at this stage of the migration, Ghazan was in the habit of riding over to Persepolis; his own palace, as he considered. There he liked to meditate on the past and, once in the year, see his people's lives in context. This autumn he had a special reason for not missing his visit. He told Rohim, who sometimes accompanied him, that he intended to go alone and, in order to avoid possible army scouts, by night. He would rejoin the tribe towards dawn.

Under a rising half-moon Ghazan rode to Persepolis and thought of his first visit, as a boy, to the same palace and yet to a very different palace. He had grown up in the belief that the huge stones of the terrace and the columns had formed the palace of Jamshid, because only two men—the legendary Persian king and Solomon—had power over angels, and only angels could have reared such massive stones. On his return from abroad, Ghazan had probed to the truth: that King Darius, ninth and greatest of the Achaemenians, had built Persepolis as capital of his empire.

The Achaemenians, originally rulers only of Fars, were Ghazan's own predecessors. They too had migrated annually—between Shush and Hamadan—a distance equal to that covered by the Falqani. Their capital dominated not only the immediate plain of Marvdasht but the once obedient surrounding country. Lying close to Ghazan's migration route, each year it drew him by its age and mass. He knew now what it was, but what did it mean? Each year he had put the question without coming nearer an answer.

After three hours' ride Ghazan saw the solid stone columns of the largest building—the Apadana—rise out of the Mountain of Mercy, from which they had been quarried and which now formed their back-cloth. Only thirteen survived out of seventy-two: battered wreck of a great ship, still afloat, still sending messages.

Next appeared the long terrace which formed the western precinct, looming sheer and high as a cliff, long as a line of a hundred horsemen. The terrace sent heralds to meet Ghazan, bee-eaters that nested in the interstices of the cut stones; with lizards the city's sole inhabitants. Their blue plumage showed in the moonlight: they circled and swooped around Ghazan, as he came up under the shadow of the place, and saw the standing stones and broken porches like a vast cuneiform script against the sky.

Cantering down the mountain track, Ghazan reined in Milk of the Moon and took a small path not generally known. This led to stone steps on the northern precincts. Ghazan rode up the steps like the kings of old, but almost at once he had to rein in before round bases of grey limestone columns, fallen horse-head capitals and walls sunk low as sheep-pens, forming a dense barrier. Dismounting, he tethered his mare to a stone lion and, skiriting the Chariot Mews, walked to the entrance hall of the Apadana. He paused before the inscriptions above the four stone piers of the eastern doorway. The inscriptions were in Persian, Elamite and Babylonian cuneiform: regular lines of straight dents in the stone, as though hacked by an axe; uncompromising, severe:

"A great god is Ahura Mazda, who created this earth, who created yonder heaven, who created man, who created welfare for man, who made Xerxes King, one king of many, one lord of many. I am Xerxes, the great king, King of Kings, king of the countries having every kind of people, king of this great earth far and wide, the son of Darius the king, the Achaemenian. Says Xerxes the great king: By the will of Ahura Mazda I made this colonnade for the representatives of all countries: much else that is beautiful I did in Persepolis, and my father did. Whatever work seems beautiful, we did it all by the will of Ahura Mazda. Says Xerxes the King: May Ahura Mazda protect me and my kingdom: my work and my father's work, may Ahura Mazda protect it."

My work and my father's work may God protect it! The cry for continuance let into the walls—Ghazan repeated the words aloud, and heard them echo from the fallen stone, as he passed to the surroundings of the Apadana, thinking all the while of his own people, his own kingship.

The raised floor of this palace was approached by the ruin's most distinctive feature: four highly decorated uncovered staircases on the north, four on the east, the sides of which formed a wall of polished fawn limestone friezes. Those on the east caught the moonlight, so that turning the corner Ghazan seemed to surprise the gliding figures to stillness: divided by lines of twelve-petalled rosettes, three rows of tribute-bearers from twenty-three satrapies of the empire. These, in profile, half-lifesize, approached from each side of the twin staircase, stone copies of the actual figures who would have mounted the long, gradual shallow degrees to lay their offerings at the great king's feet.

Ghazan scrutinized them more searchingly than ever before. These tribute-bearers who had survived the centuries must surely be wise with age; surely if he waited they would deliver the truth to him. The long stately procession, not named but each identifiable by its distinctive physiognomy, headdress and clothing, displayed the breeds of man: Medes, bearing a dagger, bracelets and coats; Elamites with bows, daggers, a lioness and two cubs; Parthians bringing a camel and skins; Babylonians with nuggets of gold and a bison; Cilicians leading two rams; Scythians offering a horse and rolls of cloth, wearing high-pointed hoods twice the length of their beards, each curl of which was still rough to the touch; Phœnicians, bringing gold flower-vases; Afghans with a two-humped camel; Indians, their offerings in baskets balanced on poles and leading a donkey: all came after many months' journey to offer in an elaborate ceremonial their treasures to a Persian king of kings. Still they marched, though the cedar roofs had long ago tumbled: Ghazan saw them with his own eyes. Past, present and future fused in the figures which only partly emerged from the fawn stone: all Asia marching here in the deserted plain, so numerous as never to have a final rank. Marching forever.

One scene showed snub-nosed Ethiopians from the Empire's southwestern satrapy, their gifts a sickle and a giraffe. Rohim had first noticed that giraffe: a horse with a very long neck—but far from long enough—its horse-head surmounted by squat horns. It had taken his fancy and Ghazan's also, that short-necked giraffe: either a deliberate slip to avoid fatal perfection or else an unwitting betrayal of the sculptor's provincialism. Either way the one freak which proved the building less than divine.

Animals and individual men—no abstract symbols, no numbers— each group offering its best produce and works of art: men who came face to face with Darius and Xerxes and their descendants. Each a satrapy, but each retaining its way of life and identity: from Africa and Thrace to the mountains of India: each retaining its own religion—even the Jews' temple at Jerusalem Cyrus had ordered rebuilt. No uniformity: a perfectly organized empire. Cyrus had founded, Darius extended it: a hundred and fifty years later it fell. And with it the palace, the largest building Persia had ever known.

Standing before the scene of that fall, Ghazan saw that his own dilemma was not a freak storm. It had broken before on this very palace. And Ghazan put to himself the crucial question, which concerned the future no less than the past: Could this fall have been averted?

Cyrus had foreseen the danger. In the fertile plains of newly-conquered Media, where his army wanted to settle, he said, "Soft lands breed soft men: rich fruits of the earth and valiant warriors do not grow from the same soil." The Persians saw that Cyrus reasoned better than they and marched out of Media, choosing rather to be rulers on a barren mountainside than slaves dwelling in tilled valleys. So, during Cyrus's lifetime, the empire gained strength. Failure came later, under his successors.

Their tombs lay around the ruined city, some in the Mountain of Mercy, others across the valley, cut into the rock, Egyptian-style. On his tomb Darius had ordered the inscription: "I was a friend to my friends: as horseman and bowman I proved myself superior to all others; as hunter I prevailed: I could do everything." Everything! The boundless pride of a king by divine right: but the boast had been vain. A small people of Europe both Darius and Xerxes his son had failed to subdue. And from Europe had arisen Persia's nemesis: Alexander the Great, Lord of the Two Horns. With only a small force he had burned Persepolis to the ground. Ten thousand mule-carts and three thousand camels had hauled away the gold and silver treasure. The library of ox-skin books, the Zoroastrian scripture, had been taken to Greece, translated for official records and thrown into the sea: repudiated with contempt. And in the Mountain of Mercy the tomb of the last king, vanquished by Alexander, gaped unfinished, still awaiting its lord.

Why, despite the prayer, "My work and my father's work, may God protect it!" had the palaces, and the empire they crowned, within two centuries fallen to fragments? The kings had become weak, aloof and cowardly; blood had run thin, the bodyguard of ten thousand Immortals had dallied away their immortality in the fat plains. Such explanations, formulated on past visits, tonight seemed to Ghazan dry bones: dissatisfied, he bit to the marrow within.

These columns had witnessed the rise and fall of all Persian dynasties. To endure, to preserve identity, again Ghazan echoed Xerxes' cry, standing alone among the cold stones, shivering a little in the autumn night. If only he could ask the right question. Everything, he believed, turned on the question. Endurance in time: was that the question?

Which dynasty, Ghazan asked himself, had endured longest? The Parthian, which for five centuries maintained its virility and kept the Roman Empire at bay. The Parthian had lasted longest, and had never lost a war. Ghazan admired the Parthians, though the wisest men he had known—the mullah Mahdi, for instance—had always disparaged them. The Parthian rulers had built no Persepolis. The Parthians had founded nothing, left no remains: they were nomads, with no standing army, almost no arts, no literature. Careless of the future, they had lived their ideas in the present, put them into action. They had not trusted in stone; had not shut out the sky with cedar roofs and the earth with marble floors.

To found, to establish, to become established—so Ghazan concluded —meant sowing the seeds of decay. Persepolis should never have been built. Once the series began, it had no end. Alexander's foundation in Egypt—Alexandria—had been put to the torch by some Roman Cæsar: the Roman cities in turn barbarously overrun.

Formulation of a way of life and beliefs—that was even more fatal than foundation. A flourish of trumpets which topple one's own walls. A fanfaronade which drew from the setting sun a locust-swarm of words to devour one's own. Impossible to write without reading: the wisdom of others, also. Two instead of one, and the satraps no longer marched in single file with their tribute.

So Ghazan generalized, but when he began to question the fallen pillars and bas-reliefs, his question was returned, an empty echo. What was the message of the past for the future? That even reiterated prayer did not avert disaster, that as soon as one sculpted tribute-bearers, the actual tribute-bearers fell away, as though from their own ghosts? If history were like a poem, these were the rhymes, but they gave no clue to the next verse. None of the answers bore on his own all-important question. If there were a treasure of truth within these ruins, it was historical truth, an epitaph, not particular prophecy.

Or was he deaf? With the disappointment of a deaf man who misses an all-important message, with disappointment no less crushing than when he had turned a second time from Fatima's tent, Ghazan walked slowly away. If he was to return to his people by daylight, he must leave now. He untethered his horse, mounted and headed from the ruins. Soon, looking back, he could see only the thirteen tall columns, sole survivors of an otherwise total deforestation.

Away from its precise details, in the semi-darkness, the presence of the place grew on Ghazan. A relic, bones of an extinct mammoth, mausoleum to a dynasty superseded by the next in line. So many had risen and fallen. Tamerlane had ridden, as he rode now, within sight of the ten-ton limestone blocks. And the first Ghazan. Even the Parthians he so admired had, after five centuries, fallen at last. All fallen at last like the palace.

All fallen. In spite of himself, Ghazan began to see his people's plight under the shadow of the fallen pillars, historically, objectively, with the eyes of his Swiss schoolteachers, of the Teheranis. A nomad people, a curious survival: they must fall into step with the world, move on to another stage of development. Better or not scarcely mattered. Perhaps, thought Ghazan, remembering the locusts, those

306

terms were inapplicable. In any case, a natural evolution which could not be resisted. Dynasties, ways of life, had a fixed term, like man, like life itself: even like the earth, for were not the Zagros to which the Falqani belonged being slowly eroded by wind and frost, chipped by rain and snow: the hardest rock riven to fragments that moved always downward to the sandy plain? One day perhaps the earth would be level, with neither peak no ocean depth. But the earth did not resist. Nature was resigned.

Resigned. Snatches of verse from his beloved mystics, from Rumi and the other Sufi poets, endorsed this line of thought. Everything human passed away; life was a moment, let it be lived in slavery or freedom. The fish caught in mountain rock, his people settled in the plain. Submit to the tide of events, careless of which way they flowed. It mattered nothing, if his people degenerated; it mattered nothing if he were forced to live among the infidel, far from all he loved. It mattered nothing for all was swept up in God's goodness. There was no such thing as evil for the humble man. Humility: Ahmad's humility, the mullah Mahdi's humility. He must become nothing, a stone figure on a stone frieze.

In the semi-darkness Ghazan had been following a mountain path to the Guyum plain, and now noticed with quickening pulse that in a few minutes he would be able to look down on the plain, on his destiny and his people's destiny. Here, unless there had been some sudden last-moment change in their plans, soldiers would already be deployed. It was the age-old battle-ground, the climacteric of their autumn migration, where Reza Shah had disarmed the Falqani in his father's day.

Easing his mare out of her gallop, Ghazan turned off the track up the rocky slopes of a tree-clad ridge overlooking the plain. Half-way he dismounted and tethered Milk of the Moon. Using the cover of yellow-leaved stunted oaks, he crept carefully forward, rustling the fallen leaves. Still below the horizon, the sun was rising behind him. He reached the top, and looked down.

The plain was crowded with brown beehive tents. A few he had expected, but not these long serried ranks. After his first surprise, Ghazan began to count them. Before he had reached a hundred he lost track, so thickly clustered they were, in the half-light. And each tent represented twelve soldiers. He had never seen such a force: at least ten times the number needed to hold up the migration. The army

307

were taking no risks: had by sheer power obviated the possibility of risk.

As the first sunbeams topped the ride and swept the plain like a searchlight, Ghazan caught his breath. Many trucks and jeeps stood behind the tents. And beyond, under camouflage nets, ranged in long ranks, gleaming in the dawn, long barrels, polished breeches of guns— pointed east, at the sun, at his people. And beside them squat mortars mounted on tripods. Then he detected thin snub-nosed machine-guns, sighted at regular intervals along the far slope. Men there had been before and rifles, but never such a harvest of arms on the sterile plain.

Ghazan lay looking at the deployment as though at his own hearse. His body grew cold as the cold earth; his mind refused to move beyond the guns. After a long time he crawled back, feeling slightly sick, and rose to his feet. He brushed oak-leaves from his palms, which were sticky with sweat, not the sweat of exertion, and mounted once more. Soon he was galloping to his own encampment. His thoughts kept pace. A division, so lightly spoken, one thing, manageable: and now spread out on the plain, many men and many guns. Anger rose in his throat at the army's strength, and as suddenly sank. Again he became a figure of stone, impassive to frost and heat, dead to his feelings. The moment of decision had come. The ruins and the guns that ruined: he had seen them both with his own eyes. No situation could be more inevitable. And so, Ghazan concluded his reasoning, there is no decision to take. No decision at all. Only resignation to the inevitable.

The chieftains must know before anyone else. He would summon them forward tonight, explain what had happened, that resistance was out of the question. They must submit as their fathers had done. He would tell them of the troops and guns: they would accept that argument. The Falqani had run their course. A good course, but finished now. It had to be: nothing mattered. A moment in eternity: not worth a tear.

CHAPTER TWENTY-TWO

"CAPTAIN SHAMI to see you, Ghazan."

Hardly had he reached his tent when Rohim brought the news.

"Shami! It can't be."

"I assure you—and not a bit put out."

"Has he no pride, to come crawling back after such a disgrace!"

Rohim laughed. "I think it's pride that brings him."

Ghazan looked up from his meal of curds and barley, puzzled. Rohim continued, "Where else can Shami find ready money for his material? With, say, eight thousand tumans he can buy back his crown."

Ghazan looked displeased. "Maybe that, or to learn my plans. He shall learn nothing one way or the other." After a pause he added, "There's no need to see him at all."

"It may be important," Rohim objected. "Let's hear what he has to say."

Ghazan acquiesced. It didn't seem to matter.

Shami was shown in, smiling, polite, his fat face shining, uniform dowdy as ever. On his shoulders he wore a captain's three stars. After an exchange of compliments, tea was served. In reaction from his own deepest feelings, Ghazan had recourse to raillery.

"Well, Shami, how did General Bahrami like his skewbald?"

Shami stirred uneasily. "Since you raise the matter, Ghazan Khan, allow me to say that I knew all along the horse's defects."

Ghazan smiled. "But didn't say so at the time?"

"As you were making a gift of the horse, naturally I did not wish to speak of its weak points. But I knew all along it wasn't much more than a nag."

Ghazan exchanged a glance with Rohim. This quartermaster really was incorrigible. "And Bahrami knew too, I daresay?"

"Not at all," said Shami smoothly. "I certainly never dreamed of giving a jade like that to General Bahrami. I found him a pure blood in Shiraz. But that is neither here no there." He paused, and lowered his voice to a solemn whisper. "Can I interest you in a light tank, Ghazan Khan?"

"A tank? Are you joking?"

"Not at all." He seemed a little hurt.

"Why should I want a light tank?"

Shami shot the cousins an oblique glance. "A very useful weapon."

Ghazan watched him gulp his tea and with his spoon scoop up the sugar at the bottom of the glass.

"But I have no enemies, Captain Shami."

Shami lifted his shoulders and spread his hands. "We all have our enemies, Ghazan Khan."

"And if the enemy, too, possesses tanks?"

"Ah, but they don't," said Shami easily. "This is the only one in Fars. It came into my hands quite by chance. The tank is of no immediate use to me and I wondered whether we could—make an exchange."

"For goats?" scoffed Ghazan.

"For, say, ten thousand tumans."

Ghazan looked at Rohim, as though to say, you were very nearly right. Turning to Shami, he said, "Where would I find such a sum?"

"Even goat's milk has cream. And cream rises to the top."

Rohim had been listening attentively and now broke in. "It all depends on the tank. What weapons does it carry?"

Ghazan did not check Rohim's interest. The tank seemed no more important than Dilbar's pink comb. He began again to brood and scarcely listened.

"A heavy machine-gun," said Shami, "with five thousand rounds."

Rohim was impressed, but he said scornfully, "What use is that? A spray of bullets into the blue—one or two men hit by chance. With a rifle I choose my target."

Putting the tips of his stubby fingers together, Shami became professional. "You have increased range—and protection of armour plating."

"True," Rohim admitted. "But you ask a large sum. First we must see the tank."

"A perfectly normal tank: there is nothing I cannot describe."

"It may look well and still not be in working order."

"I guarantee that the tank works," said Shami, drawing himself up and adopting a very self-righteous tone. "There are certain rules of war which one does not break."

310

After a silence Rohim asked, "How old is the tank?"

Shami looked displeased. He tried to get round the question. At last he put a good face on it. He announced, as though this was the tank's chief excellence, "It's exactly thirty years old."

"A tank thirty years old!"

"The best tanks were built then. It was a vintage year, you might say. And it comes from Czechoslovakia. The fact that it is working now proves it an excellent, hard-wearing tank."

"We cannot buy a tank thirty years old without seeing it," said Rohim with finality.

Shami seemed disappointed. Doubtless he had hoped to take part-payment now, leave the tank in a pre-arranged hiding place, where the Falqani could collect it and deposit the rest of the money. Now he would have to come with troops to protect himself and the tank: an awkward situation to explain to his guard.

"It's an Adamov tank," wheedled Shami. "It has slit windows in front, with little wheels you turn to open or close them." He imitated the motion. "Only the best tanks have these."

The Falqani said nothing.

Shami looked meaningfully at each in turn. "It can go in reverse—fast, very fast. The ideal vehicle for a quick escape." He paused. Ghazan stirred impatiently. "The driver's seat has a rubber cushion." Still the cousins kept silent. "Very well," sighed Shami, "you may see it. Where shall we meet?"

Rohim sugested a ruined caravanserai behind Khiareh, next day, just before dawn. Ghazan thought of intervening. That would mean telling his plans. But before anyone else—even before Rohim—the eleven chieftains must be informed, and give their approval. That was unwritten law. As for Shami, it would do him no harm to cool his heels a few hours in a ruined caravanserai.

"That will suit me," said Shami. "Bring the ten thousand." He rose to his feet. "You'll be sure to like the tank." From the tent-opening he flung the cousins a last, meaning look. "Unlike some he knows, Captain Shami always gives full value."

When Shami had left, Rohim said with enthusiasm, "A tank! I could capture Shiraz single-handed with a tank. But thirty years old—do you really think it still works?" He noticed Ghazan's silence. "You don't seem very interested."

"I'm not."

"Wait till you see it." Then, reading Ghazan's expression more carefully, "After all, you don't want to buy the tank?"

"I'm calling an assembly for tonight. Tonight you will hear everything."

Ghazan ordered tents struck at noon. The leading sections moved down on a short day's journey, allowing those behind to join them. Ghazan rode near the head. This, he thought, is my last day but one with my people. Within a few weeks I shall have left my country for ever. He breathed deeply, snatching even at the Persian air, at the scent of the dying grass. He watched his people, memorizing the scene for a lifetime. They still belonged to him: he to them. He tried to imagine it always so: tried to stretch the afternoon to the wheel of eternity. But he could not: pictures of the future broke in: of Anahita, her grey eyes like doves tumbling to another man's glance, of a remote land where he would not speak his own tongue, far from the hills where God lay hidden.

Dilbar rode near him on a donkey, Hussein held before her. She wore the red fillet bought in Meshed. Ahmad strode nearby among his sheep, calling to them from time to time, and to Dilbar. They would not pass this way again. Next spring one home and one fire. From wandering planet to fixed star—like the rest of the earth's people.

All day Ghazan had felt restless and sad. All day he had tried to check these feelings. Either course, he told himself, entailed evil. What did his feelings matter? He had reasoned out his decision dispassionately on the way from Persepolis. Now he must accept the consequences of his reasoning. He must continue impassive till the end, a figure on a stone frieze.

Ghazan cantered apart, up to a crest where he could look down on the whole body of men and beasts in motion: a dark tide drifting through the brown dust, with eddies and pools beyond on the slopes. The cloudless sky was dotted with one or two hawks far off, and one flashing blue group of bee-eaters. The dark river flowing out of the mountains into the sea, losing itself. On the other side of the hills from his people he noticed a group of five gazelle edging across the slopes: like him moving south to warmth, but to continued freedom. Sadly, taking none of his usual pleasure, he watched their graceful movement, the poised heads, the long dainty legs that flicked the ground like whips. Thin they looked: perhaps an effect of the locusts.

One of the hawks flew right above Ghazan. In the clear dry air he could see its black head, every grey and fawn breast-feather on its thin body, wheeling on motionless wings. The gazelle must have spied the hawk, but they did not start to run. Hares and partridge were the hawk's prey, not gazelle. Gazelle were too big, too powerful.

Ghazan's attention was distracted by two pack-donkeys which had strayed to an oleander bush. He drove them away with his whip and when he again looked up noticed that the hawk was no longer overhead. It had flown towards the gazelle and continued until it was almost directly above them. There it hovered.

Suddenly the hawk fell in a rushing stoop from the high air. The gazelle broke into a run and scattered. The straight line of the hawk's stoop became a parabola, pursuit and descent a single act. It swept down on the last gazelle of the herd, a big buck, striking violently between the rapier horns, from above and behind, pitching the buck forward in the dust. As he rolled over, the hawk's grip was loosened. The buck scrambled to his feet and darted away. The hawk flew after him and struck again between the horns. This time it clawed at the head and beat its wings over the gazelle's eyes.

Ghazan's first instinct was to defend the gazelle. Still watching closely, he reined in his horse, groped at his right shoulder and with a frown drew his hand back empty. He was carrying no rifle that day. Then he thought, it doesn't matter. A blow of the gazelle's hoof, and the hawk is done for.

The gazelle tottered a few paces forward, reeling and shaking, the grey shape clamped between its black horns like the crest on a helmet. Slowly he dragged to a halt. He twisted his neck wildly about, rearing up and pawing the air, then threw himself down on the earth and rolled over, trying to unloose the claws. But still the hawk clung, rolling with the gazelle, still beating its wings, so that the gazelle could not see.

Ghazan watched, almost incredulous. He had never seen such a thing before, nor heard of it happening. He felt involved, no longer a stone figure on a stone frieze, but alerted by the hawk's swoop. The hawk seemed to be rending his own flesh, something within his flesh. Still the hawk beat its wings over the gazelle's head, while it clawed

313

at the skull for a vital place. Still the gazelle lunged out with his hooves, striking the hawk glancing blows without dislodging it.

Before Ghazan had drawn two more breaths, the gazelle quivered in every limb, then lay still, while the black head jabbed at the soft parts of his breast, violently, hungrily. Starved it must have been, thought Ghazan, to reverse the natural order and strike at so huge a prey.

The hawk tore at the gazelle, overshadowed by a hill of flesh. Quickly it gorged. Then, spreading its wings, a chunk of meat in its curved beak, it flew up into the air. It came overhead, flapping tired wings slowly like a crow, then receded until it became a dark point, an invisible point in the blue sky.

Ghazan sat motionless in his saddle, breathing heavily, astounded, stirred to the extreme of excitement. This could be no chance happening. It must be a sign, a prodigy. The land had sent him a sign. Of what? Of battle, of victory. A sign, like the burning bush, overturning resignation. The land had shown its colours, had signified that it chose him and his people, would not let them go. With the image of the swooping hawk still before his eyes, Ghazan turned and looked at his people moving across the hills under the sky.

"We shall fight," he cried aloud. "We shall fight and win."

Exultant, but with a steadier pulse at his wrists, Ghazan started to ride down from the crest. He looked at the hills and his people crossing the hills under the sky. The dam of dispassion was breached—breached by the hawk's beak—and love swept free over the hills, over his people who belonged to the hills.

"We shall fight," he cried again, and began to turn over his decision, which was the earth's own decision, like a newly mined ruby. Rough and ungleaming, but heavy, easily grasped. He tried to keep it like that, tight in his fist. He would not think before or after. Such joy he felt, to have found it at last, visible, undeniable.

Before Ghazan was half-way down the slope, his mind, a deft pickpocket, wrested the jewel, and began to cut it into regular facets, hold it up to the light and show the different flushes in its cheeks. His mind mounted the gem with others in the jewelled belt of his life. His mind began to show him the devious, hidden paths which had led him to the ruby. He had to attend. Yet, even as he followed the clues, he knew that they were irrelevant beside the fact of the ruby, that many other paths led to many empty mines.

314

The notion of order played a part. That morning, riding away from Persepolis, he had seen his people's settlement as a process of natural evolution, the less highly organized, the earlier in time yielded to the better organized, the later. From the mountains to man—all had seemed caught up in that torrent, which moved only in one direction. But the swooping hawk had broken the law. The bravery and skill of a lower creature had overcome the mass and cunning of one of the higher mammals. The hawk had risked death on the rapier-horns, or from a hoof-blow, but had fought, hungrily, for survival. A law once broken was not inevitably binding.

His decision once taken had an air of destiny which set Ghazan wondering at his former doubts. Humbly he thought how little he knew himself. He had always taken pride in his logic, yet this, the most important decision of his life, had not been argued out, was not strictly logical: he had taken pride in resignation, but knew he was fulfilling himself in throwing off resignation.

What force within him demanded he fight? At what part of himself had the hawk struck? He must have been wrong in the Naked Desert, away from the hills. He was something after all—must be something to have responded to the hawk. Earth he was, and part of the earth: Ghazan saw it as though in a vision. Part of this earth. Part of the hills. His flesh was part of the hills. His flesh belonged to the hills.

But his flesh also belonged to him, to all that part of himself which was not flesh; to his spirit. His flesh linked his spirit to the hills, according to the modes of spirit, according to knowledge and love. He was part of the hills; he knew the hills; he loved the hills. He belonged doubly to the hills, because his flesh was part of them, and because he loved them.

And his people's flesh, also, was part of the hills. So that he was part of his people, and they part of him. He was linked to them by way of the earth.

And hidden in the hills was that God whom he had learned to love, his fathers' God, who had made him and his people. Not limited by the hills, but known to him and his fathers through the hills.

To hills and people and God he was linked by flesh and by love, and the three loves were one. But this love, which concerned the bulk of his being, was not capable of fluctuation. Some loves could be snapped

315

without precipitating the lover. Not this. These three were his orbit. If a star left its orbit, it burned itself out, became nothing.

This love, then, was his scattered self, which he had been so concerned to preserve. Moods passed, knowledge was forgotten, but the hills remained. His love of the hills and all that belonged to the hills— that was his past. It was his own identity, and the tribe's identity. They could sacrifice with immunity everything else, but not that.

Ghazan saw now that all his attempts to pierce to the depths of his being had been futile. He had been trying to identify the plant by its root, instead of by its flower. The flower expressed the plant's love of its own kind of life: it was an attempt, in given surroundings, to ensure continuity. The command should have been not "Know yourself", but "Know what you love."

And the will, which he had believed a judge, was in fact a lover. Only when he had thrown off knowledge, seen things as fresh in a moment of surprise, had he been able freely to love. And only then had he been able to decide. He had tried to analyse loves in terms of arguments for and against, and this had crippled his will. A stone figure on a stone frieze he had tried to be, but the stone was part of the earth, responded to earth. The decision had been a loving response.

In this long moment of sudden vision Ghazan saw also that he had decided not only as an individual, but as a Falqani. His decision was valid for all the Falqani. No amount of minor goods could outweigh this absolute good. Not even the danger from guns.

Even as he saw these facets, Ghazan knew that the "explanations" of his decision did not exhaust it, were no more than a rationalization. And he was inclined to beware of them. Once formulized, the decision was vulnerable. From clever arguments, from books and all that he had read in books.

With a sudden decisive goad of his heels he spurred his horse down the slope. It was already twilight, and camp was being pitched. He rode through the black tents to the single blue tent. Quickly he dismounted. He called to Ahmad for fuel, and in a few moments his servant hauled into the space before his tent a bundle of grey camel-thorn. Ghazan arranged it in a loose pyramid and, striking a match, lit three or four of the dry branches.

He entered his tent and opened the leather pannier where he kept the

316

books he had brought from Shiraz. He piled them in his arms and carried them close to the fire: the books whose pages he had turned with such respect and love all through his life, so that each page was like a day of his life. He squatted beside them on the earth before the leaping flames. He lifted the first volume. Abu Ali ibn Sina: *A Search for Wisdom*. Ghazan said to himself, "The true wisdom is to have no wisdom, but to respond at once, like grass, to the touch of rain and sun."

With a flick of his wrist Ghazan tossed the book into the flames. He watched the edge of the pages catch and curl. The second volume he lifted. Ibn Rushd, an ornate hand-written manuscript, two hundred years old, done by an Isfahani scribe. *On the Nature of the Self*. For seven centuries its doctrine had misled, and the pretty pages he held in his hand for two centuries. A spider's web, a dangerous extension of the self, which in emergencies could trip and tangle. Ghazan threw it into the heart of the fire.

One by one he consigned his books to the flames without hesitation until he reached the last, the fifteenth: al-Ghazali. His favourite philosopher, who had rejected every system and at last become a Sufi. With regret Ghazan turned over the well-loved pages, recalling how in the days of his studies al-Ghazali was robbed by highwaymen. The student of philosophy followed them to crave the return of his lecture-notes "which contained his knowledge". The chief robber laughed and said, "Do you pretend to have learned the knowledge in these notes? We have taken the notes from you and now you are left without knowledge." But the robber had no use for a bundle of papers and gave them back. There and then al-Ghazali had set himself to learn the notes by heart.

Perhaps it was impossible to throw knowledge once learned to the flames. He could only try. With a slight feeling of revulsion, as though he were taking life, Ghazan closed the book firmly. Al-Ghazali had preached resignation. Resignation was only half the truth, could, at times, be the supreme betrayal. Reluctantly and gently Ghazan laid the book on the pyre.

He had none of his foreign school-books with him. Some were at Garden of the Pines, most left in Lausanne. But Ghazan condemned them as heretical and consigned them in their absence to the flames. Their memory he would try to erase. The more varied his knowledge, the less he was. Not again would he lie becalmed between east wind and west.

The fire blazed high and brought sweat to his brow, but Ghazan did not move away. Steadily he watched the reasons for and against his decision go up in flames. No longer now could he argue himself out of his choice.

After the last and first pages had flared, the thick books did not burn easily. He had to stir them with a stick, turn for the last time the charred pages. Slowly they were all consumed. Possibilities were pulverized. He saw the orange flames sink to red embers. These grew ashen and at last went out. Ghazan was left alone with his red jewel.

"Chieftains of the Falqani," Ghazan looked round at eleven grave-faced men on their hunkers in the court tent. "This morning I scouted the Guyum plain. A large force is dug in on the western slopes, in prepared positions. I did not count them all, but I put them at a division of five thousand men. They are there to seize and exile your Ilkhan, to disarm you and your men and, either now or later, settle you near the Gulf.

"The army, you say, has always been there to harass us. Let us do as we did this spring, cross silently by night. That is impossible. Troops are strung all along the plain. We cannot evade them. Two courses remain. We can hand over our arms and scatter like sheep to this new fold. Or we can fight these soldiers who bar our way.

"I won't hide the danger. We are posed not man to man but against guns and mortars. We are forced to engage as a people, women and children too. We have few supplies and our hungry flocks must soon move to fresh grass. If we fight, some will lose their lives: perhaps very many. But if we do not fight, we all stand to lose everything else. And perhaps our lives too, in the pestilential plain.

"Fight, then, we shall. For ourselves and the hills, which our fathers fought to keep. Let God award the victory. Clean your rifles, prepare your ammunition, hearten your men."

Eleven grim voices discussed his words. Ghazan let them talk among themselves, then asked for their views. "We shall fight beside you, Ghazan Khan," some cried, and others, "We shall show those army scum how to shoot." But one figure rose, glowering, at the end of the tent. It was Tughril.

"If you had only listened, Ghazan Khan!" he growled. "I counselled you to strike while the army was weak. Always you answered, 'Jackals and locusts are enemies enough.' Now you fight on their terms."

Ghazan held his uncle's angry gaze. "Attacking first we should have been in the wrong. As it is, our cause is just."

"Never before have we fought the army in prepared positions."

Several leaders cried, "Enough of the past!"

"The past mirrors the future," Tughril retorted. "To fight now is a young man's foolishness. Let us hand over the rifles we carry. We have others buried in winter quarters; next spring we can buy more; then strike back when the army least expects. That is the way to victory."

He looked round the assembly, flashing his eyes like flint to catch reluctant timber. Some seemed to favour his plan, for they turned a challenging glance on their Ilkhan. For a moment Ghazan hesitated, then stiffened. Had all his debates, his final vote, taken place in sub-committee, to be annulled by this trouble-maker, his superior only in years?

"Wait till spring! But the army are stronger than ever before. They will see that we don't rearm. And would we have strength to shoot, hungry and sick and beaten? Some may think: In the plains or in the hills, what matter so long as the Falqani live together, remain intact? Do not deceive yourselves. We should not remain the people we are. In standing pools water grows stagnant, breeds flies, mixes with mud, is no longer water. Only in flowing streams does water run pure and clear and strong. Is it not so?"

"Yes," they acclaimed, all but Tughril.

"Those whose flocks weaken and die will drift away to the cities—there, in spite of themselves, become their brothers' enemies. Can you keep an ibex caged? It sickens for the hills and dies. You who have been caged once, will you be caged a second time?"

The leaders multiplied cries of "No." This rebuff angered Tughril.

"Fools," he cried. "You believe these fine words about mud and water. But I do not. What proof have we had of settlement? None at all." He had held his head square to Ghazan, but now lowered it, as though charging. "You know why your Ilkhan chooses to fight."

Some said, "He has told us himself," but others asked, "Why?"

"He fights for himself, to remain Ilkhan. It is exile he seeks to avoid.

319

And there is reason in that. For he is betrothed to a cousin named Anahita. This girl refuses to follow him into exile. Will you brave army guns to give your Ilkhan a wife?"

A surprised silence, then loud talk broke out among the chieftains. After his first angry astonishment, quickly Ghazan went over his decision. Had this been the secret motive? Not the hawk, but the grey doves? All this, for the grey eyes? It was horrible, but it might be true. For a moment he faltered. Then he cried to himself, No, I have burned my books. I have done with the subtleties of reason. I chose for my people and their land.

"Isn't it true?" cried Tughril. "Answer me, Ghazan Khan."

The chieftains looked up at him, awaiting his denial.

In a level voice Ghazan said, "It is true that I can marry the girl only as Ilkhan."

"There!" triumphed Tughril.

"But it is not for her I fight. I fight for my people. I fight for our right to choose," he suddenly cried. "The choice we make now, which is our chief glory, would be denied us in the plain."

He saw with relief that the chieftains were with him. Already they were scowling at Tughril. Of some sins they knew he might be guilty, but of that no, never.

Tughril struck his hand with a clenched fist. "My men shall not shed blood for a girl. I shall order the Shalguli to yield their arms."

"The Shalguli will fight beside their brothers."

"Not for a girl."

Ghazan was tense. He needed the Shalguli. Without the Shalguli other leaders might draw back. He looked round for a way to bring Tughril to heel. Argue against the man? Say that Tughril welcomed the exile, since he would succeed as Ilkhan? Expedient but false. Then he found what seemed a better way.

Lowering his voice, Ghazan said slowly, "This spring, Tughril, you shot a boar."

His uncle raised his eyes and Ghazan held them. "Many boar I have shot and killed."

"This spring I faced a charging boar unarmed. You rode in and shot the boar."

"What of that? It is soldiers not boar we face." But his eyelids had flickered.

"We cut off the head together. Its blood spurted on our hands. But rather the white tusks had gored my belly than have lived to see you faithless."

Tughril hunched his shoulders. "Faithless!" he snapped. "Who spoke of that?"

Ghazan watched him closely. That last word had been badly chosen. Not accuse, but call, appeal. With warmth in his voice Ghazan said:

"You proved yourself a Falqani then. Are you still a Falqani, Tughril?"

The chin sank on the great barrel chest, which rose and fell in heavy breaths. For a time there was no other sound in the crowded tent but Tughril's breathing.

Again Ghazan put the question. "Are you a Falqani, Tughril?"

Tughril lifted his head. His eyes darted here and there round the tent. Run to earth: given away by the blood of a boar, caught in the net of his own blood. The words seemed to stick in his throat, but at last he spat them out.

"And what if I am a Falqani?"

Ghazan felt his tense body slacken, like a guy-rope when the tent-peg is plucked. "Tomorrow the Falqani fight."

"It was madness not to strike earlier," Tughril muttered, sinking down on his haunches. "We shall ride, each one of us, with a shroud under our arm."

Tughril did not speak again. As one by one the leaders gave their word for battle, he began to sulk. Then Ghazan outlined his plans, taking aside each of the chieftains and detailing their movements. Afterwards they ate together, and each rejoined his group.

Later that evening Rohim came up to Ghazan, in high spirits. "To-morrow I fight like Rustam," he boasted.

"As usual then," said Ghazan, without the least flattery.

"Better than usual. For soon I shall be father of a son."

With a smile Ghazan congratulated his cousin. The wedding, and now a son—the idea of a daughter was unthinkable: a new generation whose destiny would be decided tomorrow.

"Some day," Rohim continued, "his mother will tell him how I saved the Falqani at Guyum. And in Shami's tank I shall ride through the streets of Shiraz."

Ghazan considered this. "Yes, after all, the tank will prove useful. We'll collect it tomorrow." He sat staring at the fire. "But you know, Rohim, how they will speak of this battle in Shiraz, in Teheran: we shall be called revolutionaries and reactionaries, every name under the sun, and especially wild undisciplined hordes resisting law and order. If I am captured and exiled, I want you to know the truth behind my decision, and one day I want you to tell your son."

"The truth?"

"Why I decided not to yield."

"But you had to fight. You could not do otherwise."

"Could not?" echoed Ghazan. Predestined? Had the ruby been created æons ago, with the mountain itself?

Rohim put his arm round Ghazan's shoulders. "I know you. I knew from the beginning you would not submit to exile."

"I almost did."

Rohim looked at him curiously. "I can hardly believe it."

Assured that it really had been so, Rohim questioned Ghazan, making him explain his words. Then, beginning from the spring migration Ghazan recounted the chief events, in thought and action, which Rohim had not witnessed, and which had gone to mould his mind. Each, he believed, had contributed to his decision, so that all now formed a pattern. Even his meeting with the Zoroastrian, for what was he doing now but striking a blow in the battle between Ahura Mazda and Ahriman? He recognized also for the first time that Anahita—if hers had been a choice—had chosen in the same way. They loved alike, then. Gazing into her grey eyes he would see the things he loved.

Towards midnight Ghazan ended, with a stir of triumph. "In the spring," he told Rohim, "I thought I had to take a decision only about my future. Later I saw that it involved the whole tribe and Persia itself. Now I see that even more is at stake."

"What do you mean?" his cousin asked.

"Don't you see, Rohim; sun, moon and stars, clouds winging rain from the Caspian, the intermarrying wind: we move with them. To still that spinning in one least part is unnatural, evil. These khaki troops serve the city, a head grown monstrous huge on a weakened body. They seek to drive us from our sunlit hills to a dark warren. There words wriggle, the sword becomes the scimitar, the candid face

322

assumes a set of masks. Here man carves his own life—simple or intricate, like the head of a camel-stick. There he is one of many beads sent sliding on an abacus. He becomes the mud walls his eyes reflect, is petrified to the dead chattels which are all he has to love. He falls still, he turns to stone."

Ghazan broke off, searching Rohim's eyes, wondering whether he had understood. Then, more quietly, he continued:

"It seems to me, Rohim, that we are the guardians of water and grass: we are the last whose blood moves, like oceans, to the tug of moon and sun. We are the last to love the earth as men. If we fall, the world will fall about our heads."

He saw that Rohim was only half with him. He did not care. He knew he was right. Whatever the outcome on the Guyum plain, he believed he had won his own victory with truth.

CHAPTER TWENTY-THREE

An hour before dawn Ahmad called Ghazan. He had been awake all the previous night at Persepolis, and could scarcely keep his eyes open, as he unlocked money from one of his leather panniers and rode down with Rohim to see Captain Shami and his tank. Ghazan had less faith in it than Rohim, but now they must snatch at even a minor advantage.

As Ghazan had expected, there were several soldiers posted around the ruined caravanserai. They called a signal to Shami, who came out of the mud-walled quadrangle to identify the cousins.

"So. I thought you would never arrive," he said, flinging away the end of a cigarette.

He led them into the building. In the shadow of one of the walls loomed a dark shape. Captain Shami spread a shopkeeper's arm.

"Here is the tank."

Ghazan and Rohim walked across to see it. The tank had four bogey-wheels and trapezoid tracks. Its main body, painted grey, stood high as a horse's head. Above, slightly to the fore, reared a round turret, from which projected a machine gun. On the top of the turret was an open hatch. Behind, lower than the main body, was a radiator grille.

Ghazan inspected first the tracks, then the armour plating. In a soft voice, so that his men on guard should not hear, Shami pointed out that it had been newly painted only a week before. Ghazan wondered how one decided whether or not a tank was worth buying. A horse, a buffalo: by what standard did one measure it? After they had made a tour, Ghazan turned to Rohim.

"You'd better have a look at the inside."

Rohim climbed into the hatchway and five minutes later jumped down, looking grim.

"You like my tank?" asked Shami eagerly.

Rohim did not answer. He drew Ghazan aside. "I can't drive it," he whispered.

"Why not?"

Rohim dropped his eyes. "I don't know how."

With a frown Ghazan said, "Like a car, surely."

"There's no steering wheel. All the controls are different."

Rohim was crestfallen. Ghazan could not help. He knew almost nothing about machinery. He turned to Shami.

"Perhaps you'd drive it round the caravanserai. Just once, to show us how it works."

Shami drew himself up. "Kindly remember my rank." Seeing the cousins' puzzled look, he said severely. "Surely you know officers don't drive tanks; least of all officers of the quartermaster department."

"Didn't you drive it here?"

"Certainly not. One of my men drove." He looked round with anxious impatience. "And now my ten thousand."

"We'll see about payment when the tank is working," said Ghazan. "Remember, you guaranteed it in working order."

"It is in working order."

"Not at all. The engine isn't even turning. For all we know, it may be broken."

Shami stood there, eyeing them. "My driver could start it," he said doubtfully. "But I don't want my men to know about this. None of their business."

"Quite right," said Ghazan. "And unnecessary. You, Shami, surely you know all about tanks?"

Shami's eyes did not flinch. "As a soldier, naturally, I can manipulate all my weapons."

"Then show us how to drive it. It's beneath you—yes: but just this once."

Shami pouted. "It's for you to start. You're buying it."

"But we don't know how. That's why we're asking you."

Shami considered this. "If I start the tank, will you buy it."

"You make it work, then we'll see."

Reluctantly Shami climbed into the hatchway. The engine turned very slowly on the self-starter. The cousins waited, exchanging anxious glances. Shami climbed down with a starting handle. He inserted it below the radiator grille, and began to turn. Many times he jerked up the handle, until he was sweating and growling. At last the engine turned under its own power. Shami re-entered the hatch and accelerated. The engine's roar reminded the cousins of an angry camel. A short time later they heard a grinding of gears. The tank flew back

325

into the wall, in reverse, dislodging some of the mud bricks. But the engine did not stall. Shami put his head out of the hatch, relieved and bland.

"It's working now."

Ghazan told Rohim to climb into the hatch. Shami explained how to move the gears and steer by two handles. About the control knobs he seemed more than a little vague. When Rohim had memorized the principles, both of them clambered down, leaving the engine running. "Well, Rohim, do you want the tank?" Ghazan asked.

His cousin's eyes were excited. "Certainly. It's worth a hundred horsemen—fifty Shalgulis."

Ghazan pulled out of his tunic bundles of 200-rial notes and gave them to Shami. Shami began to count them out note by note.

"It's all there," said Ghazan.

"Just to be sure," said Shami. After a few minutes he looked up, satisfied. "Ten thousand. The tank is yours. But give me time to leave with my men. Five minutes will be long enough."

Nodding affably, he walked out of the gateway.

Rohim entered the tank and when the time was up, putting the engine into gear, rumbled forward through the gateway. Ghazan followed with the two horses.

Towards sunrise Ghazan returned to the Madaleh, the most advanced section of the tribe, which extended north over a distance of several miles. Tents packed, they were waiting to move forward, a thousand strong, in the formation they had used that spring, men on the flanks; women, children and flocks in the centre. Rohim had already returned with the tank. Ghazan told him for the time being to remain where he was. Ahmad, who had volunteered as gunner, stayed too.

Ghazan rode to the head of the column and led forward the dense mass of humans, goats and sheep, of camels and donkeys and horses. They were now a mile from the Guyum plain, and some five hundred feet above it. Ghazan intended to bring up all the tribe as close as possible to the plain, so that as soon as the Falqani gained an advantage, they could cross quickly to the protecting southern hills.

They approached the plain not in a direct descent, but up and down over ranges of foothills. From the first crest Ghazan observed the plain. In the centre stood the fort, guarding the thin brown line of road. It flew no flag, the gates were open, and the walls unmanned. Beyond rose a long slope rising to a ridge, level except for one dip, which marked a re-entrant. On the left of the dip khaki tents were strung out in lines, just as he had seen them the previous morning. Figures were moving between them, and one jeep was climbing up from the dip. On the right of the dip guns and mortars had now been dug in.

The Falqani trooped down from this crest into a shallow valley, then up again towards a lower hill, five hundred paces nearer the plain. The air, unbroken by any breeze, lazed in the autumn sunshine. The dull beat of hooves on turf, an occasional whinny, the hum of insects— these were the only sounds: all as before, on every other autumn migration, as it had been for seven hundred migrations. It seemed impossible that two weeks later they would not be grazing quietly in winter quarters.

Ghazan reached the crest of the hill, about a thousand yards from the plain, well out of rifle range. Here he waited, watching the bulk of the long column gain the flat summit and begin to stream down, all in order.

A sudden clap of thunder seemed to break in the hill itself, followed by a series of even louder explosions; the earth fountained up and broke about them in stones and clods. The flocks ran wildly in all directions; riders struggled with bucking horses; donkeys threw off their baggage and bolted. Amid the whine and thud of machine-gun bullets, the crash of exploding mortar shells, Ghazan rode into the sudden ferment of men and beasts, driving them down from the exposed hill. This was soon done, for in their fear most of the flocks had instinctively followed the downward slope. When the crest was clear, Ghazan followed.

As suddenly as they had started, the deafening explosions ceased, leaving behind, like a reverberation, the bleating and howling of wounded animals. A score had been killed or so badly wounded they had to be put out of their misery. None of the tribe had been hit.

Ghazan saw that they could advance no further without loss of life. He decided to make his camp in this valley. It was sheltered and the next ridge was lightly wooded. He sent a messenger with orders that all the tribe except picked riflemen were to lie behind the crest he had just crossed, and he arranged for the non-combatant Madaleh to withdraw, later in the day, to rejoin the main body. He also sent a message telling Rohim to bring forward the tank.

He ordered one of the court tents pitched back as a dressing station. Here cotton wool and bandages left by the mission were unpacked. Another was set forward near the trees to serve as his headquarters. Here the chieftains came to report, as armed men from each group arrived and were disposed according to his orders. His potential force numbered twenty thousand men of fighting age. To the four thousand who had efficient rifles Ghazan allowed fifty rounds apiece. Others had old-fashioned rifles, but Ghazan preferred to concentrate his limited ammunition with those who could make best use of it. Marksmanship, physical strength and courage: in these the Falqani trusted.

Oak apples, acorns and fallen leaves: the scent of the dying year was carried into the open headquarters tent. Outside Ghazan saw his men cleaning and oiling their rifles: hunted, arming themselves like hunters, each species defending itself: the Falqani too. Some were joking, but their laughter, like the stir of leaves before a storm, rose and faded in a single breath, leaving the air unbroken. Ghazan felt the heightened tension: each movement, each word, seemed momentous. He saw it also in the women's faces, as they held up children to their fathers for a last farewell. Later, if they were needed, the women would be called forward to fight beside their men. Then the reds, oranges and yellows faded from the camp.

After conferring with the chieftains, Ghazan decided to lead a group of a hundred men along the ridge and to bring down fire at intervals, with the object of discovering the army's main concentration, while the rest of his force, grouped in a semicircle, held the line of foothills for the non-combatants.

With the rising sun behind them the party cantered forward, in a single line, to the last ridge overlooking the plain which, with the road, ran approximately north and south. They came over the crest five hundred yards from the enemy tents and were at once met by heavy machine-gun fire.

The Falqani replied, firing from the saddle at a trot, their hundred rifles obeying Ghazan's order so readily that there was no interval between the separate explosions. After watching for signs of movement, they swerved back behind the ridge and cantered north. Eight times they fired from the saddle at different points along the ridge, until they had swept the whole stretch of the opposite slope right and left of the dip. They discovered that most of the enemy were dug in not near

328

their tents but in three long lines in front of their guns and mortars. So accurate was the Falqani fire that only one of the machine-gun posts replied to their last burst.

Ghazan led his men back to headquarters. Near the edge of the camp stood the tank. He thought, now is the time to use it, while the enemy are still reeling from our fire.

He rode up to the tank, and found Rohim at the rear, the radiator grille removed, looking at the engine.

"Start up," he called. "I've got work for you."

Rohim turned, his face impassive. Dismally he said, "I can't. It won't go."

Ghazan frowned. "You mean, it's broken."

"The engine won't turn."

"But you drove it here."

"Just as I arrived, it suddenly stalled without warning. I've tried everything and can't get a splutter."

"Fuel?" suggested Ghazan.

"Both tanks are half full."

Ghazan looked round, searching. "Who knows about engines? Your father?"

"Karim knows most. He's had a look. But he says this engine is different from any he's seen. Being a tank and so old. He can't help."

Ghazan stared gloomily at the great mass of metal. "A tank that doesn't work!"

"It worked well in the caravanserai—and on the way here."

"Yes, Shami made it work."

They stood silent for a moment. For both of them the tank had come to stand for victory against the guns and mortars. Then Ghazan looked up and saw that Rohim was thinking the same thing.

"Shami! Shami will make the tank go."

They planned their raid that afternoon. Shami, they decided, being Shami and in charge of the quartermaster department, would be lying well back, not near the ammunition and trucks, but near the provisions. They would cross the plain at its southernmost corner, sweep round behind the ridge, approach enemy lines from the rear and bring back Shami prisoner.

Meanwhile Falqani marksmen sniped at figures on the other side of the plain. Even at that range a soldier had only to show arm or even hand for a split second to get a bullet through it. The enemy were putting their trust in mortars. An average of fifty bombs fell every hour. At first they had fallen erratically, but now they were exploding in and about the camp. Ghazan ordered his men to dig individual trenches as deep as they could with their knives, but even so on that first day three Falqani men were killed by mortar-bombs.

Soon after sunset Ghazan and Rohim, armed with pistols, set out on foot. Tughril was left in command. The moon was due to rise in two hours. They hoped to be back before.

They crossed the plain and ridge without incident, and came in sight of the first bell-shaped tents. Intermittent mortar-fire was still being directed at the tribe, but in this part of the army camp they saw no moving figures. They continued past the first line of tents, then spied a man walking ahead. They caught up with him. They saw he was a private soldier. Ghazan stopped him and asked:

"Where's Captain Shami's tent?"

The soldier looked from one to the other. It was so dark he would barely be able to distinguish their clothes. "Shami? Who's he?"

"Quartermaster department."

The soldier scratched his head.

"Where your rations are kept," continued Ghazan.

The soldier knew where those were, looked round to get his bearings, and pointed to a group of tents further back from the plain, standing apart. With a word of thanks the two Falqani started off in that direction.

They were nearing the line of tents when they were halted by a shout from a sentry, hidden near pistachio trees, armed with a rifle.

"What are you doing?" the sentry asked suspiciously.

Ghazan debated whether to use force. "We want to see Captain Shami."

The sentry looked them over. "Where are you from?"

"From Shiraz. We've just arrived."

"What do you want to see him about?"

"About a tank. It's broken down. We want to get Captain Shami to repair it."

"Oh, one of the tanks," the sentry said, as though that settled everything. "Go in."

"Which is Captain Shami's tent?"

"I'm not sure. Ask when you get up there."

They started off again.

"He spoke as if there were several tanks," said Rohim.

Ghazan nodded. "I think Shami told us less than the truth."

They reached the tents. Soldiers were moving about, carrying full sacks and cases and urns of water. The tents were in three sizes: the smallest, bell-shaped, where soldiers slept twelve to a tent; large marquees, which looked as if they held supplies, and an intermediate size of tent, of which there were four. Two of these Ghazan and Rohim scouted, walking past the entrance and taking a quick look inside. They were lighted by hurricane lamps; one was empty, the other held two officers. Through the entrance of the third tent they glimpsed Shami alone. He was undressing, and putting on pyjama trousers, grey silk pyjamas with crimson piping.

While Rohim stood on guard at the tent opening, Ghazan went in, holding his pistol. Shami's cheeks went grey: he stood absolutely motionless.

"You!" he whispered in astonishment.

Ghazan put a finger to his lips. "Pull on your trousers," he said.

"What do you want?" muttered Shami.

"The tank's broken down: you're going to mend it."

Ghazan flourished his pistol. Shami did not need a second warning. He drew on his trousers over the pyjamas, then, at Ghazan's bidding, put on his jacket and peaked cap. With their prisoner between them, the muzzles of their pistols in his ribs, the cousins retraced their steps. Again the sentry challenged them; then, recognizing Shami, saluted and let them pass.

Once out of range the Falqani put up their pistols. Shami at once broke into an angry mixture of protests and questions, asking how they had got into the camp and what they intended to do with him. The Falqani were in no mood for talk and, taking out their pistols again, escorted him in silence back to their tents.

It was too dark to think of repairs that night. Shami was guarded and next morning led to the tank.

There Ghazan confronted him. "Get to work, Shami. I want this tank repaired."

Shami put his hands on his hips. "And what if I refuse?"

331

"Come now, Shami. Did I or did I not pay you ten thousand tumans for a tank, guaranteed in working order."

"Yes, but . . ."

"Exactly. Now make it work. I give you one hour—not a minute more."

Red and blustering, Shami cried: "General Bahrami has sixteen mortars and ten light guns. He can call on three thousand reserves from Shiraz. You're mad to go on fighting."

Ghazan glowered at him. "No, Shami, I am not mad. It is the feverish patient who thinks the doctor mad. Hypercephaly and an outbreak of guns: that is Persia's disease. And I am going to bleed the patient. Now—get to work."

Fluttering like a netted partridge, Shami stayed where he was.

"Did you hear me?" snapped Ghazan, looking him dead in the eyes.

Shami shifted his stance, began an appeal, then seemed to think better of it. He walked to the tank.

"I comply under protest," he said with all the hauteur he could muster.

He took a tool box from under the driver's seat and began to strip the engine. Rohim watched him. Within the hour he found the defect: a grain of sand had clogged one of the carburettor jets. He blew the jet free and remounted the pieces. Then, inserting the starting handle, he brought the engine to life.

The engine's roar brought a gleam of satisfaction to Ghazan's eyes, but only for a moment. Shami's compliance, though useful, made Ghazan strangely uneasy. This khaki figure giving him help was the enemy. A cosmic struggle, between absolutes: Ghazan wanted to see it like that. And now this dumpy quartermaster, waddling among his men, confused the issues for him, merged white with black.

With an effort Ghazan turned his attention back to the tank. Drawing Rohim aside, he sketched out the lie of the land. "Now's your chance," he said. "I want you to drive for the tents, then swing round along the dip. Shoot up their jeeps, panic their conscripts. Our snipers will pick them off." He began to walk to the tank. "Has Ahmad got the hang of the gun?"

"Frankly, he's not very sure. But I've got a better idea. There's place for three. I'll fire the gun."

"And who's going to drive?"

332

"Shami."

"Shami?"

Ahmad can cover him, while I fire."

Ghazan considered the idea. Unorthodox, perhaps, but why not? He went up to Shami, who was standing nearby, still guarded by Ahmad.

"The battle is about to begin," he said. "Aren't you sorry to miss it?"

Shami drew himself up. "I am a quartermaster, like my uncle before me. The quartermaster department makes battle possible but rarely takes part."

Ghazan looked pointedly at three ribbons on Shami's breast. "And those medals?"

"There are other ways of serving one's country."

"It is time you earned those medals, Shami. Now's your chance to serve your country, by serving the Falqani. You are going to drive the tank against army lines."

Shami opened astonished eyes, then, swallowing hard, made a show of resistance. "I refuse. Absolutely refuse."

Ghazan flourished his pistol. "Come, Shami, be reasonable."

Eyeing the pistol, Shami raised an unsteady hand to his brow. "As an officer and prisoner of war, I have certain rights."

"If you drive well, no one will find out. It's up to you."

Shami looked doubtfully at Ghazan. "You won't give me away?"

"Not if you serve us well."

The quartermaster seemed to hesitate, then said miserably, "No, I can't. Not on the wrong side."

Ghazan signalled to Rohim, who seized Shami by the scruff of the neck and pulled him up onto the body of the tank. Before disappearing through the hatchway, Shami turned with a ruffled glance:

"You may not be aware, Ghazan Khan, but this breaks all the rules of war."

Presently the tank roared forward, watched by Ghazan and his men from positions on the ridge, rifles at the ready. The tank seemed to go very slowly, dipping like a snake to the rise and fall of the ground. Half-way across, near the road, Rohim opened fire with the machine-gun, and after some hesitation the enemy replied with rifle shots. As the tank climbed the opposite slope, a few soldiers jumped up in panic.

333

Falqani marksmen blazed at them. Ghazan thought, Rohim was right: this one weapon may turn the scales.

The tank entered enemy lines. Out of their slit trenches leaped khaki figures; some ran away, others along the slope to new positions. Mortar and enemy machine-gun fire stopped altogether, but from the most advanced gun-post grenades were thrown. The tank swung round. Slowly, steadily, like a brown turtle, it nosed its way back, dipping as it recrossed the enemy slit trenches, then gaining speed on the downward slope.

At the bottom of the dip stretched a line of qanat holes, about eighty paces apart: each a small crater surrounded with brown earth excavated from the subterranean water-course. The tank approached the line of holes. The right track struck the loose earth near one of the holes, and the tank nosed down. Ghazan could hear the engine turning still, but slowly, limping. After a pause it stalled. Ghazan was mystified. The tank was too big to be held up by the crater. Why had the engine stopped? He heard the starter turn, but the engine did not pick up. And it was too close to army lines to use the starting handle.

A moment later Rohim and Ahmad jumped out of the turret, closely followed by Shami, who turned back to his own lines. Rohim and Ahmad ran zigzag across the plain. At once Ghazan ordered heavy covering fire. His own rifle bolt flashed backwards and forwards, hot in his fingers. Between his shots he heard the crackle of army fire, but half-hearted, as though they were still uncertain about these figures from their own tank. Nearer and nearer the two Falqani came, past the fort, past the road. Ghazan could see their faces shining with sweat. At last they reached the ridge and flung themselves down on the earth.

Ghazan ran to them. Ahmad he found first, unharmed. Rohim was lying further off, panting.

"Hurt?"

"No."

Ghazan squatted down beside him. "Why did it stop?"

Rohim regained his breath. "That idiot Shami!" he growled. "We needed the throttle. Shami fumbled with the knobs, then pulled the ignition contact—cut out the engine."

"On purpose, I suppose."

334

Rohim scowled. "By mistake. He was never very sure of the controls —and with grenades bursting round him!"

Ghazan looked bleakly at the tank, wreckage of the very hopes it had excited. "Anyway, that mistake will cost him dear."

"Shami?" laughed Rohim in scorn. "Not a bit. He'll tell Bahrami he caught Ahmad and me single-handed—was bringing us back prisoner. Major Shami he'll be again."

Ghazan considered this, then muttered, "One thing he will tell—the position of our headquarters. They'll have to be shifted."

Ghazan chose a mortar-bomb crater, its sides squared off. From here he directed Falqani rifle-fire during the morning. The army were keeping very quiet. They had stopped firing mortars altogether.

At midday barley was cooked and carried forward to the riflemen, one copper bowl to each group of twenty. Hardly had he eaten his ration, when Ghazan observed an army officer, carrying a very conspicuous white flag, emerge from enemy tents and start to cross the plain. When he reached the first Falqani lines he was directed to Ghazan's headquarters.

The officer jumped down into the crater. Ghazan recognized the cast in his eye. It was Captain Morteza. With a half-bow he handed Ghazan a letter from General Bahrami. Its tone was curt and slightly impertinent. The situation of the "rebels", he declared, was desperate. Useless bloodshed would result from continued hostilities. He called for Ghazan's immediate surrender.

"The Falqani never surrender," said Ghazan. But he discussed the letter with Rohim alone. A sign of weakness, he decided, while Rohim thought it a mere trick to spy out their deployment.

They discussed the situation. Falqani rifle-fire had weakened the enemy, but until more of the mortar and machine-gun posts were wiped out, the tribe could not safely continue its march. The position of these posts was now known. Ghazan decided to attack them himself that night.

He summoned Captain Morteza and, tearing up the letter into small pieces, handed these back. "Tell General Bahrami I shall do the same to his little army—guns and mortars too."

A gesture, but there were moments for gestures.

During the afternoon Ghazan picked fifty horsemen for his raid. He told them to rest, cook themselves a hot meal and shortly before moon-

335

rise to form up behind the ridge. There he joined them. A pitch-flare stuck in the ground cast a glow. He looked round at them in turn: frank eyes, proudly arched noses, long muscular necks, lithe bodies merging with their horses. He was asking so much of them. A shadow of doubt fell across his face. Again he scrutinized their eyes, some calm, some angry: all unyielding, and the shadow passed.

Ghazan outlined his plan: to charge first at the machine-gun post from which grenades had been thrown at the tank. Like the others, the gun appeared to be on fixed sights, and useless against a flank attack. The call of the red-legged partridge would be his signal to withdraw.

Mortar shells still fell at irregular intervals. Immediately after one had exploded, the raiders galloped off in line abreast. Near the road another shell exploded behind, silhouetting them. A moment later yellow flares with comet-tails shot up, and machine-guns fired. Some horses fell. The rest gained the far slope, without flinching or swerving, for they were trained to gunfire. Up the dip they charged, the flares which made them vulnerable serving also to reveal the enemy. A hundred yards away Ghazan saw the machine-gun, its muzzle protruding down at the plain between an earthen bulwark. He led his men directly at it, firing from the hip. When they were half-way there, its crew jumped up, threw grenades and bolted.

Through the explosions and drifting smoke they charged. While his men rode on, Ghazan turned and dismounted. He dropped down into the pit behind the machine-gun and searched the ground. Here he discovered two metal grenade-boxes. One was empty: the other contained grenades. Only four—he had hoped for a dozen or so. Slipping the grenades in his cummerbund, he climbed out, and led back his horse to a distance of twenty paces. Removing the pin, he threw one of the grenades into the pit. For a few seconds nothing happened, then the grenade exploded. Earth and stones showered round him. Through the smoke he ran forward to the pit. He found the gun lying on its side, tripod broken, barrel twisted.

Meanwhile the Falqani had dismounted. One of every five riders held the horses. The rest fought hand to hand among the slit trenches, thrusting with long horn-handled knives. "Ya Ali," they shouted, calling on the saintly Imam for help. The yellow-tailed flares had sunk earthwards, leaving the sky to a pale half-moon. In the semi-darkness the soldiers believed every figure an enemy. Cries of the wounded, shouts in a strange language: these added to their fear. Some of them ran to the tents to hide. Only the officers showed much fight.

With his other grenades Ghazan blew up two machine-guns and a mortar. In each of the pits he had sought in vain for more grenades. Without them he could do no further damage. Still, he told himself, the raid had been useful.

Several times he yelled out the partridge cry: "Qah, qah." His men ran to their horses; soon they were riding back. Again a flare shot up. As the enemy regained their positions, mortars opened fire. One bomb exploded in the thick of the Falqani. Two horses fell with their riders. Several other riders were hit, but clinging to their horses reached their own lines.

Panting, bathed in sweat, Ghazan swung himself down from his saddle. He was only dimly conscious of noise and sudden glaring light. As soon as they touched the ground, his feet buckled under him: he fell heavily. Ahmad saw him first and with another tribesman carried him unconscious to his tent. There they laid the Ilkhan on his partridge-feather bedding, in the centre of his rug. He had been hit in the chest below the left lung. The shrapnel had passed sideways, leaving a gaping wound the size of a clenched fist.

As a styptic Rohim applied a paste of oak-apples on raw sheep's wool to the wounded chest. Ahmad changed the dressing repeatedly, binding it right round the body with bandages, but the bleeding did not grow less. It soon soaked through his blankets, bedding and rug to the ground. Ahmad replaced the blankets with Rohim's.

Ghazan lay in the tent all night, conscious by moments, suffering much. With him everyone suffered. The shock of the Ilkhan's wound, as it were, knocked out the poles from every court and headquarters tent. The whole spirit of the camp seemed to have collapsed. Voices, gay and confident when the raiders set off, were now continually whispering the same anxious question as tribesmen came, pale-faced, to the blue tent for news and to ask what they could do to help.

An hour before dawn Ghazan opened his eyes and looked round the tent, where a mutton-fat lamp cast a tawny glare. He asked Ahmad what had happened, then lifted himself or one elbow and tried to struggle to his feet. But he could not even raise his back from the ground.

Ahmad plied him with pomegranate juice to replace the lost blood, and encouraged him with stories of far worse wounds: of men who had survived with half their neck cut through.

A second time Ghazan tried to get up. "Help me, Ahmad," he urged. "I can't lie here any longer."

But the least movement contorted his face in pain. He fell back exhausted.

"Tell Rohim to come."

Ahmad left the tent and presently returned with Rohim, who squatted beside Ghazan.

"How many of my men came back?" His voice, though weak, was firm. His face had become very pale; jaw, cheekbones and nose were all strangely accentuated.

"Thirty-one."

"So few?"

His eyes, which had been staring at the blue canvas top of the tent, came down to meet Rohim's.

"And ten of those are wounded."

"By the mortars, Rohim. The soldiers they put to flight like hares. Are bombs still falling?"

"Less heavily. But eight men have been killed since dusk."

With angry eyes and a new twist of pain in his lips, Ghazan said, "Dig in deep."

"I've told them to use the craters."

"Good. Only the guns hold us up. There are four less now. Raid the rest tonight, Rohim."

"I'll go for the loaded trucks first. There may be grenades."

"That's right. Are the men still in good heart?"

Rohim dropped his eyes. "For the moment. Only a few know you've been hit."

"Hit and shattered. I haven't long left. It's for your father to lead them across."

Rohim answered the unspoken thought behind his cousin's challenging tone, "He won't give in now the fighting's begun."

"Urge him on, Rohim. Show him how much it matters." He lay still, listening to the distant reverberations. Now and again from a sudden stab of pain he would gasp and stifle a cry. "Those guns! Suppose you can't cross? Suppose they march you down to the plains, cage you there? No more movement. The last migration."

As though recoiling from his own words, Ghazan closed his eyes and broke off. Ahmad drew aside the blanket and looked at his chest. Already the dressing and cotton were soaked, oozing blood.

"I'll put a new bandage."

Ghazan touched Ahmad's arm. "Save it for someone else."

The shepherd looked at Rohim. It was true, there were very few bandages. Rohim motioned him to obey.

A moment later Ghazan opened his eyes. "What do you call it, Ahmad—your desert monster which preys on sleeping men?"

"The palis?"

"That's it." Ghazan put a hand to his chest and tried to smile. "I think the palis has chosen to batten here." He fumbled behind his neck at the clip of his little silver-bound Koran. "Help me with this." Rohim undid the clasp, and put the book in his hands. He tried to turn over a page, but his fingers had become weak and awkward. He handed it to Rohim. "This and Milk of the Moon—both are yours now . . . Tell Anahita to embroider the rider on the white horse—she'll know what I mean. We'll be together there." He turned to Ahmad. "My best rifle —the one with the walnut stock—that's for you."

When they had thanked him with awkward words of reassurance they did not feel, Ghazan sent for Tughril and, with two of the elders to witness the act, designated his uncle successor as Ilkhan, subject to the chieftains' approval. This seemed to exhaust his last reserves of strength. He lay back, breathing heavily.

"You must get across," he urged them, fire in his voice still.

Rohim said, "Of course we shall cross—to avenge what they've done to you."

"A chance mortar-shell. An impersonal death. No one can avenge that."

He closed his eyes. Keener still with the dawn dew, the scent of fallen oak-leaves drifted through the tent, effacing the smell of leather and wet wool. Those in the tent could not believe he was dying: so young he looked, the flesh so firm on his bones.

For a long time Ghazan said nothing. The deep chest drew steadily shallower breaths. With a last effort he whispered, "My body will lie here under the withering grass. In spring you will come thundering back over my bones. I shall hear you . . . It won't be exile."

The earth shook to a nearby explosion. The tent-skirts billowed, the

339

mutton-fat lamp flickered and went out. No one relit it. Already it was dawn.

Without speaking again Ghazan lost consciousness. Manuchehr the elder took the tablet of Kerbela dust which during his lifetime Ghazan had carried in his pocket and touched with his brow in prayer. Between two stones he ground the tablet to the dust it was, the dust where Hussein and Kazem had fallen. Taking it in his withered palm, he gently opened Ghazan's twisted lips and put a scattering of dust on his dry tongue.

A few moments later they heard a sound in his throat like the fluttering of wings, like drums beating a last retreat.

Gently the body of Ghazan Falqani was laid with his face towards Mecca, while Rohim recited the Yasein chapter from the Koran: his eyes closed, his limbs stretched, the great toes of both feet tied together and a scarf bound round the neck. Then Ahmad washed the body in water mingled with camphor and wrapped it in a shroud of blue cotton. Two willow sticks were placed under the armpits: when the angel of judgment came, these would help him to rise.

Where possible the Falqani were buried near a descendant of one of the Imams, in the shade of a large tree or close to a spring. Rohim chose the latter site, and with Ahmad dug the grave: long, because of his height, but—according to custom—very shallow. Ghazan's body was carried on a rough bier and lowered into the earth head foremost. The face was uncovered, and the body laid on the right side. Earth was piled up and all present—chieftains and elders—pressed their fingers on the soil, reciting the opening chapter of the Koran. Rohim, with his father's approval, ordered a large stone to be found and a lion carved on one side: an honour the Falqani reserved for their heroes.

The news had spread like an epidemic. Their Ilkhan dead—killed by the army. Angry tribesmen clamoured round their headmen, demanding to be led in attack. While plans were being laid, they vented some of their fury by using their scanty ammunition even when they saw no definite target, firing at tents and emplacements well out of range, sending the vultures screaming from last night's dead.

That morning brought a second shock. Six tanks like the one bought from Shami crawled over the opposite ridge and advanced abreast across the plain. Tughril and Rohim hurried among their men, telling them

340

to hold fire until they could aim on the slits. But the Falqani had never before been confronted with anything like tanks. The impossible happened: they were frightened. They fired at and hit the plated turrets and foreparts: when the tanks swept on regardless, in still greater alarm they redoubled their fire. In this way many rounds were uselessly spent. When the tanks did crawl within range, they were hit by accurate fire. One immediately burst into flames and burnt itself out, ammunition exploding in all directions. Another came to a halt, and its crew were captured. The rest turned and retreated.

By now ammunition was desperately scarce. Some men had no rounds, others one or two. Tughril gave orders that no one was to fire, however easy the target. This change the army soon noticed. They began to move freely across the slope, walking upright, carrying supplies and food; while the Falqani silently raged.

Towards midday the army launched an attack. Four companies, spread out over a front of half a mile, advanced behind each of four tanks. Heavy mortar and machine-gun fire covered their approach. They swept up the ridge without interception. At two hundred yards Tughril gave the order to fire. Some of the soldiers fell, but the majority charged on. For an hour the Falqani beat off heavily armed troops with knives and rifle-butts, but the tanks they could not halt. These swept through to open fire on the women and children. To prevent a slaughter Tughril rode across the plain and offered his surrender.

That afternoon Falqani rifles were collected under General Bahrami's supervision. When Tughril informed him of Ghazan's death, the General complained:

"Why did he fight? Against superior weapons he had no chance—he must have known that."

Manuchehr the elder, standing at Tughril's side, replied with a quotation: "'He who becomes acquainted with the mysteries of the world soon departs: whoever does his work brilliantly leaves the school.'"

"And now the school has a new master," said the General with a laugh. To Tughril he indicated a colonel in his suite. "Colonel Sirdar is the military governor appointed over the Falqani. Since Ghazan Khan is dead, the position is simple. Colonel Sirdar will take over his duties."

So the tide of sheep and goats flowed forward, herded by a depleted force, many wounded, winding out of the hills across the plain of battle,

341

with here and there a uniformed figure. Rohim's last action was to set up the tombstone carved with a lion rampant. Doubly fitting he found it, for the lion, despite its bravery, in the south-west provinces was now extinct. The cameleer named Mansur had worked continuously since Ghazan's death to finish it. There the last Ilkhan was left, to await the angel of resurrection.

The troops, even on that first day, started to exact revenge, man-handling the tribesmen, driving their vehicles through the herds as they crowded narrow gorge-roads, sending some tumbling down the cliff-side, ordering the boys to carry them water, requisitioning whatever food they fancied. In the first week over eighty complaints of assault or robbery were brought to Tughril's notice. He reported them to Colonel Sirdar, but the bullying did not grow less.

Ten days after the battle the first sections of Falqani reached the waste land south of Farrashband where some were to be settled: poor, dry soil where villages had never thrived. Once their tents were pitched they were forbidden to move: herds could be led to new pastures, but tents must not be struck. In the newly apportioned land no arrange-ments had been made for irrigation. The brackish, overworked wells steamed with flies.

Among the Shalguli, settled near marshy land close to the Gulf, malaria broke out. Tughril was one of the first stricken. In the blue tent that had belonged to Ghazan, Rohim looked after his father. He thought the great bullock body would easily throw off the fever, but it seemed, rather, to provide a larger battlefield for a more violent battle: a rearguard action which, amid delirium and cries that he had been poisoned, was lost on the eighth day. Rohim succeeded as Ilkhan of the defeated tribe.

A winter of death which, for the Falqani, spring did not resurrect. The wells dried up, spring rain fell sparsely, the ears of barley, though carefully tended, did not fill. Led far afield for pasture, led back at dusk for milking, sheep and goats grew thin, their udders flaccid. In early spring the sheep were attacked by rot-dropsy, a disease unknown in the years the Falqani had wandered. Eyes pale, hair in their scant fleeces brittle and dry, the flocks dragged thin bodies across the flat brown plain, without stamina or appetite. Stagnant water and limited pasturage spread the disease. Only the rich grass of the Zagros could have saved them, the tall grass that lazed idly on the cool slopes: forbidden. The sheep died, so many that in some sections tribesmen, unable longer to meet the sharp, sad eyes of their hungry children, resorted to the ultimate act of despair: they slaughtered lambs for food.

In the new year three herdsmen of the Ilkhan's personal following, having lost their sheep to the outbreak of rot, were driven by hunger to beg a ride on a farmer's truck carrying dates northwards. They hoped to find casual work in the Shiraz bazaars. It so happened that their journey took place on the thirteenth day after Nowruz, when Shirazis, townsmen all over Persia, had left their homes to spend the day beside running water and grass, to take back within their walls some of the fruitfulness of the spring-green earth.

As they entered the outskirts of Shiraz, to lessen the chances of being identified and oppressed, the herdsmen decided to cut off the distinctive wing-like flaps from their hats. Drawing long bone-handled knives with sharp blades, they slit the brown felt in silence, averting their eyes from each other and from the nearby hills. There already, in response to the spring sun, gazelle and ibex, partridge and francolin, with beasts and birds of prey on their trail, were beginning their long journey northwards: up the parched plain and along cooler, grass-dappled slopes—bare of men, bare of flocks—to the first crest of the Zagros, where, open to a cloudless blue sky and blending with the hills around, a rough-hewn stone marked Ghazan's last encampment.